Curso segundo

Amsco books by Marvin and Carol Wasserman

Curso primero
Curso segundo
Curso tercero
Prosa de la España moderna
Susana y Javier en España
Susana y Javier en Sudamérica

Curso segundo

Workbook
for a Second Course
in Spanish

When ordering this book, please specify:
either **R 279 W** or CURSO SEGUNDO/WORKBOOK

AMSCO SCHOOL PUBLICATIONS, INC.
315 Hudson Street/New York, N.Y. 10013

Cover illustration: The library of the National University, Mexico City

Photo credits: United Press International—pages 34, 169, 209, 282, 296, 371; Stuart Cohen—pages 11, 19, 68, 75, 160, 217, 273, 277, 287, 312, 324, 348, 355

Cover by Ted Bernstein

ISBN 0-87720-526-4

REVISED EDITION, 1996

Copyright © 1984 by AMSCO SCHOOL PUBLICATIONS, INC.

PRINTED IN THE UNITED STATES OF AMERICA

6 7 8 9 10 02 01 00 99 98 97

Preface

Curso segundo is a comprehensive course in Spanish corresponding to the second year of high school Spanish. This workbook includes several topics that extend its scope beyond a second-year course. These extra topics will be useful to teachers who want to enrich their course of study.

As in *Curso primero*, the subjects treated in the grammar chapters are divided into their smallest topical units, each of which is reinforced by one or more Practice sets. Thus, most of the major subjects treated in this workbook can be mastered in small steps. The Practice sets also serve to prepare the student to perform the summary exercises at the end of each chapter.

The distinctive features of this workbook include:

1. Nine chapters entirely in Spanish on the civilization of the Spanish-speaking world.
2. A thorough treatment of the problems involved in expressing *to be* in Spanish.
3. A comprehensive explanation of the uses of the Spanish infinitive.
4. A section on Spanish vocabulary and idioms arranged according to "situation," that is, showing how they are used in context. (See Part 7.)
5. A unit on verbs that are used like **gustar.**
6. A chapter dealing with the uses of **hace, hacía,** and the verb **llevar** in expressing the passage of time.
7. A chapter on the distinction between the passive **se** and the indefinite **se.**
8. An Appendix containing summaries of basic topics or elements introduced in Level One, as well as additional information regarding some topics that are taught in Level Two.
9. At the end of each grammar chapter: an exercise in listening comprehension that tests the student's ability to distinguish aurally between the various verb forms or other elements introduced in the chapter.
10. Chapters on the formation and uses of the present and imperfect subjunctives, for teachers who wish to teach those topics in the second year or in the early stages of the third year.

The chapters in *Curso segundo*, like those in *Curso primero*, are not arranged in a cumulative sequence; that is, the mastery of a given topic does not necessarily require mastery of the topics preceding it. Thus, the teacher can assign these chapters in any suitable order.

Students and teachers will find this workbook invaluable as a source of instruction and practice.

—THE AUTHORS

Contents

Part Three   Other Verb Forms

Part Four   Nouns, Adjectives, and Adverbs

Part Five   Pronouns

Part Six   Other Grammar Topics

Appendix

PART ONE

PRESENT TENSE
AND
COMMANDS

1
The Present Tense: Regular Verbs

	-*AR* VERBS	-*ER* VERBS	-*IR* VERBS
	visitar to visit	**correr** to run	**escribir** to write
Singular			
yo	visit**o** *I visit* *I am visiting*	corr**o** *I run* *I am running*	escrib**o** *I write* *I am writing*
tú	visit**as**	corr**es**	escrib**es**
Ud. él ella	visit**a**	corr**e**	escrib**e**
Plural			
nosotros nosotras	visit**amos**	corr**emos**	escrib**imos**
vosotros vosotras	visit**áis**	corr**éis**	escrib**ís**
Uds. ellos ellas	visit**an**	corr**en**	escrib**en**

1. The six verb forms of the present tense are obtained by dropping the **-ar, -er,** and **-ir** endings of the infinitive and replacing them with the following endings:

	-AR	-ER	-IR
yo	-o	-o	-o
tú	-as	-es	-es
usted, él, ella	-a	-e	-e
nosotros(-as)	-amos	-emos	-imos
vosotros(-as)	-áis	-éis	-ís
Uds., ellos, ellas	-an	-en	-en

Practice A: Write the indicated form of the verb in the present tense.

EXAMPLE: ella ___*vive*___
                    vivir

1. yo _____
         ayudar

2. la chica _____
              responder

3. tú _____
        recibir

4. vosotras _____
               comer

5. ellos _____
           tomar

6. el hombre _____
                dividir

7. yo _____
        comprender

8. Uds. _____
          vivir

9. nosotros _____
               contestar

10. ella y yo _____
                 permitir

2. A verb in the present tense can be translated in two ways:

Ella **visita** la ciudad dos veces por semana (todos los días).

She *visits* the city twice a week (every day).

Ella **visita** la ciudad hoy.

She *is visiting* the city today.

Visita means *visits* if this happens often or regularly in the present; it means *is visiting* if this is happening now. Similarly:

¿**Trabaja** todos los días?

Does he work every day?

¿**Trabaja** hoy?

Is he working today?

No estudiamos por la noche; **miramos** la televisión.

We *do not study* at night; we *watch* television.

No estudiamos ahora; **miramos** la televisión.

We *are not studying* now; we *are watching* television.

NEGATIVE QUESTIONS

¿**No escriben** ellos a sus padres todos los días (tres veces por mes)?

Don't they write to their parents every day (three times a month)?

¿**No escriben** ellos a sus padres hoy (en este momento)?

Aren't they writing to their parents today (at this moment)?

To express the present tense in English, one must choose between two verb forms—a fact that makes it hard for Spanish-speaking students of English to master the English present tense. A typical error of beginners in English is a sentence like "I am going to school every day."

Practice B: Translate the sentence into English in two ways if both are possible.

1. ¿Toma ella vino con la cena?

_____

_____

2. Nosotros no leemos el periódico.

_____

_____

3. Yo escribo una carta a mi primo todas las semanas.

_____

_____

4. ¿No compras tú una revista hoy?

_____

_____

Omission of the Subject Pronoun

3. The subject pronoun in Spanish is often omitted, especially when the verb ending clearly identifies the subject. Therefore, **yo, tú, nosotros,** and **vosotros** do not have to be used except for emphasis:

—¿Escribes una carta?   "Are you writing a letter?"

—Sí, escribo una carta.   "Yes, I am writing a letter."

      But:

—¿Quién escribe la carta?   "Who is writing the letter?"

—**Yo** escribo la carta.   "*I* am writing the letter."

Practice C: Translate into English.

1. Dividimos el dinero cada tarde.

_____

2. Visito muchos lugares de interés cuando voy a España.

_____

3. No comes mucho hoy, Juanito.

_____

4. ¿A qué hora llegáis esta noche?

_____

4. When a subject pronoun is omitted, we must infer the subject of the verb from an earlier sentence or trend of the conversation. If the subject is not clear, then the subject pronoun must be used:

SPEAKER 1: ¿Qué lengua habla Juan?   What language does John speak?
SPEAKER 2: Habla francés.   He speaks French.

But:

SPEAKER 1: Responde bien.   [He *or* she] is answering well.
SPEAKER 2: ¿Quién responde bien?   Who is answering well?
SPEAKER 1: **Ella** responde bien.   *She* is answering well.

Practice D: Translate into English.

1. *a.* ¿Dónde vive Felipe?   _____

   b. Vive en la Argentina.   _____

2. *a.* ¿Cómo hablan ellos español?   _____

   b. Hablan muy bien.   _____

3. *a.* ¿Aprendemos bien hoy, señor profesor? _____

   b. Sí, aprenden muy bien.   _____

Common Regular -AR, -ER, and -IR Verbs

-AR VERBS

ayudar, to help
 ayudar a alguien a + *inf.*, to help someone to

bailar, to dance

bajar, to go down
 bajar de, to get off, out of (a vehicle)

cantar, to sing

comprar, to buy

contestar, to answer

desear, to wish, want

enseñar, to teach, show
 enseñar a alguien a + *inf.*, to teach someone to

entrar (en), to enter, go (come) in

escuchar, to listen (to)

estudiar, to study

explicar, to explain

hablar, to speak, talk

llegar, to arrive
 llegar a, to arrive at; **llegar a ser (médico, -a, abogado, -a, etc.),** to become a (doctor, lawyer, etc.)

llevar, to carry, take; to wear

mirar, to look (at)
 mirar la televisión, to watch television

pagar, to pay (for)

pasar, to pass; to spend (time)

preguntar, to ask

prestar, to lend
 prestar atención, to pay attention

sacar, to take out
 sacar buenas (malas) notas, to get good (bad) marks

tomar, to take
 tomar el desayuno (café, etc.), to have breakfast (coffee, etc.)

trabajar, to work

tratar de + *inf.*, to try to

usar, to use

viajar, to travel

visitar, to visit

-ER VERBS

aprender, to learn
   aprender a + *inf.,* to learn to

beber, to drink

comer, to eat

comprender, to understand

correr, to run

deber,* to have to, must (see §5, below)

leer, to read

prometer, to promise (see §5, below)

responder, to answer

vender, to sell

-IR VERBS

abrir, to open

asistir a, to attend

cubrir, to cover

describir, to describe

dividir, to divide

escribir, to write

partir, to leave, depart

recibir, to receive

subir, to go up
   subir a, to get into or on (a vehicle)

vivir, to live

5. Some verbs are often followed directly by another verb in the infinitive, without a preposition as in English:

Deseo ir al cine.	I wish to go to the movies.
Prometo ayudar a mi madre.	I promise to help my mother.
Debo estudiar.	I have to study. (I must study.)

Practice E: Complete the Spanish sentences.

1. We wish to receive gifts.

   Deseamos _____ regalos.

2. Must I drink the milk?

   ¿Debo _____ la leche?

3. They promise to visit their grandparents.

   Prometen _____ a sus abuelos.

---

*Many Hispanics use **deber de** (+ an infinitive) to express obligation or duty, but this is incorrect. **Deber de** is used to express *probability:*

Ella **debe** estar aquí a las ocho.	She must (has to) be here at 8:00.
But:	
Ella **debe de** estar aquí ahora.	She must be here now. (= She is probably here now.)

EJERCICIOS

A. Complete each sentence with the correct form of the verb.

EXAMPLE: Mi madre vende nuestra casa y ____*compra*____ otra.
                                                  comprar

1. José y su amigo Carlos trabajan en un almacén donde _____ ropa.
                                                                        vender

2. Recibimos dinero de nuestros padres y lo _____ para comprar nuestros
                                                      usar
   libros.

3. La profesora pronuncia la palabra y luego la _____ en la pizarra.
                                                        escribir

4. ¿No lee usted los libros que _____ de la biblioteca?
                                         sacar

5. El tren parte a las seis y _____ a las diez y media.
                                     llegar

6. ¿Vendes tu bicicleta y _____ una motocicleta?
                                 comprar

7. Los ascensores bajan rápidamente y _____ despacio.
                                                subir

8. En la fiesta bailamos y _____ cerveza.
                                   beber

9. ¿Corréis porque _____ llegar temprano a la escuela?
                          desear

10. En mi cuarto estudio mis lecciones y _____ las revistas.
                                                  leer

B. Each sentence on the left is the answer to a question that begins as shown on the right. Write the rest of the question in the blank.

EXAMPLES:

Miro la televisión.   ¿Qué ____*mira Ud. (miras tú)*____ ?

Escribimos con lápiz.   ¿Con qué _*escriben Uds. (escribís vosotros)*_ ?

1. Él enseña la biología.   ¿Qué _____?

2. Leemos revistas interesantes.   ¿Qué _____?

3. Entro en la sala a las once.   ¿A qué hora _____?

4. Ellos abren las puertas a las nueve. ¿Cuándo _____?

5. Vivimos en Puerto Rico.   ¿Dónde _____?

6. Ella responde muy bien.   ¿Cómo _____?

7. Yo hablo con mi prima.   ¿Con quién _____?

8. El profesor explica el concepto a los
   estudiantes.   ¿A quiénes _____?

9. El avión para Madrid parte a la una de
   la tarde.   ¿A qué hora _____?

10. Los chicos deben comer la ensalada.   ¿Quiénes _____?

C. Answer with a complete sentence in Spanish:

1. ¿Cuándo corres por el parque?

   _____

2. ¿En qué ciudad viven Uds.?

   _____

3. ¿A qué hora entra su profesora (profesor) en la escuela?

   _____

4. ¿Siempre desea Ud. ayudar a sus padres en casa?

   _____

5. ¿Trabaja su madre en una tienda?

   _____

6. ¿Saca Ud. buenas notas en sus exámenes de español?

   _____

7. ¿Llevan todos sus profesores ropa elegante?

   _____

8. ¿Cuándo viaja su familia?

   _____

9. ¿Con quiénes llegan Uds. a la escuela por la mañana?

   _____

10. ¿Asistes a una escuela primaria, intermedia o secundaria?

   _____

D. Translate into Spanish.

EXAMPLES: Are they (*m.*) speaking?   *¿Hablan ellos?*
            I do not write.   *Yo no escribo.*

1. *a.* Are you (*tú*) listening to the music?

   _____

   b. Is she listening to the radio?

   _____

2. *a.* I am going up to (*para*) sleep now.

_____

   b. We are going up to read later.

_____

3. *a.* Does he drink ("take") wine with dinner?

_____

   b. Do they (*m. & f.*) drink milk with breakfast?

_____

4. *a.* They (*f.*) don't sing very well.

_____

   b. You (*Ud.*) sing very badly.

_____

5. *a.* Mary is not dancing with Robert.

_____

   b. The boys are not dancing at (*en*) the party.

_____

6. *a.* Helen and I are writing letters.

_____

   b. They are writing postcards.

_____

7. *a.* Are you (*tú*) eating late today?

_____

   b. Is he eating now?

_____

8. *a.* Why don't you (*Uds.*) ask the teacher?

¿_____ al profesor?

   b. Why don't we ask the lady?

¿_____ a la señora?

9. *a.* I do not want to leave the building.

_____ del edificio.

   b. Who wants to skate this afternoon?

_____

10. *a.* You (*vosotros*) are answering well today.

_____

b. I am answering the questions.

_____ a las preguntas.

E. *Idiom Review.* Translate into Spanish as shown by the examples in italics:

1. What school do you attend?   *¿A qué escuela asiste Ud.?*

What university do they attend?   _____

2. She is getting off the train.   *Ella baja del tren.*

We're getting out of the car.   _____

3. Are they getting on the bus?   *¿Suben al autobús?*

Is he getting on the train?   _____

4. You are not paying attention to the
teacher.   *Tú no prestas atención a la profesora.*

I'm not paying attention to the
speech.   _____

5. I'm trying to understand the problem. *Trato de comprender el problema.*

They are trying to sell the house.   _____

6. My sister is becoming a doctor.   *Mi hermana llega a ser médica.*

My uncle is becoming an engineer.   _____

7. She's helping the old lady to cross
the street.   *Ella ayuda a la vieja a cruzar la calle.*

I'm helping my friend to do his work. _____

8. We're learning to swim.   *Aprendemos a nadar.*

She's learning to skate.   _____

9. I'm teaching my brother to read.   *Enseño a mi hermano a leer.*

He's teaching Mary to dance.   _____

10. What do you want to have, coffee
or milk?   *¿Qué deseas tomar, café o leche?*

What do they (*f.*) want to have, beer
or soda?   _____

F. *Listening Comprehension.** * Your teacher will read to the class ten sentences in Spanish corresponding to the ten groups of sentences listed below. In each group, circle the letter (*a*, *b*, or *c*) of the correct English translation.

1. *a.* I'm taking the train now.
   b. The train is leaving now.
   c. She's taking the train now.

2. *a.* We promise to study tonight.
   b. I promise to study tonight.
   c. They promise to study tonight.

3. *a.* We're describing the programs.
   b. We don't describe the programs.
   c. We're deciding the programs.

4. *a.* Do they speak English?
   b. You speak English.
   c. Do you speak English?

5. *a.* They are not buying the watch.
   b. Is she buying the watch?
   c. She's not buying the watch.

6. *a.* Are they eating now?
   b. Aren't they eating now?
   c. Are you eating now?

7. *a.* He is covering the table.
   b. Are you covering the table?
   c. They are covering the table.

8. *a.* Is she dividing the money?
   b. Who is dividing the money?
   c. Why does he divide the money?

9. *a.* Where do we spend the night?
   b. Where are they spending the night?
   c. Where do you spend the night?

10. *a.* We pay a lot of money.
    b. They are paying a lot of money.
    c. I pay a lot of money.

**To the teacher:* For the exercises in listening comprehension, the parts that are to be read to the class will be found in the Answer Key to *Curso segundo.*

Entrada del Museo Nacional de Antropología en la ciudad de México

2
The Present Tense: Irregular Verbs

I. Verbs Irregular in the First Person Singular

GROUP A: *YO* FORM ENDING IN *-GO*

yo

caer, to fall	*caigo*
hacer, to do, make	*hago*
poner, to put, place	*pongo*
salir, to leave, go out	*salgo*
traer, to bring	*traigo*
valer, to be worth	*valgo*

GROUP B: OTHER IRREGULAR *YO* FORMS

yo

caber, to fit	*quepo*
conducir, to lead; to drive	*conduzco*
conocer, to know	*conozco*
dar, to give	*doy*
saber, to know	*sé*
ver, to see	*veo*

1. These verbs are irregular only in the **yo** form. The other forms are regular. The forms **dais** and **veis** do not have accent marks.

Practice A: In each column, write the forms of the verb that are used with the following subjects:

1. el hombre   2. Ud. y yo   3. las chicas   4. yo   5. tú

	traer	salir	saber	conducir	dar	poner
1.						
2.						
3.						
4.						
5.						

II. Verbs Irregular in All Forms Except Those for NOSOTROS and VOSOTROS

decir to say, tell	*digo*	*dices*	*dice*	decimos	decís	*dicen*
estar to be*	*estoy*	*estás*	*está*	estamos	estáis	*están*
oír to hear	*oigo*	*oyes*	*oye*	oímos	oís	*oyen*
poder to be able, can	*puedo*	*puedes*	*puede*	podemos	podéis	*pueden*
querer to want	*quiero*	*quieres*	*quiere*	queremos	queréis	*quieren*
tener to have	*tengo*	*tienes*	*tiene*	tenemos	tenéis	*tienen*
venir to come	*vengo*	*vienes*	*viene*	venimos	venís	*vienen*

III. Verbs Irregular in All Six Forms

ir, to go	*voy*	*vas*	*va*	*vamos*	*vais*	*van*
ser, to be*	*soy*	*eres*	*es*	*somos*	*sois*	*son*

2. The forms **vais** and **sois** do not have accent marks.

Practice B: Write the verb forms that are used with the given pronouns as subjects.

1. Uds. _____ _____ _____ _____
               venir   tener   poder   hacer
_____

*Both **estar** and **ser** mean *to be* but cannot be used interchangeably. See Chapter 13.

2. nosotras _____ _____ _____ _____
                querer   ser   ir   dar

3. yo _____ _____ _____ _____
           decir   ver   conocer   salir

4. ¿quién? _____ _____ _____ _____
           saber   oír   decir   ser

5. tú _____ _____ _____ _____
           poder   venir   estar   oír

Using *PODER, QUERER, IR,* and *VENIR* Before an Infinitive

3. **Poder** and **querer** are often followed directly by another verb in the infinitive form; that is, they are not followed by a preposition:

No **puedo ver** la pizarra.   I can't see the chalkboard.

¿**Quiere** (Ud.) **mirar** la televisión?   Do you want to watch television?

4. **Ir** and **venir** are followed by the preposition **a** if they precede an infinitive:

Voy **a** estudiar.   I am going to study.

Hoy mis padres vienen **a** visitar la escuela.   Today my parents are coming to visit the school.

SABER and *CONOCER*

5. **Saber** and **conocer** both mean *to know* but cannot be used interchangeably.

a. **Saber** is used for knowing facts, and also means "to know *how* (to do something)":

¿**Saben** Uds. la respuesta?   Do you know the answer?

No **sé patinar.**   I don't know how to skate.

b. **Conocer** is used in the sense of *to be acquainted* (or *familiar*) *with* people or places:

¿**Conoces** a mi amigo José?   Do you know my friend Joseph?

Mi padre **conoce** muy bien la ciudad.   My father knows the city very well.

CABER and *VALER*

6. **Caber** means *to fit* in the sense of *there is room* (or *space*) *for* someone or something:

No **quepo** en el coche.   There is no room for me in the car.

7. **Valer,** *to be worth,* is often used in the sense of *to cost:*

¿Cuánto **vale** el tocadiscos?   How much does the record player cost?

Practice C: Supply the correct form of *saber*, *conocer*, *caber*, or *valer*, in accordance with the meaning of the sentence.

1. ¿_____ tú nadar?

2. Yo _____ muy bien mi vecindario.

3. ¿Cuánto _____ estos discos?

4. Quiero _____ a tu amiga Rosa.

5. Estas revistas no _____ en la mesa.

6. Vamos a _____ la lección perfectamente.

EJERCICIOS

A. Write the appropriate forms of the verbs. (In each sentence, the two verbs have the same subject.)

1. Mi padre _____ ganar más dinero, pero no _____.
   querer   poder

2. Yo _____ a la escuela a las ocho y media y _____ a las tres.
   venir   salir

3. ¿_____ tú las ciudades que _____ a visitar?
   conocer   ir

4. Antes de la comida yo _____ la mesa y _____ los platos
   poner   traer
   de la cocina.

5. Cuando yo _____ la televisión, _____ buenos programas.
   mirar   ver

6. Los niños _____ leche, pero _____ beber café.
   beber   querer

7. Ellos _____ que _____ conducir un coche.
   decir   saber

8. ¿Dónde _____ Ud. cuando _____?
   estar   comer

9. Mi hermano _____ a hablar del coche que _____.
   venir   conducir

10. Nosotras _____ secretarias y _____ en la misma oficina.
    ser   trabajar

11. ¿Cuánto _____ esas camisas que _____ en el escaparate?
    valer   estar

12. Yo _____ en el coche pequeño porque _____ muy flaco.
    caber   ser

13. Yo _____ al señor López pero no _____ su dirección.
        conocer   saber

14. ¿_____ tú traer los discos que _____ en tu casa?
        poder   tener

15. Primero yo _____ el dinero al cajero y luego _____ a
             dar   ir

entrar en el teatro.

B. Answer with a complete sentence in Spanish:

1. ¿Qué ves en el cine?

   _____

2. ¿Qué pueden Uds. aprender en esta clase?

   _____

3. ¿Cuántos libros trae Ud. por lo general a la escuela?

   _____

4. ¿Dónde está su madre (su padre) ahora?

   _____

5. ¿Cuántas cosas hace Ud. durante una hora?

   _____

6. ¿Por qué viene Ud. a la escuela todos los días?

   _____

7. ¿En qué estación del año caen las hojas de los árboles?

   _____

8. ¿Sabes bien estos verbos irregulares?

   _____

9. ¿Quién tiene más dinero, Ud. o su padre?

   _____

10. ¿Dónde pone Ud. su ropa durante la noche?

   _____

C. Translate into Spanish:

1. *a.* I can't pay the money now. _____

   b. Can she work today? _____

2. *a.* We're going to the supermarket soon. _____

   b. I'm not going to play this afternoon. _____

3. *a.* Aren't they coming to the mall (*el centro comercial*) tonight? _____

_____

   b. I'm not coming to eat later. _____

4. *a.* I'm not leaving the house yet. _____

   b. Are they going out this morning? _____

5. *a.* Who is bringing the records tomorrow? _____

   b. I'm not bringing the record player next week. _____

_____

6. *a.* I don't know the answer. _____

   b. Do you (*tú*) know the words? _____

7. *a.* What are they (*f.*) doing here? _____

   b. Does he do his homework (*tareas*) every day? _____

_____

8. *a.* We don't hear the music. _____

   b. Don't you (*Uds.*) hear the noise? _____

9. *a.* There is no room for the table (The table does not fit) in the kitchen. _____

_____

   b. Do the books fit on the shelf? _____

10. *a.* Are you (*Uds.*) businessmen or lawyers? (Use *ser.*) _____

_____

   b. We're not neighbors. (Use *ser.*) _____

D. *Idiom Review.* Translate into Spanish as shown by the examples in italics:

1. I'm taking a trip to Spain.   *Hago un viaje a España.*

  He's taking a trip to Mexico.   _____

2. They are paying a visit to Lola.   *Hacen una visita a Lola.*

  I'm paying a visit to Philip.   _____

3. We are asking the teacher a question.   *Hacemos una pregunta a la profesora.*

  I'm asking my parents a question.   _____

4. I'm taking a walk in the park.   *Doy un paseo por el parque.*

  He's taking a walk along the street. _____

5. Are you thanking the man?

Are they thanking the lady?

¿Das las gracias al hombre?

_____

6. We have to arrive early.

I have to leave late.

Tenemos que llegar temprano.

_____

7. I am warm now.

She is warm today.

Tengo calor ahora.

_____

8. Are they very cold?

Are you (*tú*) very cold?

¿Tienen ellos mucho frío?

_____

9. Are you hungry or thirsty?

I am always hungry.

¿Tienes hambre o sed?

_____

10. Who is sleepy?

We are sleepy.

¿Quién tiene sueño?

_____

11. My grandmother is setting the table now.

I am setting the table this evening.

Mi abuela pone la mesa ahora.

_____

12. The children are leaving the house.

I am leaving the room.

Los niños salen de la casa.

_____

13. I'm leaving for Colombia tomorrow.

They are leaving for Guatemala next week.

Mañana salgo para Colombia.

_____

14. We're going out to the street.

I'm going out to the patio.

Salimos a la calle.

_____

15. Are you passing or failing the exam?

I'm failing the exam.

¿Sales bien o mal en el examen?

_____

E. *Listening Comprehension.* Your teacher will read to the class ten questions in Spanish. After each question is read to you, circle the letter (*a*, *b*, or *c*) of the most appropriate answer.

1. *a.* Aprendemos el español.
   b. Aprendo a hablar español.
   c. Tenemos una fiesta todos los días.

2. *a.* Sí, es mi amigo Juan.
   b. Sí, es mi prima Dorotea.
   c. Sí, son mis abuelos.

3. *a.* Está delante de la clase.
   b. Estoy en la sala de clase.
   c. Es muy popular.

4. *a.* Sí, porque es su padre.
   b. Sí, porque ella es muy simpática.
   c. Sí, porque el profesor da un examen.

5. *a.* Somos mecánicos.
   b. Soy estudiante.
   c. Son amigos.

6. *a.* Salgo a las tres de la tarde.
   b. Salen del teatro a las nueve de la noche.
   c. Salen a las tres de la tarde.

7. *a.* Sí, yo sé todos los verbos.
   b. No, no sabes cantar.
   c. Sí, y también sé cantar en francés.

8. *a.* Decimos «hola».
   b. Decimos «adiós, hasta mañana».
   c. Digo «hola, ¿cómo están Uds.?»

9. *a.* Veo dos libros.
   b. Vemos un libro.
   c. Vemos dos libros.

10. *a.* Oigo música en la radio.
    b. Oyen música en la discoteca.
    c. Oyes música en el concierto.

Indios con sus alpacas cerca de Cuzco, el Perú

3
The Present Tense: Stem-Changing Verbs

O to UE		

	-AR VERBS	*-ER* VERBS	*-IR* VERBS
	recordar to remember	**volver** to return	**dormir** to sleep
yo	rec**ue**rdo	v**ue**lvo	d**ue**rmo
tú	rec**ue**rdas	v**ue**lves	d**ue**rmes
Ud. él ella	rec**ue**rda	v**ue**lve	d**ue**rme
nosotros nosotras	recordamos	volvemos	dormimos
vosotros vosotras	recordáis	volvéis	dormís
Uds. ellos ellas	rec**ue**rdan	v**ue**lven	d**ue**rmen

E to IE

	-AR VERBS	-ER VERBS	-IR VERBS
	pensar to think	**entender** to understand	**sentir** to regret
yo	p*ie*nso	ent*ie*ndo	s*ie*nto
tú	p*ie*nsas	ent*ie*ndes	s*ie*ntes
Ud. él ella	p*ie*nsa	ent*ie*nde	s*ie*nte
nosotros nosotras	pensamos	entendemos	sentimos
vosotros vosotras	pensáis	entendéis	sentís
Uds. ellos ellas	p*ie*nsan	ent*ie*nden	s*ie*nten

E to I (-IR Verbs Only)

repetir, to repeat			
yo rep*i*to		nosotros(-as) repetimos	
tú rep*i*tes		vosotros(-as) repetís	
Ud. él ella	rep*i*te	Uds. ellos ellas	rep*i*ten

1. To obtain the stem of *any* verb, drop the infinitive ending (**-ar, -er,** or **-ir**). If the stem of a stem-changing verb has more than one vowel, it is the last vowel that changes: encontr-, recomend-, prefer-, etc. This vowel may be either **o** or **e.** (Not all verbs with stem-vowel **o** or **e** are stem-changing verbs.)

2. Changes in the stem-vowel occur in all the present-tense forms of the verb except those for **nosotros(-as)** and **vosotros(-as).** The stem-vowel **o** changes to **ue;** the stem-vowel **e** changes to **ie** in some verbs, to **i** in others.

Common Stem-Changing Verbs

O TO UE

-AR VERBS

acostarse,* to go to bed

almorzar, to have lunch

contar, to tell; to count

costar, to cost

encontrar, to find; to meet

jugar (u to ue), to play
  jugar al tenis (a las cartas, etc.), to play tennis (cards, etc.)

mostrar, to show

recordar, to remember

sonar, to sound; to ring

soñar (con), to dream (of)

volar, to fly

-ER VERBS

devolver, to return, give back

llover, to rain (3rd person singular only: **llueve**)

morder, to bite

mover, to move (an object)

moverse, to move (oneself)

poder, to be able, can

volver, to return, come (go) back

-IR VERBS

dormir, to sleep
  dormirse, to fall asleep

morir(se), to die

E TO IE

-AR VERBS

cerrar, to close

comenzar, to begin
  comenzar a + *inf.*, to begin to

confesar, to confess

despertar, to wake (someone)

despertarse, to wake up

empezar, to begin
  empezar a + *inf.*, to begin to

nevar, to snow (3rd person singular only: **nieva**)

pensar (en), to think (of)
  pensar + *inf.*, to intend to

sentarse, to sit down

-ER VERBS

defender, to defend

encender, to turn on (the radio, lights, etc.), to light up

entender, to understand

perder, to lose

querer, to want

-IR VERBS

divertirse, to enjoy oneself, have a good time

mentir, to (tell a) lie

preferir, to prefer

sentir, to regret, be sorry
  lo siento, I'm sorry

sentirse, to feel (sick, tired, etc.)

---

*For the conjugation of reflexive verbs, see chapter 27.

E TO I: -IR VERBS ONLY

pedir, to ask (for), request

reír(se), to laugh

repetir, to repeat

seguir, to follow; to continue

servir, to serve

sonreír, to smile

vestir, to dress (someone)

vestirse, to get dressed

3. The forms of **reír** in the present tense are:

río, ríes, ríe, reímos, reís, ríen

Sonreír is conjugated in the same way as **reír.**

4. The **yo** form of **seguir** is **sigo.** All other forms of **seguir** in the present tense retain the **u:** sig**u**es, sig**u**e, seg**u**imos, etc.

Practice: In each column, write the verb forms that are used with the given pronoun as subject.

1. *yo*	2. *nosotros*	3. *Uds.*	4. *tú*
encontrar	vestir	seguir	sonreír
mover	seguir	morir	encender
cerrar	defender	querer	almorzar
perder	devolver	comenzar	sentir
preferir	contar	mentir	jugar

EJERCICIOS

A. Repeat the sentence orally, changing the subject and verb as indicated. (Write the new verb forms in the blanks.)

1. No *recordamos* las palabras.

Yo no _____ . . . . Tú no _____ . . . .

2. ¿A qué hora *vuelven* ellos del cine?

¿A qué hora _____ Ud. del . . . ?

¿A qué hora _____ nosotras del . . . ?

3. ¿Cuántas horas *duermes* tú cada noche?

¿Cuántas horas _____ ella . . . ?

¿Cuántas horas _____ Uds . . . ?

4. Yo siempre *pienso* en las vacaciones.

Nosotros siempre _____ . . . .   Tú siempre _____ . . . .

5. ¿Cuándo *quieren* Uds. ir al cine?

¿Cuándo _____ ella . . . ?   ¿Cuándo _____ tú . . . ?

6. Ella *prefiere* ir a la discoteca.

Yo _____ . . . .   Ellas _____ . . . .

7. ¿Qué *sirve* tu mamá esta noche?

¿Qué _____ tus tías . . . ?   ¿Qué _____ Uds. . . . ?

8. Los niños *juegan* al béisbol en el parque.

Mi amigo y yo _____ . . . .

Mi prima _____ . . . .

9. Tú no *entiendes* mi pregunta.

Él no _____ . . . .   Uds. no _____ . . . .

10. Ese idiota siempre *ríe.*

Esos idiotas siempre _____ . . . .

Tú siempre _____ . . . .

B. Repeat the sentence, replacing the given verb with the appropriate form of the verb in parentheses.

EXAMPLE: Yo compro los libros. (perder)
Yo pierdo los libros.

1. Yo no sé la respuesta. (recordar)

_____

2. ¿A qué hora regresa ella? (volver)

_____

3. Nuestros amigos no dicen la verdad. (confesar)

_____

4. ¿Tienen Uds. mucho dinero? (pedir)

_____

5. La película termina a las diez. (empezar)

_____

6. No comprendo a la profesora. (entender)

_____

7. Los soldados atacan la ciudad. (defender)

_____

8. Yo nunca doy instrucciones. (seguir)

_____

9. Deseamos patinar en el hielo. (preferir)

_____

10. ¿Cuándo apagas las luces hoy? (encender)

_____

C. Answer with a complete sentence in Spanish:

1. ¿A qué hora empiezan Uds. la lección de español?

_____

2. ¿Siempre sigues las instrucciones del profesor?

_____

3. ¿Qué hacen el avión y el pájaro?

_____

4. ¿Qué lleva Ud. cuando llueve mucho?

_____

5. ¿Qué puede Ud. ver en el cielo en una noche clara?

_____

6. ¿A qué hora encienden Uds. las luces en su casa?

_____

7. ¿A dónde piensa Ud. ir esta noche?

_____

8. ¿Vuelve Ud. a casa temprano o tarde los sábados por la noche?

_____

9. ¿Cuánto dinero pide Ud. a sus padres todos los días?

_____

10. ¿Cuánto cuesta un buen par de zapatos para mujeres (o para hombres)?

_____

D. *Optional Exercise: Reflexive Verbs* (*See chapter 27*). Answer with a complete sentence in Spanish:

1. ¿A qué hora te acuestas por lo general?

_____

2. ¿Se duerme Ud. en seguida después de trabajar muchas horas?

_____

3. ¿Dónde se sienta la profesora (el profesor) en la sala de clase?

_____

4. ¿Qué hace una persona cuando se siente enferma?

_____

5. ¿Se viste Ud. rápidamente por la mañana antes de ir a la escuela?

_____

E. Translate into Spanish:

1. *a.* We have lunch at noon. _____

   b. They have lunch at 1:00. _____

2. *a.* Can you come early tonight? _____

   b. Can they come late tomorrow? _____

3. *a.* I'm not repeating the question. _____

   b. She's not repeating the answer. _____

4. *a.* Why don't they close the window now? _____

_____

   b. Why doesn't he close the door at once? _____

_____

5. *a.* Isn't she returning the money tomorrow? _____

_____

   b. Aren't you (*Ud.*) returning the books yet? _____

_____

6. *a.* They're losing a lot of time. _____

   b. We're losing a lot of money. _____

7. *a.* I'm sorry, sir.   Lo _____

   b. She's sorry, miss.   Lo _____

8. *a.* You (*Vosotros*) are always smiling. _____

    b. She never smiles. _____

9. *a.* It's not snowing today. _____

    b. It's raining all day (*todo el día*). _____

10. *a.* I'm dreaming of (*con*) the weekend. _____

    b. They (*Ellas*) are dreaming of their teachers. _____

_____

F. *Listening Comprehension.* Your teacher will read to the class ten statements in Spanish. After each statement is read, circle the letter (*a*, *b*, or *c*) of the most logical reply among the three choices.

1. *a.* Pero yo quiero salir.
    b. Las hojas mueren.
    c. Ella lo confiesa.

2. *a.* No, defiendo mi ciudad.
    b. No, yo digo la verdad.
    c. Sí, y también como papas.

3. *a.* Al contrario, es muy barata: cuesta sólo diez dólares.
    b. Sí, cuesta cinco centavos.
    c. Nieva mucho hoy.

4. *a.* Sí, lo sentimos mucho.
    b. Sí, es muy fácil.
    c. No, ella sirve pasteles.

5. *a.* Sí, quiero comer dulces en la escuela.
    b. No, los perros muerden a los niños.
    c. Sí, queremos ir a España y Francia.

6. *a.* Sí, ella almuerza a la una de la tarde.
    b. Sí, almuerzo a medianoche, como siempre.
    c. No, almuerzo a mediodía, como todos los días.

7. *a.* Muy bien; entonces podemos comer a tiempo.
    b. Duerma Ud. en la cocina.
    c. Repita Ud. la pregunta, por favor.

8. *a.* Es verdad, ella siempre vuela por el aire.
    b. ¡Claro! Ella es una cocinera excelente.
    c. Sí, él es un buen mecánico.

9. *a.* Tú siempre juegas bien al tenis.
    b. No sé por qué. El profesor enseña muy bien.
    c. Nunca nieva en el verano.

10. *a.* Debemos llevar un paraguas.
    b. Es un buen día para ir a la playa.
    c. El arroz con pollo es delicioso.

4
Formal Commands

mirar:
Mire Ud. (Miren Uds.) el mapa.   Look at the map.

beber:
Beba Ud. (Beban Uds.) el café.   Drink the coffee.

subir:
Suba Ud. (Suban Uds.) la escalera.   Go up the stairs.
No suba Ud. (No suban Uds.).   Don't go up(stairs).

1. To form the command, start with the **yo** form of the present tense. Drop the **-o** ending and replace it as follows:

-AR verbs: add **-e** or **-en.**
-ER and *-IR* verbs: add **-a** or **-an.**

2. The command is made negative by placing **no** before the verb.

3. The pronoun **Ud.** or **Uds.** follows the command form but need not be expressed:

> **¡Miren Uds.!** }
> **¡Miren!** }   Look!

4. Whether a verb is regular, irregular, or stem-changing, the same rule applies: to form the command, always start with the **yo** form of the present tense:

yo **traigo**:
   Traiga Ud. (**Traigan** Uds.) la sopa.   Bring the soup.

yo **vengo**:
   Venga Ud. (**Vengan** Uds.) mañana.   Come tomorrow.

yo **recuerdo**:
   Recuerde Ud. (**Recuerden** Uds.)   Remember.

yo **repito**:
   Repita Ud. (**Repitan** Uds.).   Repeat.

Practice A: Write the **yo** form, then the singular and plural command forms.

EXAMPLES:

| ver | *yo veo* | *vea Ud.* | *vean Uds.* |
| no tomar | *yo no tomo* | *no tome Ud.* | *no tomen Uds.* |

1. contestar _____ _____ _____
2. no comer _____ _____ _____
3. vivir _____ _____ _____
4. no salir _____ _____ _____
5. hacer _____ _____ _____
6. traducir _____ _____ _____
7. decir _____ _____ _____
8. tener _____ _____ _____
9. no mostrar _____ _____ _____
10. devolver _____ _____ _____
11. dormir _____ _____ _____
12. no confesar _____ _____ _____
13. defender _____ _____ _____
14. no mentir _____ _____ _____
15. pedir _____ _____ _____

Irregular Command Forms

dar, to give	*dé* Ud.	*den* Uds.
estar, to be	*esté* Ud.	*estén* Uds.
ir, to go	*vaya* Ud.	*vayan* Uds.
saber, to know	*sepa* Ud.	*sepan* Uds.
ser, to be	*sea* Ud.	*sean* Uds.

5. The command form of **dar** has an accent mark in the singular (**dé** Ud.) but not in the plural (**den** Uds.).

Practice B: Complete the Spanish sentences.

1. Go home. _____ Ud. a casa.
2. Be good. _____ Uds. buenos.
(Use *ser.*)

3. Know the lesson. _____ Ud. la lección.

4. Don't be here late. No _____ Uds. aquí tarde.
(Use *estar*.)

5. Don't give the hat to Mary. No _____ Ud. el sombrero
a María.

Forming Commands With Reflexive Verbs

quedarse, to remain, to stay

    Quédese Ud. (**Quédense** Uds.) en casa   Stay home today.
    hoy.

    No se quede Ud. (**No se queden** Uds.)   Do not stay home today.
    en casa hoy.

sentarse, to sit down

    Siéntese (Siéntense) aquí.   Sit down here.

    No se siente (No se sienten) allí.   Don't sit down there.

6. To express a command with a reflexive verb, attach **se** to the command form of the verb. Note the accent mark on the stressed vowel.

7. To make the command negative, place **se** between **no** and the verb. (Omit the accent mark in negative commands.)

Practice C: Change each command from the affirmative to the negative or vice versa.

EXAMPLES:

Levántese Ud. temprano.   *No se levante Ud. temprano.*

No se quiten Uds. los guantes.   *Quítense Uds. los guantes.*

1. Lávense las manos.   _____

2. No se acueste Ud. ahora.   _____

3. Diviértase en España.   _____

4. No se despierten Uds. antes de las seis.   _____

EJERCICIOS

A. As shown in the examples, write a sentence in Spanish that has the same meaning as the given sentence, then translate into English.

EXAMPLES:

Haga Ud. el favor de venir.   *Venga Ud., por favor.*

                     Please come.

Hagan Uds. el favor de no entrar.   *No entren Uds., por favor.*

                  Please do not enter.

1. Haga Ud. el favor de volver temprano. _____

        _____

2. Hagan Uds. el favor de traer las cartas. _____

        _____

3. Haga el favor de no decir eso. _____

        _____

4. Hagan el favor de no salir ahora. _____

        _____

5. Haga Ud. el favor de usar la escalera. _____

        _____

EXAMPLES:

Tenga Ud. la bondad de escribir.   *Escriba Ud., por favor.*

                 Please write.

Tengan Uds. la bondad de no gritar.   *No griten Uds., por favor.*

               Please do not shout.

6. Tenga Ud. la bondad de repetir la pregunta. _____

        _____

7. Tengan Uds. la bondad de ser sinceros. _____

        _____

8. Tenga la bondad de estar aquí a las siete. _____

        _____

9. Tenga Ud. la bondad de no salir de casa. _____

        _____

10. Tengan la bondad de no cerrar la puerta. _____

        _____

On lines *a* and *b*, write sentences in Spanish that have the same meaning as the given sentence; on line *c*, translate them into English.

EXAMPLES:

Tenga Ud. la bondad de sentarse allí.

a. *Haga Ud. el favor de sentarse allí.*
b. *Siéntese Ud. allí, por favor.*
c. *Please sit (down) there.*

Hagan Uds. el favor de no dormirse en la clase.

a. *Tengan Uds. la bondad de no dormirse en la clase.*
b. *No se duerman Uds. en la clase, por favor.*
c. *Please do not fall asleep in class.*

11. Tenga Ud. la bondad de no sentarse en esta silla.

a. _____

b. _____

c. _____

12. Hagan Uds. el favor de no quedarse en esta habitación.

a. _____

b. _____

c. _____

13. Tenga la bondad de quitarse el sombrero.

a. _____

b. _____

c. _____

14. Hagan el favor de callarse.

a. _____

b. _____

c. _____

15. Tengan Uds. la bondad de vestirse ahora.

a. _____

b. _____

c. _____

B. Translate into Spanish. (Items 16 to 20 require the use of reflexive verbs.)

1. Be there at six o'clock, Mrs. Rodríguez. (Use *estar*.)

_____

2. Take the medicine three times a day (*al día*), Mr. López.

_____

3. Steven and Lola, don't go to the city today.

_____

4. Boys, don't fall into the lake (*al lago*).

_____

5. Finish the job now, men.

_____

6. Know the answers tomorrow, students.

_____

7. Boys and girls, write the words on the paper.

_____

8. Have patience, madame.

_____

9. Listen to the music, girls.

_____

10. Read the article tonight, gentlemen.

_____

11. Young man, please put the newspaper on the table. (Use *por favor*.)

_____

12. Please close the door, Miss Sánchez. (Use *por favor*.)

_____

13. Do not return here before five o'clock, sir.

_____

14. Employees, don't ask for more money. (to ask for = *pedir*)

_____

15. Know the words for the test, John.

_____

16. Stay here this afternoon, gentlemen.

_____

17. Please put on your jacket (*la chaqueta*). (Use *por favor.*)

_____

18. Ladies, don't get angry.

_____

19. Please sit down here, Mr. González. (Use *por favor.*)

_____

20. Don't go to bed late tonight, Mrs. Benítez.

_____

La Bahía de Acapulco, México

5
Familiar Commands

canta	**Canta** (tú) ahora.	Sing now.
come	**Come** (tú) la ensalada.	Eat the salad.
escribe	**Escribe** (tú) la carta.	Write the letter.
empieza	**Empieza** a leer.	Begin reading.
vuelve	**Vuelve** pronto.	Come back soon.
da	**Da** el dinero a José.	Give the money to Joseph.
está	**Está** aquí a las dos.	Be here at two o'clock.

1. The familiar command* is identical in form to the third person singular of the present tense. With a few exceptions (see page 36), this is true of *all* verbs.

2. The pronoun **tú** follows the verb but is most often omitted.

3. Compare:

¡Oiga Ud.!	**¡Oye** (tú)!	Hear! (Listen!)
¡Siga Ud.!	**¡Sigue** (tú)!	Follow! (Continue!)
¡Traduzca Ud.!	**¡Traduce** (tú)!	Translate!
¡Traiga Ud.!	**¡Trae** (tú)!	Bring!

Practice A: Change the form of the command from the formal to the familiar.

1. Almuerce Ud. a mediodía.

_____ tú

2. Confiese Ud. la verdad.

_____ tú

3. Tome Ud. café.

_____ tú

4. Viva Ud. en México.

_____ tú

5. Traiga Ud. el dinero.

_____ tú

6. Oiga Ud. la música.

_____ tú

7. Sepa Ud. la lección.

_____ tú

8. Conduzca Ud. con cuidado.

_____ tú

---

*This chapter deals with commands in the familiar *singular*, or **tú** form. For the familiar plural, or **vosotros** form, see Appendix X.

Irregular Familiar Commands

DECIR: *Di* (tú) la verdad.   Tell the truth.
HACER: *Haz* el trabajo.   Do the work.
IR: *Ve* a casa.   Go home.
PONER: *Pon* el libro aquí.   Put the book here.
SALIR: *Sal* temprano.   Leave early.
SER: *Sé* bueno.   Be good.
TENER: *Ten* paciencia.   Have patience.
VENIR: *Ven* acá.   Come here.

4. These eight command forms are irregular because they differ from the third-person-singular form of the verb and must be learned individually.

5. Other irregular verbs have *regular* **tú** commands. For example:

TRAER: **Trae** (tú) los discos.   Bring the records.
ESTAR: **Está** aquí a las dos.   Be here at two o'clock.
DAR: **Da** el dinero a José.   Give the money to Joseph.
OIR: **Oye** el ruido.   Hear the noise.

Practice B: Change the command from the formal to the familiar.

1. Salga Ud. de mi casa.

   _____ tú

2. Haga Ud. el favor de escuchar.

   _____ tú

3. Ponga Ud. la silla aquí, por favor.

   _____ tú

4. Diga Ud. algo.

   _____ tú

5. Venga Ud. conmigo en seguida.

   _____ tú

Negative Familiar Commands

Habla tú bien.
Speak well.

No habl**es** en voz baja.
Don't speak in a low voice.

Vuelve pronto.
Return soon.

No vuelv**as** tarde.
Don't return late.

Divide el pastel.
Divide the pie.

No divid**as** el dinero.
Don't divide the money.

Haz la tarea.
Do the task.

No ha**gas** ese trabajo.
Don't do that work.

Di la respuesta.
Tell the answer.

No di**gas** nada.
Don't say anything.

6. To form the negative **tú** command, add **-s** to the **Ud.** command form: **diga** Ud.—no diga**s** (tú), etc.:

Mira tú.	**Mire** Ud.	No **mires** tú.
Duerme tú.	**Duerma** Ud.	No **duermas** tú.
Ven tú.	**Venga** Ud.	No **vengas** tú.

Practice C: Change to the negative.

1. Mira la televisión esta noche.

   No _____

2. Aprende esta lección.

   No _____

3. Asiste al concierto.

   No _____

4. Cierra la puerta.

   No _____

5. Envuelve el paquete.

   No _____

6. Pon el espejo allí.

   No _____

7. Ven con nosotros.

   No _____

8. Haz el favor.

   No _____

9. Ve al museo con Roberto.

   No _____

10. Contesta a mi pregunta.

   No _____

Familiar Commands Used With Object Pronouns*

Háblame, niño.
Speak to me, child.

Duérmete en seguida.
Fall asleep at once.

Ponlo en la mesa.
Put it on the table.

Hazme un favor.
Do me a favor.

Tráemelo ahora.
Bring it to me now.

Díselo más tarde.
Tell it to him later.

No **me** hables, por favor.
Don't speak to me, please.

No **te** duermas todavía.
Don't fall asleep yet.

No **lo** pongas allí.
Don't put it there.

No **me** hagas ese favor.
Don't do me that favor.

No **me lo** traigas hoy.
Don't bring it to me today.

No **se lo** digas ahora.
Don't tell it to him now.

---

*For the forms of object pronouns, see chapters 24 and 25.

7. Object pronouns are attached to the verb in **tú** commands in the same way as they are to the **Ud.** commands. When the command is negative, object pronouns are placed between **no** and the verb. Note that the single-syllable command forms take no accent mark when one pronoun is attached but take an accent mark on the third syllable from the end when two pronouns are added. (Dinos, but Dínos**lo**.)

Practice D: Change to the negative or affirmative.

EXAMPLES: No te levantes tarde.   *Levántate* temprano.
                Hazlo hoy.   *No lo hagas* mañana.

1. No me mires así.   _____ ahora.

2. Hazlos en seguida.   _____ nunca.

3. No la pongas en la mesa.   _____ en la silla.

4. Siéntate junto a mí.   _____ junto a él.

5. No nos hables de eso.   _____ de algo mejor.

EJERCICIOS

A. Complete the response with a *tú* command as shown in the example.

EXAMPLE: Yo quiero comer ensalada.
           Pues, *come ensalada*, si quieres.

1. Yo quiero tomar café.

Pues, _____, si quieres.

2. Yo quiero volver tarde.

Pues, _____, si quieres.

3. Yo quiero vender el tocadiscos.

Pues, _____, si quieres.

4. Yo quiero ser el Presidente de los Estados Unidos.

Pues, _____, si quieres.

5. Yo quiero hacer las tareas.

Pues, _____, si quieres.

B. Reply with a *tú* command as shown in the example.

EXAMPLE: Yo voy a prepararla.
           Pues, *prepárala*.

1. Yo voy a sentarme aquí.

Pues, _____.

2. Yo voy a ponerlas en la cama.

Pues, _____.

3. Yo voy a escribirles.

Pues, _____.

4. Yo voy a besarte ahora.

Pues, _____.

5. Yo voy a devolvérselo a ella.

Pues, _____.

C. Reply with a negative *tú* command as shown in the example.

EXAMPLE: Yo no quiero hablar.
  Entonces, *no hables*.

1. Yo no quiero venir hoy.
Entonces _____.

2. Yo no quiero ir al cine.

Entonces, _____.

3. Yo no quiero cantar.

Entonces, _____.

4. No quiero beber leche.

Entonces, _____.

5. No quiero decir eso.

Entonces, _____.

D. Complete the response with a negative *tú* command as shown in the example.

EXAMPLE: No voy a decírtelo.
  No me importa; *no me lo digas*.

1. Yo no voy a vendérsela a nadie.

No me importa; _____.

2. No voy a pedirlos.

No me importa; _____.

3. No voy a quejarme de ella.

No me importa; _____.

4. No voy a darte el dinero.

No me importa; _____.

5. No voy a hacerlo.

No me importa; _____.

E. Translate into Spanish. (Use the *tú* command form.)

1. *a.* Sleep here tonight. _____

    b. Don't sleep at home. _____

2. *a.* Take John to the movies this afternoon. (Use *llevar*.) _____

    _____

    b. Don't take him to the Mall (*centro comercial*). _____

    _____

3. *a.* Return early this evening. _____

    b. Don't return late. _____

4. *a.* Sit here near me. _____

    b. Don't sit there, near her. _____

5. *a.* Tell them the truth. _____

    b. Don't tell them a lie. _____

6. *a.* Have patience. _____

    b. Don't be afraid. _____

7. *a.* Stay at home tonight. _____

    b. Don't stay in the street. _____

8. *a.* Go to bed on time. _____

    b. Don't go to bed after midnight. _____

9. *a.* Be good. _____

    b. Don't be bad. _____

10. *a.* Show it (*f.*) to me. _____

    b. Don't show it to him. _____

PART TWO

PAST TENSES

6
The Preterite Tense: Regular Verbs

	-AR VERBS	*-ER* AND *-IR* VERBS	
	prestar to lend	**romper** to break	**recibir** to receive
	Singular		
yo	prest**é** *I lent*	romp**í** *I broke*	recib**í** *I received*
tú	prest**aste**	romp**iste**	recib**iste**
Ud. él ella	prest**ó**	romp**ió**	recib**ió**
	Plural		
nosotros nosotras	prest**amos**	romp**imos**	recib**imos**
vosotros vosotras	prest**asteis**	romp**isteis**	recib**isteis**
Uds. ellos ellas	prest**aron**	romp**ieron**	recib**ieron**

1. The preterite tense is equivalent to the past tense in English: *I ate, she went, we talked, did he work?, we did not speak.*

2. To form the preterite, add the following endings to the stem of the infinitive:

	-*AR*	-*ER* AND -*IR*
yo	-**é**	-**í**
tú	-**aste**	-**iste**
Ud., él, ella	-**ó**	-**ió**
nosotros(-as)	-**amos**	-**imos**
vosotros(-as)	-**asteis**	-**isteis**
Uds., ellos, ellas	-**aron**	-**ieron**

3. The **nosotros** form of the -*AR* and -*IR* verbs in the preterite is identical to the **nosotros** form in the present tense:

hablamos $\begin{cases} \text{we speak (are speaking)} \\ \text{we spoke} \end{cases}$

escribimos $\begin{cases} \text{we write (are writing)} \\ \text{we wrote} \end{cases}$

4. -*ER* and -*IR* verbs have the same endings in the preterite.

5. Stem-vowel changes in the present-tense forms of -*AR* and -*ER* verbs do not occur in the preterite:*

	PRESENT	PRETERITE
pensar	yo **pie**nso	yo pensé
defender	Ud. defie**nde**	Ud. defendió
encontrar	ellos encue**ntran**	ellos encontraron
mover	tú mue**ves**	tú moviste

6. The verb **ver** has regular preterite endings but its first and third person singular forms are now written without accent marks: **vi,** viste, **vio,** vimos, visteis, vieron.

Practice A: Write the preterite forms of the verbs that are used with the given pronouns as subjects.

EXAMPLE:

Uds.	*contestaron*	*perdieron*	*describieron*
	contestar	perder	describir
1. yo	_____	_____	_____
	abrir	comer	encontrar

*-*IR* verbs that have stem changes in the present tense also undergo some stem changes in the preterite: see page 58.

2. tú   _____   _____   _____
            recordar   responder   escribir

3. nosotros   _____   _____   _____
            entender   pasar   salir

4. ella   _____   _____   _____
            subir   prometer   entrar

5. Uds.   _____   _____   _____
            cantar   partir   volver

7. The following adverbial phrases are typical of the kinds of expressions that are often used with the preterite tense:

ayer, yesterday

ayer por la mañana, yesterday morning

ayer por la tarde, yesterday afternoon

anoche, last night

la semana pasada, last week

el mes pasado, last month

el año pasado, last year

hace tres días, three days ago*

hace diez años, ten years ago

> *Practice B:* Complete the English translations.

EXAMPLES: Vivo en Nueva York.   Viví en Madrid hace dos años.
               I *live* in New York.   I *lived* in Madrid two years ago.

¿Dónde vive ella ahora?
Where *does* she *live* now?

1. Escriben cartas a sus parientes.

    They _____ letters to their relatives.

    Escribieron una carta anoche.

    They _____ a letter last night.

2. ¿Encuentra interesante la ciudad?

    _____ she _____ the city interesting?

    ¿Encontró ella su libro?

    _____ she _____ her book?

---

*See page 59.

3. Bebemos cerveza todos los días.

   We _____ beer every day.

   Bebimos vino anoche.

   We _____ wine last night.

4. Yo no escucho la música ahora.

   I _____ not _____ to the music now.

   Yo no escuché el disco antes.

   I _____ not _____ to the record before.

5. ¿A qué hora salen del museo esta tarde?

   At what time _____ they _____ the museum this afternoon?

   ¿A qué hora salieron ayer por la tarde?

   At what time _____ they _____ yesterday afternoon?

6. Mi lección de tenis termina a las cinco hoy.

   My tennis lesson _____ at five o'clock today.

   Mi lección de piano terminó a las ocho ayer.

   My piano lesson _____ at eight o'clock yesterday.

7. El avión vuela a 800 kilómetros por hora.

   The plane _____ at 800 kilometers an hour.

   El avión voló a 500 kilómetros por hora hace diez años.

   The plane _____ at 500 kilometers an hour ten years ago.

8. Este invierno no nieva mucho.

   This winter it _____ not _____ a lot.

   El invierno pasado nevó mucho.

   Last winter it _____ a lot.

9. Ella no devuelve los libros a la biblioteca hoy.

   She _____ not _____ the books to the library today.

   Ella no devolvió los libros a la biblioteca ayer.

   She _____ not _____ the books to the library yesterday.

10. ¿Qué programa ves esta noche en la televisión?

    What program _____ you _____ tonight on television?

    ¿Qué programa viste anoche en la televisión?

    What program _____ you _____ last night on television?

EJERCICIOS

A. Repeat the sentence, using the new subject.

 EXAMPLE: Yo viví en Madrid el verano pasado.
 Mis padres *vivieron en Madrid el verano pasado.*

1. Nosotros admiramos las pinturas en el museo.

 Yo _____.

2. ¿Quién compró el coche?

 ¿Quiénes _____?

3. Ellos dividieron el pastel en cuatro partes.

 Él _____.

4. El vestido costó cien dólares.

 Los trajes _____.

5. Tú no confesaste la verdad al juez.

 Vosotros _____.

6. Los chicos subieron la escalera muy de prisa.

 La niña _____.

7. ¿Cuántas copas de vino bebieron Uds.?

 ¿_____ ella?

8. ¿Viste tú el programa anoche?

 ¿_____ él _____?

9. ¿A qué hora encendió Ud. la luz de la cocina?

 ¿_____ tú _____?

10. Nosotras devolvimos los regalos a la tienda.

 Yo _____.

B. Change the verb to the preterite.

 EXAMPLE: Ud. vuelve tarde hoy.
 Ud. _____*volvió*_____ tarde anoche.

1. Hoy visito a mis primos en Los Angeles.

 El mes pasado _____ a mis parientes en San Diego.

2. Ahora bebemos leche.

 Esta mañana _____ café.

3. En este momento escuchan la música *rock*.

Anoche _____ la música clásica.

4. ¿Qué venden hoy en el mercado?

¿Qué _____ ayer?

5. ¿A qué hora sales de la escuela generalmente?

¿A qué hora _____ ayer?

6. Mi padre compra un coche nuevo hoy.

La semana pasada _____ un televisor en colores.

7. Siempre vuelve a la misma hora.

Anoche _____ a las siete y media.

8. Este invierno nieva muy poco.

El invierno pasado _____ muchísimo.

9. Hoy escribo una carta a mi amigo en San Juan.

_____ a mis tíos en Miami hace tres días.

10. Ya no llueve.

_____ mucho hace una hora.

C. Answer with a complete sentence in Spanish:

1. ¿Cuánto costó una buena chaqueta de cuero hace cinco años?

_____

2. ¿A qué hora de la noche volvió Ud. a casa el sábado pasado?

_____

3. ¿Qué programa interesante vio Ud. en la televisión anoche?

_____

4. ¿Tomó su familia vino anoche con la cena?

_____

5. ¿Qué aprendieron Uds. ayer en la clase de español?

_____

6. ¿A qué hora empezó esta clase ayer?

_____

7. ¿Voló Ud. a la luna el año pasado?

_____

8. ¿Tomaste un buen desayuno ayer por la mañana?

_____

9. ¿A qué escuela asistió Ud. hace cinco años?

_____

10. ¿Dónde vivió su familia hace cuatro meses?

_____

D. Translate into Spanish:

1. _a._ Did you sell your bicycle last week?

_____

_b._ Did she sell her car yesterday?

_____

2. _a._ Last night I studied three hours.

_____

_b._ Yesterday my brothers studied all evening (_toda la noche_).

_____

3. _a._ Didn't you (_tú_) understand the lesson this morning?

_____

_b._ Didn't you (_Ud._) understand the program last night?

_____

4. _a._ Where did your father work last year?

_____

_b._ Where did they (_f._) work yesterday afternoon?

_____

5. _a._ We attended the same university ten years ago.

_____

_b._ Susan attended the same high school last year.

_____

6. _a._ Where did you (_tú_) lose your watch?

_____

_b._ When did they (_m._) lose their money?

_____

7. *a.* You (*tú*) promised to bring the tapes.

_____

    b. You (*vosotros*) promised to send postcards.

_____

8. *a.* Who (*Quién*) opened the windows?

_____

    b. Who (*Quiénes*) opened the doors?

_____

9. *a.* When did she travel through Europe?

_____

    b. When did they (*f.*) travel through Spain?

_____

10. *a.* I lived in Argentina two years ago.

_____

    b. Our grandparents lived in Florida six months ago.

_____

E. *Listening Comprehension.* Your teacher will read to the class ten questions in Spanish. After each question is read to you, circle the letter (*a*, *b*, or *c*) of the most appropriate answer.

1. *a.* Cantamos canciones populares.
   b. Vimos a muchas chicas.
   c. Canté una canción puertorriqueña.

2. *a.* Nacimos en 1960.
   b. Nací en Panamá.
   c. Nacimos en Guatemala.

3. *a.* El viento entra.
   b. Siempre cierro las ventanas.
   c. Abro el libro.

4. *a.* No visité a México.
   b. Siempre visitamos países hispanos.
   c. Visitamos a Chile.

5. *a.* Sí, bajé a la calle.
   b. No bajé del coche.
   c. Sí, bajamos al segundo piso.

6. *a.* Sí, lo vimos a las siete.
   b. No, vi otro más interesante.
   c. Sí, viví en California.

7. *a.* Recibí el paquete ayer.
   b. Recibimos 10 pesos la semana pasada.
   c. Recibí cinco dólares anoche.

8. *a.* Aprendieron la historia de Sudamérica.
   b. Aprendiste muchas cosas.
   c. Aprendí los verbos irregulares.

9. *a.* Sí, nevó mucho.
   b. No, nuestros abuelos volaron por el aire.
   c. Sí, y por eso nos quedamos en casa.

10. *a.* Bebió vino.
   b. Bebimos leche.
   c. Bebiste agua.

7
The Preterite Tense: Irregular Verbs

Group 1: Verbs With Special Preterite Stems

-U- STEMS

andar, to walk, go (**anduv-**)	*anduve*	*anduviste*	*anduvo*	*anduvimos*	*anduvisteis*	*anduvieron*
caber, to fit (**cup-**)	*cupe*	*cupiste*	*cupo*	*cupimos*	*cupisteis*	*cupieron*
estar, to be (**estuv-**)	*estuve*	*estuviste*	*estuvo*	*estuvimos*	*estuvisteis*	*estuvieron*
poder, to be able, can (**pud-**)	*pude*	*pudiste*	*pudo*	*pudimos*	*pudisteis*	*pudieron*
poner, to put (**pus-**)	*puse*	*pusiste*	*puso*	*pusimos*	*pusisteis*	*pusieron*
saber, to know (**sup-**)	*supe*	*supiste*	*supo*	*supimos*	*supisteis*	*supieron*
tener, to have (**tuv-**)	*tuve*	*tuviste*	*tuvo*	*tuvimos*	*tuvisteis*	*tuvieron*

-I- STEMS

hacer, to do, make (**hic-**)	*hice*	*hiciste*	*hizo*	*hicimos*	*hicisteis*	*hicieron*
querer, to want (**quis-**)	*quise*	*quisiste*	*quiso*	*quisimos*	*quisisteis*	*quisieron*
venir, to come (**vin-**)	*vine*	*viniste*	*vino*	*vinimos*	*vinisteis*	*vinieron*

-J- STEMS

Conducir (to lead, drive), **decir** (to say, tell), and **traer** (to bring) have preterite stems that end in **j.** The ending **-ieron** becomes **-eron:**

conducir (conduj-)	conduje	condujiste	condujo	condujimos	condujisteis	condujeron
decir (dij-)	dije	dijiste	dijo	dijimos	dijisteis	dijeron
traer (traj-)	traje	trajiste	trajo	trajimos	trajisteis	trajeron

1. These preterite forms have no accent marks.

2. The endings that are added to these special preterite stems are:

-e, -iste, -o, -imos, -isteis, -ieron (sometimes **-eron**)

3. The third person singular of **hacer** is **hizo.** In this form, the **c** changes to **z** to represent the same sound before the letter **o.**

4. The preterite of **saber** means *learned* or *found out.* The preterite of **tener** sometimes means *got* or *received:*

Supimos la verdad anoche.   We learned the truth last night.

Tuve una carta ayer.   I got a letter yesterday.

Practice A: Complete each sentence with the preterite form of the verb.

1. ¿Dónde _____ tú la revista?
   (poner)

2. ¿Cuándo _____ Uds. a casa?
   (venir)

3. Nosotras _____ en casa anoche.
   (estar)

4. El no _____ venir a la fiesta.
   (poder)

5. Ellas _____ la comida a la mesa.
   (traer)

6. Elena no _____ la tarea.
   (hacer)

7. Yo _____ el paquete ayer por la mañana.
   (tener)

8. Los chicos _____ por las calles.
   (andar)

9. ¿Por qué no _____ Uds. bailar?
   (querer)

10. ¿Qué _____ tú al profesor?
    (decir)

Group 2: Verbs With Third-Person Preterite Endings -YÓ and -YERON

caer, to fall	caí	caíste	*cayó*	caímos	caísteis	*cayeron*
creer, to believe	creí	creíste	*creyó*	creímos	creísteis	*creyeron*
leer, to read	leí	leíste	*leyó*	leímos	leísteis	*leyeron*
oír, to hear	oí	oíste	*oyó*	oímos	oísteis	*oyeron*

5. In this group of verbs, **i** changes to **y** in the endings of the third person singular and plural. All other endings have an accented **i**.

Group 3: DAR, IR, SER

dar, to give	*di*	*diste*	*dio*	*dimos*	*disteis*	*dieron*
ir, to go } **ser,** to be }	*fui*	*fuiste*	*fue*	*fuimos*	*fuisteis*	*fueron*

6. The preterite endings of **dar** are the same as those for regular *-ER* and *-IR* verbs.

7. The preterite forms of **ir** and **ser** are identical.

8. The forms **di, dio, fui,** and **fue,** which were once accented, are no longer written with accent marks.

Practice B: Indicate whether the verb is a form of *ser* or *ir* by writing either *ser* or *ir* in parentheses at the beginning of your answer; then translate the sentence into English.

1. Fueron a California la semana pasada. _____

2. Fueron buenos profesores. _____

3. ¿Quién fue esa mujer? _____

4. ¿Quién fue al cine anoche? _____

Practice C: Complete the sentence with the preterite form of the verb.

1. ¿Qué le _____ Ud.?
   (dar)

2. Carlos y yo _____ buenos amigos hace diez años.
   (ser)

3. ¿Qué _____ del árbol?
   (caer)

4. Ellos _____ mucho ruido en la calle.
   (oír)

5. Tú no _____ ese libro.
   (leer)

6. ¿Adónde _____ Uds. anoche?
   (ir)

7. Yo no le _____ nada.
   (dar)

8. Mi hermana _____ a Inglaterra el verano pasado.
   (ir)

EJERCICIOS

A. Change the verb from the present tense to the preterite. (Write the preterite form in the blank at the right.)

EXAMPLE: Mi padre *es* profesor. _____*fue*_____

1. ¿Qué *traen* ellos a la tertulia? _____

2. Yo no *quiero* oír esa música. _____

3. Él no *hace* bien el trabajo. _____

4. ¿Adónde *vas*? _____

5. Los alumnos de la clase de inglés *leen* tres novelas. _____

6. Nosotros *venimos* a casa muy tarde. _____

7. ¿Dónde *está* ella? _____

8. Por fin ellas *saben* la verdad. _____

9. Yo le *digo* la respuesta. _____

10. Él me *da* todo el dinero. _____

11. ¿Quiénes *son* esos señores? _____

12. ¿No *oyes* la televisión? _____

13. ¿Quién no *puede* ver la película? _____

14. ¿*Andáis* vosotros con ella? _____

15. El profesor no *cree* la excusa. _____

16. ¿Qué *dicen* Uds.? _____

17. Estos libros no *caben* en el estante. _____

18. No *sabemos* la respuesta. _____

19. Ella *conduce* su coche rápidamente. _____

20. ¿Dónde *pongo* las revistas? _____

B. Answer with a complete sentence in Spanish:

1. ¿Dónde estuvo Ud. ayer por la mañana?

_____

2. ¿Fueron Uds. a España el verano pasado?

_____

3. ¿Cuántos libros leíste la semana pasada?

_____

4. ¿Tuvo Ud. una carta ayer de Puerto Rico?

_____

5. ¿A qué hora vino Ud. a la escuela hoy?

_____

6. ¿Quién fue el último alcalde de su ciudad?

_____

7. ¿Trajo Ud. su radio a la escuela hoy?

_____

8. ¿Dijo Ud. una mentira a su profesor ayer?

_____

9. ¿Qué quiso Ud. hacer el domingo pasado?

_____

10. ¿Oyeron Uds. la música _rock_ ayer en la clase de matemáticas?

_____

C. Each statement is the answer to a question that begins as shown. Write the rest of the question.

EXAMPLES: Puse la carta en la mesa.   Yo vine a las ocho.
            ¿Dónde _pusiste la carta_?   ¿Quién _vino a las ocho_?

1. Mi padre condujo el coche ayer por la tarde.

   ¿Quién _____?

2. Supe la buena noticia anoche.

   ¿Cuándo _____?

3. Ellos no dijeron nada.

   ¿Qué _____?

4. Estuvimos en el supermercado.

¿Dónde _____?

5. Yo lo hice hace cuatro días.

¿Cuándo _____?

6. No, no quise ir a la fiesta.

¿_____ tú _____?

7. Cinco personas cupieron en el coche.

¿Cuántas _____?

8. Anduve por el parque.

¿Por dónde _____?

9. Fue a Inglaterra.

¿Adónde _____?

10. Fue mi sobrino José.

¿Quién _____?

D. Translate into Spanish:

1. *a.* They (*f.*) brought the records yesterday.

_____

b. We brought the record player last night.

_____

2. *a.* Did you (*tú*) go to the country last summer?

_____

b. Did he go to the concert last Saturday?

_____

3. *a.* When did you (*Ud.*) come home?

_____

b. When did they (*m.*) come to school?

_____

4. *a.* I didn't say anything (*nada*).

_____

b. They (*m.*) didn't say very much.

_____

5. *a.* To whom did he give the stamps?

_____

   b. To whom did they (*f.*) give the money?

_____

6. *a.* Last night we didn't walk very far. (Use *andar*.)

_____

   b. Yesterday morning I didn't walk to school.

_____

7. *a.* What did you (*Uds.*) do last summer?

_____

   b. What did the child do this morning?

_____

8. *a.* A lot of snow fell last winter.

_____

   b. Very little rain fell in April.

_____

9. *a.* They were friends twenty years ago.

_____

   b. I was his friend fifteen years ago.

_____

10. *a.* Did John get the tennis racket? (Use *tener*.)

_____

   b. Did the girls get the bracelets?

_____

11. *a.* We didn't believe the story.

_____

   b. Robert did not believe his brother.

_____

12. *a.* How many books fit on the shelf yesterday?

_____

   b. How many bottles fit in the box that you (*tú*) brought?

_____

13. *a.* I could not (= was not able to) arrive on time.

_____

b. We couldn't hear the program.

_____

14. *a.* Who wanted to see the movie?

_____

b. Susan and Arthur wanted to buy the tape recorder.

_____

15. *a.* Where were you (*vosotras*) last night?

_____

b. Where was he two days ago?

_____

E. *Listening Comprehension.* Your teacher will read to the class ten questions in Spanish. After each question is read to you, circle the letter (*a*, *b*, or *c*) of the most appropriate answer.

1. *a.* No leí nada.
   b. Leímos tres libros.
   c. Leyeron una buena novela.

2. *a.* Hice mi tarea.
   b. Aprendimos los verbos irregulares.
   c. Hicieron cosas interesantes.

3. *a.* Visitó a mis abuelos.
   b. Fui a California.
   c. Tomó el tren para Europa.

4. *a.* Sí, los trajimos ayer.
   b. No, los comieron en casa.
   c. Sí, los trajeron esta mañana.

5. *a.* Lo pusiste en la mesa.
   b. Lo puse en la silla.
   c. Lo pusieron en la cama.

6. *a.* Vino a las siete.
   b. Vine a casa.
   c. Vine a las cuatro y media.

7. *a.* Anduvimos por la plaza principal.
   b. Anduvimos por la comida.
   c. Anduve por el centro comercial.

8. *a.* Le dijimos la verdad.
   b. Le dijo una mentira.
   c. Le dije algo interesante.

9. *a.* La supimos ayer por la tarde.
   b. La supe mañana.
   c. La supe esta mañana.

10. *a.* Pudiste terminar la tarea.
    b. Pude traer los discos.
    c. Pudimos comer una ensalada.

SUPPLEMENT 1: -IR Verbs With Stem Changes in the Preterite

-IR verbs that have stem changes in the present tense will also undergo stem changes in the third-person forms of the preterite. In these forms, the stem vowel of the infinitive changes as follows:

1. **e** becomes **i**.

preferir:	preferí	preferimos
	preferiste	preferisteis

pref**i**rió	pref**i**rieron

Other verbs in this group: **corregir, divertirse, herir, mentir, pedir, reír (sonreír), repetir, seguir, sentir, servir, vestir.** Note the conjugation of **reír** and **sonreír**:

(son)reír:	(son)reí	(son)reímos
	(son)reíste	(son)reísteis

(son)r**ió**	(son)r**i**eron

2. **o** becomes **u**.

dormir:	dormí	dormimos
	dormiste	dormisteis

d**u**rmió	d**u**rmieron

Also in this group: **morir.**

EJERCICIO

F. Complete each sentence with the appropriate preterite form of the verb:

1. Anoche mis padres _____ mucho en la fiesta.
   (divertirse)

2. ¿Cuántos discos _____ José?
   (pedir)

3. Ayer en un accidente de coches _____ seis personas.
   (morir)

4. ¿Qué _____ su tía anoche?
   (servir)

5. ¿A qué hora _____ Ud. esta mañana?
   (vestirse)

6. Ayer mi abuela _____ enferma.
   (sentirse)

7. ¿Dónde _____ tu primo anoche?
   (dormir)

8. El profesor _____ al oír mi respuesta.
   (sonreír)

9. Yo _____ las faltas de mi amigo y él _____
   (corregir)   (corregir)
   las mías.

10. ¿_____ tu padre cuando oyó el chiste?
    (reír)

SUPPLEMENT 2: Expressing "Ago" in Spanish

Ago = **hace,** which is used with the preterite tense. *Ago* can be expressed in Spanish in two ways:

I saw her two hours ago.	La vi **hace dos horas.** **Hace dos horas que** la vi.
They arrived a week ago.	Llegaron **hace una semana.** **Hace una semana que** llegaron.

EJERCICIOS

G. Write the alternate construction, then translate into English.

EXAMPLE: Partieron hace dos días.
   Hace dos días que partieron.   They left two days ago.

1. Hace tres años que vinieron a Nueva York.

   _____

2. Fuimos al concierto hace un mes.

   _____

3. Hace seis meses que nació.

   _____

4. Trajeron las cintas hace una hora.

   _____

5. Hace cinco minutos que la profesora explicó el concepto.

   _____

6. Me dio el dinero hace cuatro días.

   _____

H. Express in Spanish in *two* ways:

1. We learned those verbs two years ago. _____

   _____

2. I arrived at school twenty minutes ago. _____

   _____

3. They went home an hour ago. _____

   _____

4. She was here six weeks ago. _____

   _____

5. We had breakfast a half hour ago. _____

8
The Imperfect Tense

	-AR VERBS	-ER AND -IR VERBS	
	contestar to answer	**vender** to sell	**dormir** to sleep
	I answered *I was answering* *I used to answer*	*I sold* *I was selling* *I used to sell*	*I slept* *I was sleeping* *I used to sleep*
yo	contest*aba*	vend*ía*	dorm*ía*
tú	contest*abas*	vend*ías*	dorm*ías*
Ud., él, ella	contest*aba*	vend*ía*	dorm*ía*
nosotros, nosotras	contest*ábamos*	vend*íamos*	dorm*íamos*
vosotros, vosotras	contest*abais*	vend*íais*	dorm*íais*
Uds., ellos, ellas	contest*aban*	vend*ían*	dorm*ían*

1. To form the imperfect tense of all verbs except **ir, ser,** and **ver,** add the following endings to the stem of the infinitive:

	-AR VERBS	-ER AND -IR VERBS
yo	**-aba**	**-ía**
tú	**-abas**	**-ías**
Ud., él, ella	**-aba**	**-ía**
nosotros(-as)	**-ábamos**	**-íamos**
vosotros(-as)	**-abais**	**-íais**
Uds., ellos, ellas	**-aban**	**-ían**

2. Note the accent mark on the first **a** of the ending **-ábamos.**

3. The imperfect tense is often equivalent to English *used to . . .* or *was (were) . . . -ing:**

---

*The imperfect tense of **hacer** has a special meaning when used idiomatically in expressions such as **hacía dos años que vivíamos allí.** See chapter 32.

ella **escribía** $\begin{cases} \text{she was writing} \\ \text{she used to write} \end{cases}$

hablábamos $\begin{cases} \text{we were speaking} \\ \text{we used to speak} \end{cases}$

4. The imperfect tense expresses an action in the past that (1) occurred regularly or repeatedly *or* (2) was in progress:

(1) **Jugábamos** al béisbol todos los sábados.   We played (used to play) baseball every Saturday.

(2) María **estudiaba** y Raúl **escribía** cartas.   Mary was studying and Raúl was writing letters.

Practice A: For each verb, write the form of the imperfect tense that is used with the given pronoun as subject.

1. ella   _____ comprender   _____ estar   _____ venir

2. nosotros   _____ ayudar   _____ escribir   _____ comer

3. Uds.   _____ sentir   _____ defender   _____ andar

4. tú   _____ poner   _____ salir   _____ preguntar

Irregular Verbs in the Imperfect Tense

There are only three verbs that are irregular in the imperfect tense: **ser, ir,** and **ver.**

	ser, to be	**ir,** to go	**ver,** to see
	I was *I used to be*	*I went* *I was going* *I used to go*	*I saw* *I was seeing* *I used to see*
yo	*era*	*iba*	*veía*
tú	*eras*	*ibas*	*veías*
Ud., él, ella	*era*	*iba*	*veía*
nosotros(-as)	*éramos*	*íbamos*	*veíamos*
vosotros(-as)	*erais*	*ibais*	*veíais*
Uds., ellos, ellas	*eran*	*iban*	*veían*

5. Note the accent marks on the **e** of **éramos** and the **i** of **íbamos.**

6. The imperfect tense of **ver** is irregular in that it retains the **e** of the infinitive ending **-er.**

Practice B: For each verb, write the form of the imperfect tense that is used with the indicated subject.

1. ella y yo   _____   _____   _____
                    ser   ir   ver

2. usted no   _____   _____   _____
                    ir   ser   ver

3. los chicos _____   _____   _____
                    ver   ir   ser

Expressions Often Used With the Imperfect Tense

---

7. The following adverbial phrases are typical of the kinds of expressions that often occur with verbs in the imperfect tense:

algunas veces, sometimes   **generalmente,** generally
a menudo }   **siempre,** always
muchas veces } often   **todos los días,** every day

Note that such phrases indicate a repeated or recurrent action. Thus, they may serve as a clue to the proper tense if you have to choose between the preterite and the imperfect.

Practice C: Complete the English translations.

EXAMPLES: Vivíamos en Chicago.

We __*lived (were living, used to live)*__ in Chicago.

Me visitaban a menudo.

They __*visited (used to visit)*__ me often.

1. Yo estudiaba mis lecciones todos los días.

   I _____ my lessons every day.

2. Ellos comían en la cafetería.

   They _____ in the cafeteria.

3. ¿Que hacían Uds. mientras ellos dormían?

   What _____ while they _____?

4. ¿Qué leías cuando yo miraba la televisión?

   What _____ when I _____
   television?

5. Íbamos al cine los sábados.

We _____ to the movies on Saturdays.

6. Siempre salíamos de casa temprano.

We always _____ the house early.

Practice D: Complete the Spanish sentence with the appropriate form of the verb.

1. (ser) They used to be good students.

_____ buenos estudiantes.

2. (ir) My parents went to the country every summer.

Mis padres _____ al campo cada verano.

3. (ver) Which program were you watching?

¿Qué programa _____ Uds.?

4. (ver) We often saw her at school.

La _____ muchas veces en la escuela.

5. (irse) Sometimes I left early.

Algunas veces me _____ temprano.

6. (ser) Annie and I were close friends.

Anita y yo _____ amigas íntimas.

7. (ser, ir) When you (*tú*) were young, did you often go to the movies?

Cuando _____ joven, ¿_____ a menudo al cine?

EJERCICIOS

A. Write the appropriate form of the verb in the imperfect tense.

EXAMPLE: (decir) Los niños nunca _____*decían*_____ la verdad.

1. (ir) ¿Adónde _____ Uds. cuando encontraron a Juan?

2. (hacer) ¿Qué _____ Ud. en el museo?

3. (llegar) A menudo nosotros _____ tarde a la escuela.

4. (pensar) ¿Qué _____ tú de ese hombre?

5. (ser) _____ las siete cuando llegaron a casa.

6. (partir) El tren siempre _____ a las ocho en punto.

7. (beber) En el verano yo generalmente _____ cerveza.

8. (leer/mirar) Mientras mis padres _____ las revistas, mi hermano y yo _____ la televisión.

9. (ir) Nosotras _____ al cine cuando vimos a Carlos.

10. (viajar) Nuestra familia siempre _____ durante el verano.

11. (volver) ¿A qué hora _____ ellos los domingos?

12. (ver) Mi hermana y yo siempre _____ buenas películas en ese cine.

13. (acostarse) ¿A qué hora te _____ tú los viernes?

14. (levantarse) Yo me _____ a las siete todos los días.

15. (dormirse/estar) Mi abuelo siempre se _____ cuando _____ sentado en el sillón.

B. Change the verb to the imperfect tense. (Write the new verb form in the blank at the right.)

EXAMPLE: Ella *es* mi amiga. _____*era*_____

1. ¿Dónde *estás*, Roberto? _____

2. Siempre *repiten* la misma pregunta. _____

3. Mi padre *trabaja* en una oficina grande. _____

4. ¿Adónde *vamos* todas las semanas? _____

5. A menudo *llueve* en las montañas. _____

6. ¿A qué hora *cierran* las puertas por la noche? _____

7. Generalmente *ven* buenos partidos de béisbol en el estadio. _____

8. Jorge y yo no *somos* buenos jugadores de tenis. _____

9. Ella no *sabe* cocinar bien. _____

10. ¿Qué *tienes* en la mano? _____

_____

C. Answer with a complete sentence in Spanish.

1. ¿Sonó el teléfono anoche mientras Ud. escuchaba sus discos?

_____

2. ¿A qué escuela iba Ud. cuando tenía diez años?

_____

3. ¿Dónde quería su familia pasar las vacaciones?

_____

4. ¿Siempre sabía Ud. hablar español?

_____

5. ¿Qué hora era cuando saliste de casa esta mañana?

_____

6. ¿Cuántos programas veía Ud. generalmente en la televisión cuando estaba de vacaciones?

_____

7. Cuando Ud. era niña (niño), ¿a qué hora iba a la cama?

_____

8. ¿Qué hacía Ud. esta mañana mientras tomaba el desayuno?

_____

9. ¿Bebía Ud. vino cuando tenía tres años?

_____

10. Cuando Ud. estaba en el quinto grado, ¿cómo se llamaba su mejor amigo (amiga)?

_____

D. Translate into Spanish:

1. _a._ We were coming to school. _____

   _b._ I was coming home. _____

2. _a._ Where (_Adónde_) were they going? _____

   _b._ Was she going to the movies? _____

3. _a._ My uncle used to live in Mexico. _____

   _b._ My aunts used to live in Chile. _____

4. _a._ I always used to see my friends. _____

   _b._ We always used to see our relatives. _____

5. _a._ My father traveled (= used to travel) to Spain every summer. _____

   _____

   _b._ My grandparents always traveled through Mexico. _____

   _____

6. _a._ We were walking through the department store. _____

   _b._ Who was walking through the garden? _____

7. _a._ The child used to sleep for (_por_) ten hours. _____

   _____

   _b._ The children used to sleep all afternoon. _____

   _____

8. *a.* It was raining a lot yesterday. _____

    b. It was snowing for two days. _____

9. *a.* I used to get up early on Sundays. _____

    b. My cousin used to get up late on Saturdays. _____

10. *a.* Were you (*tú*) eating hamburgers? _____

    b. What was Mary eating? _____

11. *a.* We used to be good friends. _____

    b. They (*m.*) used to be good tennis players (*jugadores de tenis*). _____

_____

12. *a.* Were you (*tú*) writing to your grandmother? _____

_____

    b. Was she writing to her teacher? _____

13. *a.* He used to go to bed at eleven o'clock. _____

    b. We used to go to bed at half past ten. _____

14. *a.* Were you (*Uds.*) drinking wine or beer? _____

    b. Was John drinking coffee or tea? _____

15. *a.* Where were William and Frank before? _____

    b. Where was the child afterwards? _____

E. *Listening Comprehension.* Your teacher will read to the class ten sentences in Spanish. After each sentence is read to you, circle the letter (*a*, *b*, or *c*) of the correct English translation.

1. *a.* Where were you going?
    b. Where were they going?
    c. Where was he going?

2. *a.* It snowed every day.
    b. It was snowing all day.
    c. It was raining all day.

3. *a.* We could not arrive on time.
    b. They couldn't arrive on time.
    c. Could she arrive on time?

4. *a.* She always got up at 6:00.
    b. We always get up at 6:00.
    c. We always used to get up at 6:00.

5. *a.* We used to see interesting programs.
    b. We see interesting programs.
    c. They used to see interesting programs.

6. *a.* What did she want to do?
   b. What did you wish to do?
   c. Where did you want to go?

7. *a.* While we were reading, the telephone rang.
   b. While they read, the telephone rang.
   c. While she read, the telephone rang.

8. *a.* What was the teacher saying?
   b. What were you saying to the teacher?
   c. What did the teachers say?

9. *a.* They used to be rich lawyers.
   b. He was a rich lawyer.
   c. He is a rich lawyer.

10. *a.* Did they live in San Juan?
    b. I lived in San Juan.
    c. We used to live in San Juan.

Una calle del centro, Bogotá, Colombia

9
The Preterite and Imperfect Tenses Compared

1. *Verbs in a sentence are in the same tense if their actions occur at the same time:*

¿Qué **hicieron** Uds. cuando ellos **entraron**?

What did you do when they came in?

¿Qué **hacían** Uds. mientras yo **estudiaba**?

What were you doing while I studied (was studying)?

2. *The preterite interrupts the imperfect:*

La profesora **explicaba** la regla cuando **sonó** el timbre.

The teacher was explaining the rule when the bell rang.

3. *Verbs in a narration are in the preterite if their actions occurred at one time in the past. They are in the imperfect if their actions occurred regularly or repeatedly in the past.*

a. **Esa mañana** José **fue** el primero en levantarse. Se **vistió** de prisa, se **lavó, bajó** a la cocina, **tomó** una taza de café y **salió** de casa sin despertar a nadie.

b. **Todas las mañanas** José **era** el primero en levantarse. Se **vestía** de prisa, se **lavaba, bajaba** a la cocina, **tomaba** una taza de café y **salía** de casa sin despertar a nadie.

. . . Joseph was the first to arise. He dressed quickly, washed up, went downstairs to the kitchen, drank a cup of coffee, and left the house without waking anyone.

Passage **a** describes what José did on a particular morning; a phrase such as **Esa mañana** is either expressed or implied. Passage **b** describes what José did regularly or repeatedly or often; a phrase such as **Todas las mañanas** is either expressed or implied. Aside from such clues, note that the two passsages can have the same English translation.

Practice A: Underline the more appropriate verb form.

1. While I was studying, she listened to the tapes.

   Mientras yo (estudié / estudiaba), ella (escuchó / escuchaba) las cintas.

2. This morning I got up early, dressed, and had a cup of coffee.

   Esta mañana me (levanté / levantaba) temprano, me (vestí / vestía) y (tomé / tomaba) una taza de café.

3. Yesterday afternoon she wrote a letter.

   Ayer por la tarde (escribió / escribía) una carta.

4. While she wrote, it started to snow.

   Mientras (escribió / escribía), (empezó / empezaba) a nevar.

4. *The time of day in the past is expressed by the imperfect:*

Eran las siete cuando llegaron.

It was seven o'clock when they arrived.

5. *The imperfect is used to describe people, places, or events in the past:*

a. **Había** una vez una muchacha que **era** muy linda. Ella **tenía** los ojos azules y el pelo negro. Cuando **andaba** por las calles, todos los muchachos la **admiraban.**

There was once a girl who was very pretty. She had blue eyes and black hair. When she walked through the streets, all the boys admired her.

b. Las montañas de ese país **eran** altas y hermosas.

The mountains of that country were high and beautiful.

c. Cuando mi tío **vivía** en Puerto Rico, a menudo **iba** a Ponce.

When my uncle lived in Puerto Rico, he often went to Ponce.

In **c**, the verb **vivía** is in the imperfect because it expresses a continuous action in the past ("lived" = "was living").

6. *The preterite is used if the action ended in the past:*

Cuando mi tío vivía en Puerto Rico, **fue** a Ponce para visitar a un amigo, y **se quedó** por dos días.

When my uncle lived in Puerto Rico, he went to Ponce to visit a friend, and he stayed for two days.

Practice B: Underline the more appropriate verb.

1. What time was it when they came in?

   ¿Qué hora (fue / era) cuando (entraron / entraban)?

2. My friend's house was big.

   La casa de mi amigo (fue / era) grande.

3. When we were in Spain we went to Seville, where we stayed for five days.

Cuando (estuvimos / estábamos) en España (fuimos / íbamos) a Sevilla, donde nos (quedamos / quedábamos) cinco días.

4. It was nine o'clock in the evening and the streets were empty.

(Fueron / Eran) las nueve de la noche y las calles (estuvieron / estaban) vacías.

Verbs With Special Meanings in the Preterite or the Imperfect

Preterite	*Imperfect*

conocer

Conocí a Pepe en Panamá.
I *met* (= became acquainted with) Joe in Panama.

Conocía a la mayoría de los invitados.
I *knew* most of the guests.

saber

Supe la verdad ayer.
I *learned* (*found out*) the truth yesterday.

Sabía que el cuento era verdadero.
I *knew* that the story was true.

tener

Tuve un regalo de mi abuelo.
I *got* (*received*) a gift from my grandfather.

Tenía un regalo para mi prima.
I *had* a gift for my cousin.

Note: Care is also needed in choosing between the preterite and the imperfect of **ser, estar, poder,** and **querer.** In some cases, using one tense rather than the other may result in a slight shift in meaning:

Pude llegar a tiempo.
I managed to arrive on time.

Podía llegar a tiempo.
I was able to arrive on time.

When in doubt, it is best to use the imperfect since that tense is most likely to convey the "ordinary" past-tense meanings of these four verbs.

EJERCICIOS

A. Change the verb from the imperfect to the preterite or vice versa.

EXAMPLE: Yo siempre *comía* a las siete.

Ayer ____*comí*____ a las ocho.

1. Todos los días *estudiábamos* por la tarde.

Ayer _____ por la noche.

2. ¿Qué *hicieron* Uds. anoche?

¿Qué _____ Uds. cuando empezó a llover?

3. Mis parientes de Nevada *vinieron* a visitarnos la semana pasada.

Mis parientes de Colorado _____ todos los veranos.

4. Mientras yo *andaba* por el parque, encontré a Lola.

Primero _____ por el parque; luego encontré a Lola.

5. Todos los años *viajábamos* por Europa.

El año pasado _____ por Sudamérica.

6. Yo *dormí* siete horas anoche.

Yo _____ ocho horas cuando tenía once años.

7. Esta tarde vi a mi primo y *fui* al cine con él.

Mientras yo _____ al cine, vi a mi primo.

8. Cuando estaban en Madrid, *visitaban* muchos sitios de interés.

Cuando estaban en Madrid, _____ el museo del Prado un domingo por la tarde.

9. Todas las noches *veíamos* los mismos programas en la televisión.

Anoche _____ un programa excelente.

10. ¿Dónde *viviste* hace cuatro años?

¿_____ en la Argentina mientras tu padre trabajaba en Buenos Aires?

B. Write the appropriate form of the verb in each blank, choosing either the preterite or the imperfect tense in accordance with the meaning of the sentence:

Esta mañana yo _____ a las seis. En seguida _____ en el
    1. levantarse   **2.** entrar

cuarto de baño donde _____. Mientras _____ en el cuarto
    3. lavarse   **4.** estar

de baño, _____ la radio. De repente mi madre me _____
    5. escuchar   **6.** llamar

y me _____ que _____ que salir porque mi padre
    7. decir   **8.** tener

_____ entrar y _____ las siete ya. Yo _____
    9. querer   **10.** ser   **11.** salir

inmediatamente y _____ a tomar el desayuno. Mientras _____
    12. ir   **13.** pasar

al comedor, _____ a mi hermano y le _____. Yo
    14. ver   **15.** saludar

_____ que _____ tarde; por eso _____ muy
    16. saber   **17.** ser   **18.** vestirse

rápidamente. _____ de casa a las siete y media y _____ con
    19. salir   **20.** encontrarse

mi amigo José en la esquina.

C. Answer with a complete sentence in Spanish:

1. ¿Tenían sus padres otros hijos cuando Ud. nació?

_____

2. ¿Qué hacían los estudiantes cuando el profesor (la profesora) entró en la clase?

_____

3. ¿Qué hora era cuando Ud. vino a la escuela hoy?

_____

4. ¿Dónde estaba Ud. ayer por la tarde, y qué tiempo hacía?

_____

5. Cuando Ud. era muy joven, ¿visitaba con frecuencia a sus parientes?

_____

6. Mientras Uds. venían a la clase de español, ¿hablaban de sus estudios o de otra cosa?

_____

7. Mientras Ud. venía a la escuela esta mañana, ¿encontró a algunas personas interesantes?

_____

8. ¿Podía Ud. hacer su tarea sin dificultad?

_____

9. ¿Dónde estaba su madre ayer cuando Ud. estaba en la escuela?

_____

10. ¿Adónde quería Ud. ir con sus amigos el sábado por la noche?

_____

D. Translate into Spanish:

1. _a._ While we were in school, the weather was nice ("good").

_____

_b._ While they were home, the weather was bad.

_____

2. _a._ What were you (_tú_) doing when we came?

_____

_b._ What was she doing when they came?

_____

3. *a.* This morning I left my house, waited for the bus, and went downtown. (to wait for = *esperar*)

_____

b. Last night he left the theater, waited for the train, and went home.

_____

4. *a.* While I was going to the city, I saw my friend Dorothy.

_____

b. While we were going to school, we saw our friends.

_____

5. *a.* It was ten o'clock when they finally arrived.

_____

b. It was midnight when my father finally arrived home.

_____

6. *a.* Last night we watched television for three hours.

_____

b. Yesterday morning we listened to records for an hour. (to listen to = *escuchar*)

_____

7. *a.* Then we had ("took") lunch and went downtown.

_____

b. Afterwards I had dinner and then went to the theater.

_____

8. *a.* While we slept, it rained a lot.

_____

b. While they traveled, it snowed a lot.

_____

9. *a.* Did you know that she was an actress?

_____

b. Did they know that I was a teacher?

_____

10. *a.* She also used to dance very well, but one night she fell. (to fall = *caerse*)

_____

b. You (*tú*) were a good player until (*hasta que*) you fell.

_____

E. *Listening Comprehension.* Your teacher will read to the class ten sentences in Spanish. After each sentence is read to you, circle the letter (*a, b,* or *c*) of the correct English translation.

1. *a.* Where were you when I called?
   b. Where were they when I called?
   c. Where was he when they called?

2. *a.* They used to stay there four hours.
   b. He stayed there four hours.
   c. They stayed there four hours.

3. *a.* It was one o'clock when she came in.
   b. It was one o'clock when they came in.
   c. It was one o'clock when I came in.

4. *a.* He got up, got dressed, and had coffee.
   b. I got up, got dressed, and had coffee.
   c. I was getting up, getting dressed, and having coffee.

5. *a.* While we were walking through the street, Charles saw us.
   b. While we walked through the street, we saw Charles.
   c. While they walked through the street, they saw Charles.

6. *a.* When he studied at the University of California, he took a trip to Mexico.
   b. When they studied at the University of California, they took trips to Mexico.
   c. When I studied at the University of California, I used to take trips to Mexico.

7. *a.* What time was it when they arrived?
   b. What time was it when she arrived?
   c. What time was it when they were arriving?

8. *a.* We always wear gloves when it is cold.
   b. We always wore gloves when it was cold.
   c. She always wore gloves when she was cold.

9. *a.* I did not know the answer to that question.
   b. Didn't you know the answer to that question?
   c. Did you know the answer to that question?

10. *a.* We used to sleep all night.
    b. We slept all night.
    c. They slept all night.

Bailadoras folklóricas (folk dancers), Cuzco, el Perú

10
The Present Perfect and Pluperfect Tenses

A. The Present Perfect (*el Perfecto*)

Hemos andado cinco millas hoy.

We have walked five miles today.

¿Has comprendido la lección?

Have you understood the lesson?

Yo no **he dormido** en toda la noche.

I haven't slept all night.

1. The Spanish *perfecto* corresponds to the English present perfect tense.

2. The *perfecto* is translated as shown in the three model sentences above. Other examples:

¿Han ido?
Ella no **ha estudiado.**
Yo no lo **he visto.**

Have they gone?
She has not studied.
I have not seen it.

3. The *perfecto* is made up of two elements, the present-tense form of the verb **haber** followed by a past participle:

	andar to walk	**comprender** to understand	**dormir** to sleep
	I have walked	*I have understood*	*I have slept*
yo	*he andado*	*he comprendido*	*he dormido*
tú	*has andado*	*has comprendido*	*has dormido*
Ud. él ella	*ha andado*	*ha comprendido*	*ha dormido*
nosotros nosotras	*hemos andado*	*hemos comprendido*	*hemos dormido*
vosotros vosotras	*habéis andado*	*habéis comprendido*	*habéis dormido*
Uds. ellos ellas	*han andado*	*han comprendido*	*han dormido*

4. The present tense of **haber** is conjugated as follows: **he, has, ha, hemos, habéis, han.** These forms cannot stand alone. They must be followed by a past participle.

THE PAST PARTICIPLE

5. Past participles of Spanish verbs are formed by adding the following endings to the stem of the infinitive:

-AR verbs add **-ado:**   hablar ⟶ hablado, *spoken*

-ER and *-IR* verbs add **-ido:**   { comer ⟶ comido, *eaten*
                               vivir ⟶ vivido, *lived*

6. The **-o** ending of the past participle does not change for number or gender.

Practice A: Write the past participle of the verb and translate into English.

EXAMPLE: yo he ___*tomado*___   *I have taken*
               (tomar)

1. tú has _____ (aprender)   _____

2. hemos _____ (jugar)   _____

3. Uds. han _____ (pedir)   _____

4. ¿quién ha _____? (salir)   _____

5. yo he _____ (comprender)   _____

6. habéis _____ (hablar)   _____

USING THE *PERFECTO* IN NEGATIVE STATEMENTS AND QUESTIONS

Roberto ha tomado café.	Robert has had coffee.
Roberto **no** ha tomado café.	Robert has not had coffee.
Ellos **han comido** mucho.	They have eaten a lot.
¿**Han comido** ellos mucho?	Have they eaten a lot?
¿**Han comido** mucho los muchachos?*	Have the boys eaten a lot?

7. To change a statement in the *perfecto* to the negative, place **no** directly before the form of **haber.**

*If a question is short and its complete subject is "long," that is, has almost as many syllables as the rest of the sentence, the subject is often placed at the end of the question.

8. To change a statement in the *perfecto* to a question, place the subject after the past participle.

Note: If no subject noun or pronoun is expressed, the statement is changed to a question by a rising intonation in the voice:

Ha llegado tarde.	He has arrived late.
¿Ha llegado tarde?	Has he arrived late?

Practice B: Change to (*a*) the negative and (*b*) a question.

EXAMPLE: Ella ha recibido un paquete.
          a. Ella no ha recibido un paquete.
          b. ¿Ha recibido ella un paquete?

1. Ellas han mirado la televisión.

    a. _____

    b. _____

2. Hemos respondido bien.

    a. _____

    b. _____

3. Mis padres han salido de la casa.

    a. _____

    b. _____

4. Tú has admirado a los jugadores de béisbol.

    a. _____

    b. _____

5. Los estudiantes han estudiado mucho.

    a. _____

    b. _____

IRREGULAR PAST PARTICIPLES

A. Past participles ending in **-ído:**

Infinitive	*Past Participle*
caer, to fall	*caído,* fallen
creer, to believe	*creído,* believed
leer, to read	*leído,* read
oír, to hear	*oído,* heard
traer, to bring	*traído,* brought

B. Other irregular past participles:

Infinitive	*Past Participle*
abrir, to open	*abierto,* opened
cubrir, to cover	*cubierto,* covered
decir, to say, tell	*dicho,* said, told
descubrir, to discover	*descubierto,* discovered
escribir, to write	*escrito,* written
hacer, to make, do	*hecho,* made, done
morir, to die	*muerto,* died
poner, to put, place	*puesto,* put, placed
romper, to break	*roto,* broken
ver, to see	*visto,* seen
volver, to return	*vuelto,* returned

Practice C: Complete each sentence with the appropriate form of the verb in the present perfect.

EXAMPLE: Nosotros ___*hemos escrito*___ las cartas.
(escribir)

1. Ellos no _____ la ciudad.
(ver)

2. ¿Qué _____ Ud.?
(decir)

3. Yo _____ las ventanas.
(abrir)

4. ¿_____ tú los vasos?
(traer)

5. Un actor famoso _____ esta mañana.
(morir)

6. Los alumnos _____ a las preguntas del profesor.
(contestar)

7. Mi primo y yo _____ temprano.
(volver)

8. ¿Qué _____ los chicos?
(perder)

9. ¿No _____ Ud. esa novela?
(leer)

10. La clase ya _____ .
(empezar)

B. The Pluperfect (*el Pluscuamperfecto*)

¿A qué hora **habían salido** ellos?	At what time had they left?
Alberto dijo que **había visto** la película.	Albert said that he had seen the film.

9. The *pluscuamperfecto* consists of the imperfect tense of **haber** + a past participle: **habían salido, había visto,** etc. This corresponds to the English pluperfect tense: *they had left, I had seen,* etc.

Practice D: Complete the English translations.

1. Hemos hablado con los profesores.

   _____ with the teachers.

2. Creo que han ido al concierto.

   I believe that _____ to the concert.

3. Creíamos que ella había dicho una mentira.

   We believed that she _____ a lie.

4. Era evidente que ellos habían muerto en seguida.

   It was evident that they _____ immediately.

5. ¿Dónde has puesto las revistas?

   Where _____ the magazines?

6. ¿Cuánto tiempo habías pasado en el campo?

   How long _____ in the country?

Practice E: Write the verb in the appropriate form of the *pluscuamperfecto.*

1. Los abuelos _____ la semana pasada.

(llegar)

2. Yo no _____ el programa esa noche.

(ver)

3. ¿Quién _____ bien a las preguntas?

(responder)

4. Juan y yo _____ temprano.

(volver)

5. Tú no _____ nada en la escuela.

(hacer)

EJERCICIOS

A. Supply the missing verb, which is the *perfecto* form of the verb used at the beginning of the sentence. (The subjects are the same.)

   EXAMPLE: María no habla con Ricardo ahora, pero creo que ___*ha hablado*___ con él esta mañana.

   1. Los jóvenes no comen mucho en este momento, pero creo que _____ mucho antes.

2. Mi padre no trabaja en Madrid, pero dicen que _____ allí en otros años.

3. No recibes nada de tus abuelos ahora, pero quiero saber lo que _____ antes.

4. Esta noche no vemos buenos programas en la televisión, pero es verdad que _____ buenos programas en otras noches.

5. "¿A qué hora vuelve Juana del baile?" "Yo creo que ella _____ ya."

6. "¿Qué hace el niño en casa ahora?" "No lo sé, pero dicen que _____ mucho ruido esta mañana."

7. Ahora pongo los discos en la mesa, pero antes _____ los discos en la cama.

8. Ahora abre las puertas; ya _____ las ventanas.

9. Niño, ahora no rompes los juguetes, pero esta mañana _____ tres.

10. No comprendemos la gramática de esta lección, pero _____ la gramática de la otra lección.

B.

Proceed as in exercise **A**, but this time the missing verb is in the *pluscuamperfecto*.

EXAMPLE: Yo escribí una novela. Ellos dijeron que yo ___*había escrito*___ una buena novela.

1. ¿A qué piso de la casa subiste? ¿Sabían ellos a qué piso _____?

2. Encontramos estos objetos en la calle. Ellos declararon que nosotros _____ unos objetos de mucho valor.

3. El enfermo murió en el hospital. El médico dijo que él _____ de una enfermedad rara.

4. ¿Qué comió ella en la cena? Dijeron que _____ demasiado.

5. ¿Visteis la película? ¿Sabían ellos que _____ la película?

6. Ellos fueron a Inglaterra. Escribieron que _____ a Inglaterra y a España también.

7. Pusimos las cintas en el estante. Ellos vieron que _____ las cintas allí.

8. José leyó una revista vieja. Él me dijo que _____ un periódico también.

9. Los chicos rompieron la ventana de la sala. Los padres dijeron que ellos _____ la ventana de la cocina también.

10. Yo no volví a casa temprano. Mi madre le dijo a mi padre que yo no _____ antes de la medianoche.

C. Answer with a complete sentence in Spanish:

1. ¿Ha descubierto Ud. algo interesante en su clase de español?

_____

2. ¿Qué libro ha leído Ud. recientemente?

_____

3. ¿Qué había hecho Ud. antes de venir a la escuela hoy?

_____

4. ¿Han comprendido Uds. todos los verbos?

_____

5. ¿Qué ha traído Ud. hoy a la escuela?

_____

6. ¿Había escrito Ud. novelas cuando era muy joven?

_____

7. ¿Qué ha dicho a la clase hoy la profesora (el profesor) de español?

_____

8. ¿Ha roto su papá todos los platos del desayuno?

_____

9. ¿Habían muerto muchos soldados americanos en la Segunda Guerra Mundial?

_____

10. ¿Dijeron en la radio que había nevado anoche?

_____

D. Translate into Spanish:

1. _a._ We have not gone to the movies. _____

   _b._ They had not gone to the fair. _____

2. _a._ Have you (_tú_) seen my records today? _____

   _b._ Had you (_Uds._) seen the game (_el partido_) the other day? _____

   _____

3. _a._ I have already eaten the dessert. _____

   _b._ She had already eaten the meat. _____

4. _a._ He hasn't read the magazine yet. _____

   _b._ Lola hadn't read the article yet. _____

5. *a.* You (*Ud.*) have broken the dish. _____

   b. You (*tú*) had broken the glass too. _____

6. *a.* Had the authors written more books? _____

_____

   b. Has the author written another novel? _____

_____

7. *a.* My father had not sold the car. _____

   b. I haven't sold my bicycle. _____

8. *a.* Where had your cousins worked? _____

   b. Where has your uncle worked? _____

9. *a.* Had the boys heard the program? _____

   b. Have you (*vosotras*) heard the news? _____

10. *a.* What had the girl seen? _____

   b. What have the men seen? _____

11. *a.* He thinks I have bought the tickets. _____

_____

   b. I thought he had bought the wine. _____

_____

12. *a.* Do they know who (*quién*) has driven the new car? _____

_____

   b. Did they know who (*quiénes*) had driven the motorcycles? _____

_____

13. *a.* She says that the child has spent all the money. _____

_____

   b. She said that the children had spent ten dollars. _____

_____

14. *a.* It seems that you (*tú*) have returned early tonight. _____

_____

   b. It seemed that you (*Ud.*) had returned late that night. _____

_____

15. *a.* Do you (*tú*) know that we've brought the skates? _____

_____

b. Did you (*tú*) know that we had brought the tape recorder? _____

_____

E. *Listening Comprehension.* Your teacher will read to the class ten sentences in Spanish. After each sentence is read to you, circle the letter (*a*, *b*, or *c*) of the correct English translation.

1. *a.* What have you done?
   b. What has she done?
   c. What had you done?

2. *a.* I hadn't returned yet.
   b. They hadn't returned yet.
   c. They haven't returned yet.

3. *a.* When had you arrived?
   b. When had they arrived?
   c. When has he arrived?

4. *a.* I have not had good luck.
   b. You have not had good luck.
   c. Hasn't she had good luck?

5. *a.* They had already died.
   b. Have they already died?
   c. Had they already died?

6. *a.* What has fallen?
   b. What had fallen?
   c. What fell?

7. *a.* I had come to see you.
   b. I've come to see you.
   c. We have come to see you.

8. *a.* I had not covered the table.
   b. I have not covered the table.
   c. You haven't covered the table.

9. *a.* We've received the packages.
   b. He had received the packages.
   c. I had received the packages.

10. *a.* They have worked all day.
    b. Had they worked all day?
    c. They had worked all day.

PART THREE

OTHER VERB FORMS

11
The Future Tense
and
the Conditional

The Future Tense

Mañana yo **iré** al cine.

¿Dónde **estarás** tú más tarde?

El verano próximo **viajaremos** por España.

Tomorrow I shall go to the movies.

Where will you be later?

Next summer we will travel through Spain.

1. The future tense is formed with the Spanish infinitive, and is expressed in English by two words: I *shall go* (or *will go*), they *will take* (or *shall take*), etc.

2. The following phrases are typical of the kinds of expressions often used with the future tense:

más tarde, later
mañana, tomorrow
mañana por la mañana, tomorrow morning
mañana por la tarde, tomorrow afternoon
mañana por la noche { tomorrow evening
tomorrow night

la semana próxima
la semana que viene } next week

el mes próximo
el mes que viene } next month

el año próximo
el año que viene } next year

Regular Verbs in the Future Tense

	tomar	prometer	escribir
	I will take, etc.	*I will promise,* etc.	*I will write,* etc.
yo	tomar**é**	prometer**é**	escribir**é**
tú	tomar**ás**	prometer**ás**	escribir**ás**
Ud., él, ella	tomar**á**	prometer**á**	escribir**á**
nosotros, nosotras	tomar**emos**	prometer**emos**	escribir**emos**
vosotros, vosotras	tomar**éis**	prometer**éis**	escribir**éis**
Uds., ellos, ellas	tomar**án**	prometer**án**	escribir**án**

3. For all three conjugations, the future tense is formed by adding the following endings to the infinitive: **-é, -ás, -á, -emos, -éis, -án.**

Practice A: Write the indicated form of the verb in the future tense.

EXAMPLE: ellos ___*practicarán*___   ___*volverán*___   ___*permitirán*___
                        practicar   volver   permitir

1. yo   _____   _____   _____
                   aprender   bailar   recibir

2. tú   _____   _____   _____
                    partir   mirar   responder

3. los chicos _____   _____   _____
                    jugar   perder   subir

4. Ana y yo no _____   _____   _____
                    comer   trabajar   vivir

5. ¿quién . . . ? _____   _____   _____
                    dormir   beber   cantar

Practice B: Translate the words in italics into English.

EXAMPLE: ¿A qué hora *llegarán* mañana?   ___*will they arrive*___

1. ¿Cuándo *venderás* tu casa?   _____

2. Yo creo que *ellos recibirán* mucho dinero.   _____

3. *No hablaré* con ese chico.   _____

4. Ellos dicen que *irán* mañana si hace buen tiempo.   _____

5. *Comeremos* en un restaurante esta noche.   _____

Irregular Verbs in the Future Tense

Verbs that are irregular in the future tense are divided into three groups:

GROUP A: The **e** in the infinitive ending **-er** is dropped.

caber to fit	**cabr**é	**cabr**ás	**cabr**á	**cabr**emos	**cabr**éis	**cabr**án
haber* to have (helping verb)	**habr**é	**habr**ás	**habr**á	**habr**emos	**habr**éis	**habr**án
poder to be able	**podr**é	**podr**ás	**podr**á	**podr**emos	**podr**éis	**podr**án
querer to want	**querr**é	**querr**ás	**querr**á	**querr**emos	**querr**éis	**querr**án
saber to know	**sabr**é	**sabr**ás	**sabr**á	**sabr**emos	**sabr**éis	**sabr**án

GROUP B: The **e** or **i** in the infinitive endings **-er** and **-ir** is changed to **d**.

poner to put	**pondr**é	**pondr**ás	**pondr**á	**pondr**emos	**pondr**éis	**pondr**án
salir to leave, go out	**saldr**é	**saldr**ás	**saldr**á	**saldr**emos	**saldr**éis	**saldr**án
tener to have	**tendr**é	**tendr**ás	**tendr**á	**tendr**emos	**tendr**éis	**tendr**án
valer to be worth, cost	**valdr**é	**valdr**ás	**valdr**á	**valdr**emos	**valdr**éis	**valdr**án
venir to come	**vendr**é	**vendr**ás	**vendr**á	**vendr**emos	**vendr**éis	**vendr**án

GROUP C: The verbs **decir** (future stem **dir-**) and **hacer** (future stem **har-**).

decir to say, tell	**dir**é	**dir**ás	**dir**á	**dir**emos	**dir**éis	**dir**án
hacer to do, make	**har**é	**har**ás	**har**á	**har**emos	**har**éis	**har**án

Note: All verbs in the future, whether regular or irregular, take the same endings: **-é, -ás, -á, -emos, -éis, -án.**

---

*These forms of **haber** are used in the future perfect (**habré hablado,** *I will have spoken*), which is not taught in this book. The third person singular, **habrá,** is used as the future tense of **hay.** See Appendix VII-C.

Practice C: Write the indicated forms of the future tense.

1. nosotros no _____ _____ _____ _____
                           venir   decir   saber   tener

2. ellos _____ _____ _____ _____
                  poner   hacer   poder   querer

3. yo _____ _____ _____ _____
              decir   salir   caber   hacer

4. ¿quién . . . ? _____ _____ _____ _____
                  poner   saber   decir   tener

5. tú _____ _____ _____ _____
            querer   hacer   valer   saber

Practice D: Complete the Spanish translations with the appropriate form of the verb in parentheses.

1. There will be no classes on Wednesday. (*haber*)

   No _____ clases el miércoles.

2. The packages won't fit in the car. (*caber*)

   Los paquetes no _____ en el coche.

3. Some day these paintings will be worth a lot of money. (*valer*)

   Algún día estas pinturas _____ mucho dinero.

4. We will not be able to attend the meeting. (*poder*)

   No _____ asistir a la reunión.

5. Will you (*tú*) come with us? (*venir*)

   ¿_____ con nosotras?

SUPPLEMENT: Using the Present Tense With Future Meaning

In spoken Spanish, the near future is often expressed in the present tense, which is used:

a. instead of the future tense.

    Te **veo** mañana.   I'll see you tomorrow.
    Dentro de poco **vienen.**   They will come shortly.

b. in the expression **ir a** + *infinitive.*

    Voy a hacerlo más tarde.   I'm going to do it later.

    Van a ver una película esta noche.   They're going to see a movie tonight.

Practice E: Complete the Spanish sentences in three ways that show how the near future may be expressed.

EXAMPLE: Later we will see a good program.

Más tarde _____*veremos*_____ un buen programa.

_____*vemos*_____

_____*vamos a ver*_____

1. In five minutes the train will leave.

    Dentro de cinco minutos _____ el tren.

    _____

    _____

2. Tonight we're going to the movies.

    Esta noche _____ al cine.

    _____

    _____

3. What are you doing Saturday night? (you = *tú*)

    ¿Qué _____ el sábado por la noche?

    _____

    _____

4. We'll have a ham sandwich. (Use the verb *tomar*.)

    _____ un sandwich de jamón.

    _____.

    _____

5. I'm visiting my relatives next week.

    La semana que viene _____ a mis parientes.

    _____

    _____

The Conditional

Yo **iría** al cine, pero no tengo dinero.   I would go to the movies, but I don't have any money.

¿Dónde **estarías** sin mí?   Where would you be without me?

¿Cuánto **valdría** ese libro?   How much would that book cost?

4. The conditional is formed in the same way as the future tense: by adding endings to the infinitive.

5. The conditional is translated into English by using the helping verb *would:* "I *would go,*" "*would* you *speak?*," "they *would* not *run,*" etc.

Regular Verbs in the Conditional

	tomar	prometer	escribir
	I would take, etc.	*I would promise,* etc.	*I would write,* etc.
yo	tomar*ía*	prometer*ía*	escribir*ía*
tú	tomar*ías*	prometer*ías*	escribir*ías*
Ud., él, ella	tomar*ía*	prometer*ía*	escribir*ía*
nosotros, nosotras	tomar*íamos*	prometer*íamos*	escribir*íamos*
vosotros, vosotras	tomar*íais*	prometer*íais*	escribir*íais*
Uds., ellos, ellas	tomar*ían*	prometer*ían*	escribir*ían*

Irregular Verbs in the Conditional

Verbs that have irregular stems in the future tense have the same irregular stems in the conditional.

GROUP A: The **e** in the infinitive ending **-er** is dropped.

caber:	cabría	cabrías	cabría	cabríamos	cabríais	cabrían
haber:	habría	habrías	habría	habríamos	habríais	habrían
poder:	podría	podrías	podría	podríamos	podríais	podrían
querer:	querría	querrías	querría	querríamos	querríais	querrían
saber:	sabría	sabrías	sabría	sabríamos	sabríais	sabrían

GROUP B: The **e** or **i** in the infinitive endings **-er** and **-ir** is changed to **d**.

poner:	pondría	pondrías	pondría	pondríamos	pondríais	pondrían
salir:	saldría	saldrías	saldría	saldríamos	saldríais	saldrían
tener:	tendría	tendrías	tendría	tendríamos	tendríais	tendrían
valer:	valdría	valdrías	valdría	valdríamos	valdríais	valdrían
venir:	vendría	vendrías	vendría	vendríamos	vendríais	vendrían

GROUP C: The verbs **decir** (conditional stem **dir-**) and **hacer** (conditional stem **har-**).

| **decir:** | **diría** | **dirías** | **diría** | **diríamos** | **diríais** | **dirían** |
| **hacer:** | **haría** | **harías** | **haría** | **haríamos** | **haríais** | **harían** |

Practice F: Write the indicated form of the conditional.

1. la niña	_____	_____	_____	_____
	comer	venir	decir	hablar
2. ¿quiénes . . . ?	_____	_____	_____	_____
	hacer	tener	saber	dividir
3. tú y yo	_____	_____	_____	_____
	contestar	poner	poder	decir
4. yo	_____	_____	_____	_____
	querer	comprar	salir	hacer
5. tú	_____	_____	_____	_____
	dormir	decir	saber	venir

Practice G: Translate the italicized words into English.

1. El profesor dijo que *daría* un examen. _____

2. ¿Qué *usaríamos* para arreglar los patines? _____

3. *Yo no tomaría* el autobús para llegar allí. _____

4. ¿Qué *sabrías* de eso? _____

5. *Ella no diría* una mentira. _____

6. Supimos ayer que *habría* unos alumnos nuevos en la clase. _____

7. Sin dinero, ¿qué *podríamos* hacer? _____

EJERCICIOS

A. In each sentence, the verb in italics is used again with a change of subject. Supply the missing verb form.

EXAMPLE: Yo no *haré* el trabajo pero él lo ____*hará*____.

1. Nosotros *tomaremos* el tren, pero ellos _____ el autobús.

2. Ellos no *podrán* ir a la tienda, pero yo _____ ir.

3. Mi amiga no *aprenderá* los verbos irregulares, pero Uds. los _____.

4. Ud. no *tendrá* el dinero, pero mis padres lo _____.

5. Ella *saldrá* temprano y yo _____ tarde.

6. Yo *venderé* mi bicicleta y mi tío _____ su coche.

7. Yo te *diré* un secreto. ¿Qué me _____ tú?

8. Esta noche *veremos* un buen programa en la televisión. ¿Qué _____ vosotros?

9. María *llegará* a la fiesta a las seis. ¿A qué hora _____ sus amigas?

10. ¿Quién *querrá* acompañarnos al teatro? Nuestros padres _____ acompañarnos.

B. Proceed as in exercise **A**, but this time supply the *conditional* form of the missing verb.

EXAMPLE: Tú *dirías* la verdad, pero él ____*diría*____ una mentira.

1. Ella *iría* al centro, pero nosotros no _____.

2. ¿*Escribirían* Uds. las tarjetas, o las _____ José?

3. Ud. no *tendría* el dinero necesario, pero mis padres lo _____.

4. ¿Quiénes *harían* las tareas? Mis tíos las _____.

5. ¿*Trabajarían* los chicos? No, pero yo _____.

6. ¿Dónde *pondrías* los paquetes? Yo los _____ en la mesa.

7. Mi padre *iría* a España, pero mis hermanos _____ a Portugal.

8. Una revista *valdría* un dólar. ¿Cuánto _____ dos?

9. "¿Qué serías sin mí?" "Yo _____ muy feliz."

10. Nosotros *vendríamos* con Pepe y Lola. ¿Con quiénes _____ Uds.?

C. Without changing the subject, write the appropriate form of the verb in the future tense.

EXAMPLE: Ella dice que ____*hará*____ el trabajo.
　　　　　　　　　　　(hacer)

1. Yo digo que _____ el dinero mañana.
　　　　　　　　　(tener)

2. ¿Piensa él que _____ los discos esta noche?
　　　　　　　　　　(traer)

3. Decimos que _____ mañana a las dos de la tarde.
　　　　　　　　　(salir)

4. Los niños prometen que _____ buenos.
　　　　　　　　　　　(ser)

5. ¿Declaras tú que _____ la verdad?
　　　　　　　　　　(decir)

6. Yo sé que _____ comprar la camisa.
　　　　　　　(querer)

7. Escriben que _____ el viaje el mes próximo.
　　　　　　　　(hacer)

8. ¿Juráis que _____ el dinero en el banco?
　　　　　　　　(poner)

9. ¿Dice ella que _____ en casa antes de las siete?
　　　　　　　　(estar)

10. ¿Promete Ud. que no _____ tarde esta noche?
　　　　　　　　　(volver)

D. Without changing the subject, write the appropriate form of the verb in the conditional.

EXAMPLE: Ellos dijeron que ___*vendrían*___ temprano.
                                    (venir)

1. Julio dijo que _____ con nosotros.
                        (ir)

2. Pensábamos que _____ el programa.
                          (ver)

3. ¿Dijiste que _____ para el examen?
                    (estudiar)

4. Yo le prometí que le _____ con su trabajo.
                              (ayudar)

5. Ellos declararon que _____ ganar el premio.
                              (querer)

6. Sabíamos que _____ el domingo.
                      (venir)

7. Escribieron que _____ en Bolivia el mes próximo.
                          (estar)

8. Ud. juró que me _____ la verdad.
                        (decir)

9. Ella prometió a la profesora que _____ la lección.
                                          (saber)

10. ¿Dijeron ellas que _____ esas cosas?
                            (hacer)

E. Answer with a complete sentence in Spanish:

1. ¿Qué dirá Ud. mañana a su profesora (profesor) de español?

   _____

2. ¿Qué haría Ud. con un millón de dólares?

   _____

3. ¿Lloverá mañana o no?

   _____

4. ¿Cuánto valdría una buena bicicleta?

   _____

5. ¿Cuántos programas de televisión verá su familia esta noche?

   _____

6. ¿Dónde nevaría en julio?

   _____

7. ¿Viajará su familia por un país extranjero el año que viene?

   _____

8. ¿Cuánto pagarían Uds. por un buen tocadiscos estereofónico?

_____

9. ¿Cómo llegarán Uds. mañana a la escuela?

_____

10. ¿Por cuántas horas podrías correr?

_____

11. ¿Quién servirá la comida en su casa esta noche?

_____

12. ¿Cuántas personas cabrían en el coche de sus padres?

_____

13. ¿Jugarán Uds. en el parque el domingo próximo?

_____

14. ¿Viviría Ud. en un apartamento de dos piezas?

_____

15. ¿Cuántas horas dormirás esta noche?

_____

16. ¿En qué clase de restaurante le gustaría comer?

_____

17. ¿A qué hora se acostará Ud. el sábado próximo?

_____

18. ¿Se divertirían Uds. en una discoteca?

_____

19. ¿Con qué se lavará Ud. la cara y las manos mañana por la mañana?

_____

20. ¿Se quejaría Ud. al sacar una nota de 98 en su próximo examen de español?

_____

F. Translate into Spanish:

1. _a._ Where will you go next week? (you = _tú_)

_____

　　_b._ Where would you go afterwards? (you = _Uds._)

_____

2. _a._ She says that she will have the tickets tonight.

_____

b. He said that he would have the money tomorrow afternoon.

_____

3. *a.* We believe that we will know the answer.

_____

b. We believed that we would know the lesson.

_____

4. *a.* I promise that I will come to school on time.

_____

b. I promised that I would come home early.

_____

5. *a.* What will they do next month?

_____

b. What would you do with all the money? (you = *vosotras*)

_____

6. *a.* Will your brother work next Saturday?

_____

b. Would your sisters work all day (*todo el día*)?

_____

7. *a.* The teacher promises that he will give an easy test.

_____

b. The teachers promised that they would not give a difficult test.

_____

8. *a.* Will you be able to go to the party? (you = *Uds.*)

_____

b. Would you be able to come to dinner (*a comer*)? (you = *Ud.*)

_____

9. *a.* What will your father say?

_____

b. What would your parents say?

_____

10. *a.* Where will she be tomorrow?

_____

b. Would he be there later?

_____

11. *a.* In five minutes it will be one o'clock.

_____

b. It is five o'clock in New York; what time would it be in Spain?

_____

12. *a.* Will your grandparents buy a color TV set? (TV set = *el televisor*; in color = *en colores*)

_____

b. What would your uncle buy for your birthday?

_____

13. *a.* Where will we stay in Mexico City?

_____

b. Where would I stay in Madrid?

_____

14. *a.* Some people (*personas*) will sit in the orchestra (*la platea*).

_____

b. Where would the others sit?

_____

15. *a.* I'll put on a coat if it's cold.

_____

b. He would put on a hat, but he doesn't have any (*no lo tiene*).

_____

G. *Listening Comprehension.* Your teacher will read to the class ten statements or questions in Spanish. In each case, circle the letter of the correct translation.

1. *a.* I will not tell the answer.
   b. He will not tell the answer.
   c. I would not tell the answer.

2. *a.* At what time will she come?
   b. At what time would she come?
   c. At what time would you come?

3. *a.* Who will bring the tapes?
   b. Who would bring the tapes?
   c. Who brought the tapes?

4. *a.* Who would take a walk with me?
   b. Who will take a walk with me?
   c. Will you take a walk with me?

5. *a.* Will you know how to skate?
   b. Would they know how to skate?
   c. Would you know how to skate?

6. *a.* Would they like to ski this winter?
   b. Do you like skiing this winter?
   c. Would you like to ski this winter?

7. *a.* Will there be room for us in that small car?
    b. Will we go riding in that small car?
    c. Would there be room for us in that small car?

8. *a.* I know they will be good friends.
    b. I knew they would be good friends.
    c. I know they were good friends.

9. *a.* What would she be without us?
    b. What would she do without us?
    c. What will she do without us?

10. *a.* Will you have wine with your meal?
    b. Would they have wine with their meal?
    c. Would you have wine with your meal?

11. *a.* I'll eat an apple.
    b. I'd eat an apple.
    c. She'll eat an apple.

12. *a.* How many hours will they work?
    b. How many hours would they work?
    c. How many hours will you work?

13. *a.* I wouldn't play tennis with her.
    b. He won't play tennis with her.
    c. He will not play tennis with her.

14. *a.* Joseph would drive his father's car.
    b. Joseph will drive his father's car.
    c. Will Joseph drive his father's car?

15. *a.* How much would the tickets cost?
    b. How much will the ticket cost?
    c. How much will the tickets cost?

16. *a.* I'll watch TV in the living room.
    b. We'll watch TV in the living room.
    c. We would watch TV in the living room.

17. *a.* At what time would she get up?
    b. At what time would they get up?
    c. At what time will they get up?

18. *a.* He won't stay home this afternoon.
    b. They would stay home this afternoon?
    c. Will he stay home this afternoon?

19. *a.* Will he leave early?
    b. Will you leave early?
    c. Would they leave early?

20. *a.* He would wash with cold water.
    b. I'll wash with cold water.
    c. Would you wash with cold water?

12
The Progressive Tenses

Ramón **está hablando.**	Raymond is speaking.
Ramón **estaba hablando.**	Raymond *was* speaking.
¿Están comiendo ellos?	Are they eating?
¿Estaban escribiendo las muchachas?	Were the girls writing?

1. The progressive tenses consist of a form of **estar** + a *present participle.*

The Present Participle

ha**blar**	com**er**	viv**ir**
habl**ando,** speaking	com**iendo,** eating	viv**iendo,** living

2. To form the Spanish present participle, or *gerundio,* drop the infinitive endings and add as follows:

-AR VERBS	-ER AND -IR VERBS
Add **-ando.**	Add **-iendo.**

3. The Spanish *gerundio* usually has the same meaning as the English present participle, which ends in *-ing.**

4. In questions, the subject of the verb follows the *gerundio,* except for **Ud.** and **Uds.:**

¿Estaban corriendo **ellos**?	Were they running?
¿Qué está mirando **él**?	What is he looking at?
¿Está estudiando **María**?	Is Mary studying?

---

*The *gerundio* can be used as an adverb meaning *by . . . -ing:*

Gana su dinero **trabajando** mucho.	He earns his money *by working* hard.
Partiendo temprano llegarás allí antes del anochecer.	*By leaving* early you will get there before nightfall.

This use of the *gerundio* should not be confused with the use of the English gerund as a verbal noun:

Smoking is bad for the health = **El fumar** es malo para la salud.

Swimming is a good sport = **El nadar** es un buen deporte.

But:

¿Estaba **Ud.** corriendo?	Were you running?
¿Qué están **Uds.** mirando?	What are you looking at?

Practice A: Write the *gerundio* of each verb and translate it into English.

EXAMPLE: beber: *bebiendo, drinking*

1. volver: _____

2. recibir: _____

3. viajar: _____

4. hacer: _____

5. pensar: _____

6. subir: _____

Practice B: Change each sentence to a question.

EXAMPLE: Alberto está cantando.   *¿Está cantando Alberto?*

1. Ellos no estaban trabajando.   _____

2. Uds. están comiendo.   _____

3. El chico está jugando.   _____

4. Ud. estaba escribiendo.   _____

Gerundios With Short Stems

dar	ser	ver
dando, giving	*siendo*, being	*viendo*, seeing

Irregular *Gerundios*

A. Ending in **-yendo:**

caer	*cayendo*, falling
construir	*construyendo*, constructing
creer	*creyendo*, believing
ir	*yendo*, going
leer	*leyendo*, reading
oír	*oyendo*, hearing
traer	*trayendo*, bringing

B. Others:*

decir	*diciendo*, saying, telling
dormir	*durmiendo*, sleeping
poder	*pudiendo*, being able
venir	*viniendo*, coming

Practice C: Complete each Spanish sentence and its English translation with the appropriate present participles.

EXAMPLE: Están _____*trabajando*_____ en la ciudad.
 (trabajar)

 They are _____*working*_____ in the city.

1. Estamos _____ la casa.   We are _____ the house.
 (vender)

2. Tú estabas _____ mucho ruido.   You were _____ a lot of
 (hacer)   noise.

3. Estoy _____ una buena novela.   I am _____ a good novel.
 (leer)

4. ¿Qué estaban _____ ellas?   What were they _____?
 (decir)

5. Él está _____ en la sala.   He is _____ in the living
 (dormir)   room.

Note: The present participles of the verbs **ir** and **venir** are generally not used with **estar** to form the progressive tenses. The simple (one-word) tenses are used instead.

¿Adónde **ibas**?   Where were you going?
Mañana **vienen** a casa.   Tomorrow they are coming home.

Practice D: Translate into Spanish.

1. I am going home.   _____ a casa.

2. I was going to school.   _____ a la escuela.

3. She was coming to the city.   _____ a la ciudad.

4. She is coming to our house.   _____ a nuestra casa.

CONTINUAR } **+ Present Participle**
SEGUIR

Siguen durmiendo.   They continue (keep on) sleeping.

¿Continuaba bailando?   Did she continue to dance? (Did she keep on dancing?)

---

*See page 106.

5. **Continuar** or **seguir** followed by the *gerundio* means *to continue* (*keep on*) *doing something.*

Practice E: Translate the italicized words into English.

1. *Sigo trabajando* en la fábrica. _____ in the factory.

2. ¿Por qué *sigues leyendo* ese libro   Why _____ that boring
   aburrido?   book?

3. *Continuamos viendo* los mismos   _____ the same
   programas.   programs.

The Relation Between the Simple and Progressive Tenses in English and Spanish

I buy = yo **compro**   I am buying = $\begin{cases} \text{yo } \textbf{compro} \\ \textbf{estoy comprando} \end{cases}$

What was she writing? = $\begin{cases} \text{¿Qué } \textbf{escribía} \text{ ella?} \\ \text{¿Qué } \textbf{estaba escribiendo} \text{ ella?} \end{cases}$

6. The English present progressive tense (*I am buying*, etc.) can be expressed in Spanish in two ways:

a. by using the present tense (yo **compro**).

b. by using the present progressive (yo **estoy comprando**). This tense consists of the present tense of **estar** + a present participle.

7. The English past progressive tense (*she was writing*, etc.) can be expressed in Spanish in two ways:

a. by using the imperfect tense (ella **escribía**).

b. by using the imperfect progressive (ella **estaba escribiendo**). This tense consists of the imperfect tense of **estar** + a present participle.

Practice F: Express the same thought by using **estar** + a present participle.

EXAMPLES: Ellas bailan ahora.   *Ellas están bailando ahora.*
           ¿Dormías tranquilamente?   *¿Estabas durmiendo tranquilamente?*

1. No escriben a sus padres. _____

2. Tú leías muy bien. _____

3. ¿Quién toma vino? _____

4. ¿Almuerzan Uds. temprano? _____

5. Dábamos un paseo por la playa. _____

EJERCICIOS

A. Each statement is the answer to a question that begins as shown. Write the rest of the question. (Pronouns in parentheses indicate to whom the question is addressed.)

EXAMPLE: Ella estaba patinando sobre el lago.

¿Quién _____estaba patinando sobre el lago_____ ?

¿Dónde _____estaba patinando ella_____ ?

1. Estamos trayendo las cintas y los discos.

¿Qué _____? (Uds.)

2. Estoy trabajando en casa.

¿Dónde _____ hoy? (tú)

3. Ricardo y María estaban bailando.

¿Quiénes _____?

4. Estábamos recibiendo mensajes.

¿Qué _____? (vosotras)

5. Roberto está durmiendo ahora.

¿Quién _____ ahora?

6. Yo no estaba haciendo nada.

¿Qué _____? (tú)

7. Estoy llevando unos libros escolares.

¿Qué _____ en esa cartera? (Ud.)

8. Estábamos vendiendo cien discos.

¿Cuántos _____? (Uds.)

9. Sí, está tomando el desayuno.

¿ _____ el desayuno?

10. Están construyendo una fábrica grande.

¿Qué _____ los hombres?

B. Answer in the corresponding form of the progressive tense.

EXAMPLES: ¿Comen Uds. ahora?   ¿Qué decían ellos?
             Sí, estamos comiendo ahora.   *Ellos estaban diciendo una mentira.*

1. ¿Qué escriben ellos a sus padres?

_____

2. ¿Qué ponías en el estante?

_____

3. ¿No oyen Uds. buena música?

_____

4. ¿Qué leía la madre a sus hijos?

_____

5. ¿Ve Juana un programa interesante?

_____

6. ¿Dormía yo durante el concierto?

_____

7. ¿Cómo cantaban los niños?

_____

8. ¿Quién abre las ventanas en la escuela?

_____

9. ¿Dónde pasa Ud. este verano?

_____

10. ¿Juegan los amigos en la piscina?

_____

C. Translate into Spanish in two ways, as shown in the examples.

EXAMPLES: What is he doing now?   _¿Qué hace él ahora?_   _¿Qué está haciendo él ahora?_
They were writing letters.   _Escribían cartas._   _Estaban escribiendo cartas._

1. _a._ Where are they sleeping tonight?

_____

_b._ Where was Mary sleeping that night?

_____

2. _a._ The children are playing in the pool.

_____

_b._ The girls were playing in the garden.

_____

3. _a._ What were you bringing to class? (you = _tú_)

_____

_b._ What are you bringing to the party? (you = _Uds._)

_____

4. _a._ Is she using those skates?

_____

b. Were you using these skis? (you = *Ud.*)

_____

5. *a.* We were eating in the car.

_____

b. We're eating at this moment.

_____

6. *a.* What was he telling his parents?

¿Qué les _____ a sus padres? ¿Qué les _____ a sus padres?

b. What is he telling his friends?

¿Qué les _____ a sus amigos? ¿Qué les _____ a sus amigos?

7. *a.* Were you doing that (*eso*)? (you = *vosotros*)

_____

b. I'm not doing this (*esto*).

_____

8. *a.* We're going up in the elevator.

_____

b. We were going up the stairs.

_____

9. *a.* They're constructing an apartment house.

_____

b. They were constructing a school.

_____

(In #**10,** translate as shown on page 101.)

10. *a.* I continue going to that school.

_____

b. I continued to go to work.

_____

D. *Listening Comprehension.* Your teacher will read to the class ten questions in Spanish. After each question is read to you, circle the letter of the most appropriate reply.

1. *a.* Estoy mirando las nubes.
   b. Estamos mirando la casa.
   c. Estaba mirando el edificio.

2. *a.* Está comiendo.
   b. Estábamos practicando el español.
   c. Estaba jugando al béisbol.

3. *a.* Vivo en Guatemala.
   b. Estaba viviendo en Chile.
   c. Ud. está viviendo en Segovia.

4. *a.* Estás diciendo eso al profesor.
   b. Estoy diciendo eso a mi tío.
   c. Estaba diciendo eso a mis abuelos.

5. *a.* Sí, sigo viniendo.
   b. No, no queremos venir más.
   c. No, siguen viniendo.

6. *a.* Estaba leyendo una novela clásica.
   b. Leen una revista importante.
   c. Está leyendo un artículo interesante.

7. *a.* No, estamos dando una fiesta.
   b. Sí, estoy dando una fiesta grande.
   c. Sí, damos la fiesta en casa de Ramón.

8. *a.* Estoy durmiendo ahora.
   b. No puedo dormir esta noche.
   c. Estamos durmiendo en este momento.

9. *a.* Sí, y pronto podemos ir a esquiar.
   b. Sí, estaba nevando mucho ayer.
   c. No es posible, porque estamos en invierno.

10. *a.* Sí, está lloviendo mucho.
    b. No, la lluvia estaba cayendo.
    c. No, hacía buen tiempo.

SUPPLEMENT: *-IR* Verbs That Have a Stem Change in the Present Participle

If an -IR verb has a stem change in the third-person forms of the preterite (see page 58), the same change occurs in the present participle. The stem vowel of the infinitive changes as follows:

PRESENT PARTICIPLE

1. **e** becomes **i:**   sentir   s*i*ntiendo
                             pedir   p*i*diendo

2. **o** becomes **u:**   dormir   d*u*rmiendo

Practice G: Complete each sentence with the *gerundio* of the indicated verb.

1. La clase está _____ las frases.
   (repetir)

2. ¿Estaban _____ los chicos?
   (mentir)

3. Estamos _____ la misma ruta.
   (seguir)

4. ¿Quiénes estaban _____ en esa habitación?
   (dormir)

5. Todo el mundo está _____.
   (reír)

6. Dijeron que el viejo estaba _____.
   (morir)

13
Expressing "to Be" in Spanish: *SER* and *ESTAR*; Some Idioms With *HACER* and *TENER*

Some Spanish Equivalents of "To Be"

Mi madre **es** abogada.	My mother *is* a lawyer.
Estoy en casa.	I *am* at home.
Hoy **hace** frío.	Today it *is* cold.
Ella **tiene** hambre.	She *is* hungry.
Trabajan en una fábrica.	They *are* working in a factory.
Hay treinta alumnos en la clase.	There *are* thirty pupils in the class.

1. *To be* is expressed in Spanish by using (1) **ser** or **estar,** (2) the third-person-singular forms of **hacer** in weather expressions, and (3) the verb **tener** in certain idioms. The forms of *to be* used as helping verbs in the English present progressive "disappear" when the tense is expressed by the Spanish simple present (*they are working* = **trabajan**). They also vanish when the English idiom *there is, there are* is expressed as **hay.***

Uses of *SER*

A. *To Express Identity*

¿Qué **es** eso?	What is that?
Es una casa.	It is a house.
¿Qué **son** ellos?	What are they?
Son mecánicos.	They are mechanics.
¿Quién **es** esa mujer?	Who is that woman?
Es mi madre.	She is my mother.

---

*When *there* means "in that place," *there is* (*are*) is expressed by **allí está(n):**

> *There are* the books you are looking for.   **Allí están** los libros que buscas.

B. *To Describe a Personal Trait or Physical Characteristic*

¿Cómo **es** su profesora?	How is your teacher? (= What sort of person is she?)
Es muy inteligerte.	She is very smart.
Juan **es** alto y fuerte.	John is tall and strong.
La ciudad **es** grande y hermosa.	The city is large and beautiful.

C. *To Express Nationality, Religious Affiliation, Place of Origin, Material of Which Something is Made*

¿**Es** Ud. cubano?	Are you Cuban?
No, **soy** puertorriqueño.	No, I am Puerto Rican.
¿**Es** Ud. católica?	Are you (a) Catholic?
No, **soy** protestante.	No, I am (a) Protestant.
¿De dónde **son** Uds.?	Where are you from?
Somos de España.	We are from Spain.
¿De qué **es** su reloj?	What is your watch made of?
Es de oro. No **es** de plata.	It is (made of) gold. It is not silver.

D. *To Tell the Time, Date, or Day of the Week (see Appendix III, IV, V, VI)*

¿Qué hora **es**?	What time is it?
Son las siete.	It is seven o'clock.
¿Cuál **es** la fecha?	What is the date?
Es el tres de enero.	It is January 3rd.
¿Qué día **es**?	What day is it?
Es lunes.	It is Monday.

Uses of *ESTAR*

A. *To Express Location or Position*

¿Dónde **están** sus amigos?	Where are your friends?
Están en el banco.	They are in the bank.
¿Dónde **está** San Juan?	Where is San Juan?
Está en Puerto Rico.	It is in Puerto Rico.

B. *To Express a Reversible State That Often Alternates With Its Opposite: Well and Sick, Sad and Happy, Hot and Cold, Seated and Standing, etc.**

¿Cómo **estás**?	How are you? (= How do you feel?)
Estoy bien. No **estoy** enfermo.	I am well. I am not sick.

---

*But not such opposites as *rich and poor* or *young and old*, which are not alternating states. Such adjectives are used with **ser**.

¿**Está** abierta o cerrada la puerta? | Is the door open or closed?
Está cerrada. No **está** abierta. | It is closed. It is not open.

¿**Estás** triste o contento? | Are you sad or happy?
Estoy contento. No **estoy** triste. | I am happy. I am not sad.

C. *As a Helping Verb in the Progressive Tenses* (*See Chapter 12*)

¿Qué **estás** haciendo? | What are you doing?
Estoy comiendo ahora. | I am eating now.

¿**Están** Uds. leyendo una novela? | Are you reading a novel?
No, **estamos** mirando la televisión. | No, we are watching television.

Some Comments Concerning *SER* and *ESTAR*

2. Both **ser** and **estar** may be followed by an adjective:*

Ella **es alta.** Los hombres **están tristes.**

3. Only **ser** may be followed by a noun:

Somos profesoras. Soy médico.

4. Although they have similar meanings, **feliz** is used with **ser** but **alegre** and **contento** are used with **estar**:

¿**Eres feliz?**
¿**Estás contento?** } Are you happy?

Practice A: Underline the correct verb.

1. Mi tía (es / está) enferma hoy.

2. El señor González (es / está) de Nicaragua.

3. Mamá, la sopa (es / está) fría.

4. Felipe y yo (somos / estamos) buenos amigos.

5. ¿(Son / Están) contentas ellas?

6. Nuestra casa (es / está) de madera.

7. Mis parientes no (son / están) pobres.

8. Esas mujeres (son / están) portuguesas.

9. ¿Qué (son / están) Uds. haciendo ahora?

10. ¿Quién (es / está) esa persona?

11. Mi madre (es / está) muy cansada esta noche.

---

*The adjective must agree in gender and number with the noun or pronoun that it modifies. See chapter 19.

12. Esos perros (son / están) estúpidos.

13. ¿Qué (es / está) eso?

14. Hoy (es /está) sábado.

15. ¿Dónde (es / está) él?

16. ¿De dónde (son / están) ellas?

17. Nuestro pueblo (es / está) pequeño.

18. ¿(Es / Está) abierta la ventana?

19. Mi amiga Rosa (es / está) muy bonita.

20. Yo (soy / estoy) el presidente de nuestro club.

21. ¿Quiénes (son / están) esos hombres?

22. Mis padres (son / están) visitando a mis abuelos.

23. ¿(Eres / Estás) tú mi amigo o no?

24. Uds. (son / están) hermanos, ¿verdad?

25. ¿Por qué (eres / estás) triste?

Idioms With *HACER* and *TENER*

A. **Hacer** + noun = *to be* + adjective

| ¿Qué tiempo **hace**? | How is the weather? |
| Hoy **hace calor**. No **hace frío**. | Today it is warm. It is not cold. |

5. The verb **hacer** is used in the third person singular to talk about the weather. (See Appendix VII–B.)

B. **Tener** + noun = *to be* + adjective

Tengo frío.	I am cold.
¿Tienes sed?	Are you thirsty?
¿Cuántos años **tiene** ella?	How old is she?
Tiene veinte años.	She is twenty years old.

6. In certain idioms, **tener** is translated as *to be*. (See Appendix VII–A.)

The Relation Between the Spanish Present Tense and "To Be" as Helping Verb

Leo una novela.	I *am reading* a novel.
Ellas **van** al cine esta noche.	They *are going* to the movies tonight.
¿Viene Ud. a nuestra casa?	*Are* you *coming* to our house?

7. The progressive tenses in English, which take the form *to be . . . -ing*, can be expressed in Spanish in two ways; see page 102. When the English present progressive (for example, I *am reading*) is expressed in Spanish by the present tense, the helping verb *to be* is not translated.

The Idiom *HAY*

Hay algo interesante aquí.   *There is* something interesting here.
¿**Hay** muchas personas allí?   *Are there* many people there?

8. **Hay** means *there is, there are, is there?* and *are there?* (See Appendix VII–C.)

Practice B: Underline the verb that completes the sentence correctly, that is, the verb corresponding to *am, are, is,* or *there are* in the equivalent English sentence.

1. Vamos a la playa si (es / está / hace) calor.

2. ¿(Es / Está / Tiene) interesante su libro?

3. ¿Dónde (hacen / están / tienen) los niños?

4. Esta noche yo (tengo / soy / estoy) sueño.

5. Luisa no (tiene / es / está) bien esta mañana.

6. En mi ciudad (hay / son / tienen) edificios grandes.

7. El vestido de Isabel (está / tiene / es) de lana.

8. Los señores López (están / son / tienen) de Venezuela.

9. Nosotros (somos / estamos / tenemos) alegres porque hoy no hay clases.

10. ¿Qué hora (es / está / hace) ahora?

EJERCICIOS

A. Supply the missing words in accordance with the change of subject.

EXAMPLE: Mi hermana está enferma hoy.

　　　　Nosotros ____*estamos enfermos*____ hoy.

1. Mi familia es de Bolivia. Mis tíos _____ de Colombia.

2. ¿Están cerradas las puertas? ¿_____ el edificio?

3. Yo no soy rico. Nuestra familia no _____ tampoco.

4. Su primo es argentino. Mis amigas _____ también.

5. Nuestras clases son grandes. Mi clase de inglés _____ también.

6. ¿Dónde están Uds.? ¿Dónde _____ tú?

7. "Tenemos mucho frío." "Yo _____ también."

8. Mis primos son jóvenes. Tú _____ también.

9. El reloj es de plata. Los platos _____ de plata también.

10. Las habitaciones son pequeñas. El cuarto no _____.

B. In each pair of sentences, one sentence requires a form of *ser*, the other, a form of *estar*. Complete the sentences with the correct verb forms.

EXAMPLES: Ella ___*es*___ mi amiga.   Hoy no ___*está*___ bien.

Ellos ___*están*___ allí.   ___*Son*___ mis primos.

1. Juan _____ en casa ahora.   Él _____ un buen chico.

2. Mi camisa _____ de seda.   _____ en la cama.

3. Nosotros _____ enfermos hoy.   _____ amigos.

4. ¿Quién _____ tú?   ¿Dónde _____ tú?

5. ¿_____ Uds. bomberos?   ¿_____ Uds. cansados?

6. Mis padres _____ jóvenes.   _____ en California.

7. Yo _____ triste ahora.   _____ profesor de español.

8. Ellos _____ bien.   _____ de Alemania.

9. Yo _____ feliz.   _____ alegre.

10. ¿Cómo _____ ellas?   ¿_____ ellas bonitas?

C. Each statement is a reply to a question. Write the question.

EXAMPLE: Sí, soy cubano.   *¿Es Ud. (or Eres tú) cubano?*

1. No, no estamos cansados. _____

2. Sí, somos felices. _____

3. Sí, están muy bien. _____

4. No soy española; soy norteamericana. _____

5. Estoy bien, gracias. _____

6. Son las tres y cuarto. _____

7. No, tengo calor. _____

8. Es blanca. _____

9. Hace mal tiempo. _____

10. Ella está trabajando hoy. _____

D. Form a sentence with each group of words.

1. ¿ / está / no / María / escuela / hoy / la / en / por / qué / ?

_____

2. interesantes / de / estos / son / televisión / programas / muy

_____

3. y / son / mis / simpáticos / jóvenes / tíos

_____

4. de / nuestra / es / delgada / profesora / español / y / alta

_____

5. de / sala / las / de / clase / abiertas / están / puertas / la

_____

E. Make each expression a complete sentence by adding a form of _ser_ or _estar_.

EXAMPLE: las chicas pobres: _Las chicas son pobres._

1. su habitación cerrada: _____

2. la mujer simpática: _____

3. los alumnos tristes: _____

4. nuestro vecino inglés: _____

5. la casa diferente: _____

6. los amigos extraordinarios: _____

7. mis hermanas contentas: _____

8. la comida fría: _____

9. el arquitecto famoso: _____

10. los gatos estúpidos: _____

11. la señora de Cuba: _____

12. los hombres en la calle: _____

13. el sombrero de fieltro: _____

14. ese profesor inteligente: _____

15. el abuelo enfermo: _____

F. Translate into Spanish:

1. _a._ Where is your bicycle? _____

_b._ It is in the basement. _____

2. *a.* My room is large and light. _____

    b. The kitchen is small and dark. _____

3. *a.* The chairs are old. _____

    b. The tables are new. _____

4. *a.* We (*f.*) are seated. _____

    b. They are standing. _____

5. *a.* He is very sleepy. _____

    b. Are you hungry? _____

6. *a.* The school is situated in the center of the city. _____

_____

    b. There is a library near the bookstore. _____

_____

7. *a.* The men are from Guatemala. _____

    b. I am from Mexico. _____

8. *a.* What day is today? _____

    b. Today is Sunday. It is not Saturday. _____

9. *a.* They are not well today. _____

    b. The girls are sick this evening. _____

10. We are listening to the records. (Translate in two ways.)

    a. _____ *b.* _____

11. *a.* My sweater is woolen. _____

    b. Our table is wooden. _____

12. *a.* My brother is happy. (Use *contento, -a.*) _____

    b. My friends are happy. (Use *feliz, felices.*) _____

13. *a.* Your grandparents are not old. _____

    b. The singers are very rich. _____

14. *a.* His letters are very interesting. _____

    b. The meeting is very important. _____

15. *a.* Today it is very cold. _____

    b. We are very warm here. _____

16. *a.* Who are they? _____

    b. They are my relatives. _____

17. *a.* What is this? _____

    b. It's a tennis racquet. _____

18. *a.* What time is it? Is it late? _____

    b. It is half past eleven. It is not early. _____

_____

19. *a.* Are the doors open? _____

    b. No, they are closed. _____

20. *a.* How old is she? _____

    b. She is fifteen years old. She is young. _____

_____

G. *Listening Comprehension.* Your teacher will read to the class ten questions in Spanish. After each question is read, circle the letter of the most appropriate answer.

1. *a.* Está enferma.
    b. Está enfermo.
    c. Es bonita.

2. *a.* Estoy en Chicago.
    b. Son de Los Ángeles.
    c. Soy de Nueva York.

3. *a.* Está en la cama.
    b. Es de nilón.
    c. Somos de Panamá.

4. *a.* Está allí.
    b. Está enfermo.
    c. Es inteligente.

5. *a.* Están muy bien.
    b. Somos felices.
    c. Son muy simpáticos.

6. *a.* No, es abogado.
    b. Sí, está en casa.
    c. No, son arquitectos.

7. *a.* Sí, es un buen hombre.
    b. No, está enfermo hoy.
    c. Sí, estoy en casa.

8. *a.* Tengo un dólar.
    b. Tenemos doce años.
    c. Tengo catorce años.

9. *a.* No, somos jóvenes.
    b. No, son muy jóvenes.
    c. Sí, es muy vieja.

10. *a.* Hace calor.
    b. Son las ocho.
    c. Es jueves.

14
Uses of the Infinitive

Quiero hablar contigo.	I want to speak with you.
Voy a ver una película.	I'm going to see a film.
Trato de aprender.	I'm trying to learn.
Antes de salir, tomo el desayuno.	Before going out, I have breakfast.

1. In Spanish, an infinitive may follow a conjugated verb directly, a conjugated verb + a preposition, or a preposition by itself.

Some Verbs That Are Followed Directly by an Infinitive

---

deber, should, ought to, have to, to be supposed to
    Debemos asistir a la reunión.　　　We have to (are supposed to) attend the meeting.

desear, to wish, want
    Deseamos partir en seguida.　　　We wish to leave at once.

esperar, to hope
    Esperan llegar a tiempo.　　　They hope to arrive on time.

pensar, to intend
    Ella **piensa quedarse** en casa.　　　She intends to stay home.

poder, to be able, can
    No **puedo oír** la música.　　　I can't hear the music.

preferir, to prefer
    Preferimos tomar vino.　　　We prefer to have wine.

querer, to want
    ¿**Quiere** (Ud.) **ver** el menú?　　　Do you want to see the menu?

saber, to know how
    Él no **sabe manejar.**　　　He doesn't know how to drive.

Practice A: Answer each question as indicated.

1. ¿Esperas llegar temprano?   Sí, _____

2. ¿Piensa Ud. viajar este verano?   No, no _____

3. ¿Quiere José jugar?   No, no _____

4. ¿Sabes nadar?   Sí, _____

5. ¿Deben Uds. beber mucha agua?   Sí, _____

Some Verbs That Require the Preposition *A* Before an Infinitive

aprender a, to learn to
¿**Aprendes a** patinar?   Are you learning to skate?

ayudar a, to help to
¿Quién la **ayudó a** levantarse?   Who helped her to get up?

enseñar a, to teach to
El maestro nos **enseñó a** escribir.   The teacher taught us to write.

comenzar a ⎫
          ⎬ to begin to
empezar a ⎭
  Comienzan a comprender.   They are beginning to understand.
  Empezó a llover.   It began to rain.

invitar a, to invite to
Invítelos **a** comer con nosotros. Invite them to eat with us.

ir a, to be going to
Voy a hablar con ella.   I'm going to speak with her.

venir a, to be coming to
Venimos a verlo.   We're coming to see it.

salir a, to go (come) out to
¿**Sales a** jugar?   Are you coming out to play?

volver a, (to do something) again
El alumno **volvió a** hacer la tarea. The student did the homework again.

Practice B: Express in Spanish.

1. My brother is learning to talk. _____

2. Are you going to have breakfast now? _____

3. It is beginning to snow. _____

4. I'm inviting her to go with us. _____

5. He is sleeping again. _____

Some Verbs That Require the Preposition *DE* Before an Infinitive

acabar de, to have just
    Acaban de llegar.   They have just arrived.
    Acababan de llegar.   They had just arrived.

acordarse de, to remember
    Se acordaron de ir a la tienda.   They remembered to go to the store.

alegrarse de, to be glad
    Me alegro de verte.   I'm glad to see you.

cesar de ⎫
dejar de ⎬ to stop (doing something)
    Cesaron de comer.   They stopped eating.
    Él nunca **deja de** hablar.   He never stops talking.

olvidarse de, to forget
    Me olvidé de traer el paquete.   I forgot to bring the package.

tratar de, to try
    Trata de acabar sus tareas.   He is trying to finish his homework.

Practice C: Express in Spanish.

1. They have just come in. _____

2. She is glad to do it. _____

3. Stop shouting. _____

4. We're trying to study. _____

5. Is she forgetting to bring the records? _____

Infinitives as Objects of Prepositions

Antes de salir, apagamos las luces.   Before going out, we put out the lights.

Al ver el accidente, llamé a la policía.   On seeing the accident, I called the police.

Sin estudiar no se puede aprender.   Without studying you can't learn.

Trabajo **para ganar** dinero.   I work (in order) to earn money.

2. Any verb that follows a preposition must be in the infinitive form. In phrases such as **antes de salir** and **sin estudiar**, the meaning of the infinitive is generally expressed in English by a form that ends in *-ing*. This should not be confused with the Spanish present participle (**hablando, comiendo,** etc.)* when translating the equivalent English phrases into Spanish.

_____

*See page 99.

3. Compare the following sentences:

Buscando su anillo, encontró el reloj que había perdido.

(While) looking for her ring, she found the watch she had lost.

Al salir del edificio, vimos a nuestros amigos.

(On) leaving the building, we saw our friends.

Practice D: Express in Spanish.

1. Running down the street, he bumped into his friend Charlie.

   _____ por la calle, dio con su amigo Carlitos.

2. Instead of going to the movies, I stayed home.

   _____ al cine, me quedé en casa.

3. On arriving home, they turned on the television.

   _____ a casa, pusieron la televisión.

4. After closing the door, I opened the windows.

   _____ la puerta, abrí las ventanas.

5. Without eating, one can't live.

   _____ no se puede vivir.

6. Before entering, take off your hat.

   _____, quítese el sombrero.

EJERCICIOS

A. Complete the sentences with the correct preposition (**a** or **de**). If the sentence does not require a preposition, do not write one.

1. ¿Qué piensan Uds. _____ hacer hoy?

2. ¿Quién te invitó _____ ir al cine?

3. Volvieron _____ ver el film.

4. Ud. se ha olvidado _____ traer el libro.

5. ¿Prefieren Uds. _____ ver el menú?

6. Ella no sabe _____ hablar inglés.

7. Después _____ llegar, se sentaron a comer.

8. ¿Quieres _____ tomar algo en este café?

9. ¿Cuándo empezaron _____ ganar dinero?

10. Los invitados acaban _____ entrar.

B. Underline the expression in parentheses that could *not* be used to complete the sentence.

1. Mi madre nos (ayuda a, trata de, invita a) preparar la comida.

2. (Aprendemos a, Esperamos, Venimos a) verlos a Uds. mañana.

3. La clase (empieza a, trata de, enseña a) comprender el concepto.

4. Los niños (invitan a, vuelven a, van a) jugar al béisbol.

5. (Acaban de, Aprenden a, Se alegran de) salir de la escuela.

C. Write the questions that are answered by the given statements.

EXAMPLE: Sí, vamos a verla.
    ¿Van Uds. a ver la película?

1. Sí, me alegro de tener el coche esta noche.

   _____

2. Nuestros abuelos van a llegar mañana.

   ¿Cuándo _____?

   ¿Quiénes _____?

3. Esperamos visitar a Madrid.

   ¿Qué _____?

4. Lo hacemos antes de salir.

   ¿Cuándo _____?

5. Al terminar la comida, pasé a la sala.

   ¿Qué _____?

6. No, no puedo oírla.

   _____

7. Queremos ir a México.

   ¿Adónde _____?

8. Después de ver el programa, se sentaron a comer.

   ¿Qué _____?

9. Sí, sé patinar muy bien.

   _____

10. No pensamos viajar porque no tenemos suficiente dinero.

    ¿Por qué _____?

D. Express in Spanish:

1. *a.* Can you bring the tapes tomorrow?

_____

   b. Are you going to bring the money tonight?

_____

2. *a.* She has just paid for the dinner.

_____

   b. She should pay the bill.

_____

3. *a.* Are you (*Ud.*) playing the music again?

_____

   b. Are you (*Ud.*) coming to play in our band?

_____

4. *a.* Our students are learning to speak Spanish.

_____

   b. They are also trying to speak fast.

_____

5. *a.* He left without saying good-bye.

_____

   b. They left before seeing my father.

_____

6. *a.* I'm coming to hear the music.

_____

   b. I don't want to hear the news.

_____

7. *a.* Are you (*Uds.*) glad to be here?

_____

   b. Do you (*Uds.*) prefer to be here?

_____

8. *a.* Stop talking so much.

_____

   b. Learn to speak Spanish.

_____

9. *a.* I hope to listen to the records later.

_____

   b. I tried to listen to the program.

_____

10. *a.* Were they able to go to the concert?

_____

   b. Did they forget to go to the store?

_____

E. *Listening Comprehension.* Your teacher will read aloud ten questions in Spanish. After each question is read, circle the letter of the most appropriate answer.

1. *a.* No, pero espero aprender algún día.
   b. Sí, me alegro de verte.
   c. No, pero sabemos ir en bicicleta.

2. *a.* Van a ver una película.
   b. Puedo hacerlo muy bien.
   c. Voy a visitar a mi tío.

3. *a.* Sí, pero nos olvidamos de apagar las luces.
   b. Sí, y también volvimos a ver a Rosa.
   c. No, porque debemos llegar temprano.

4. *a.* Acabo de recibir un telegrama.
   b. Llamaré por teléfono a José.
   c. Después de salir, tomaré el autobús.

5. *a.* Dejamos de correr a las siete.
   b. Debo correr rápidamente.
   c. Comenzamos dentro de cinco minutos.

6. *a.* Debo llegar temprano.
   b. Debes pagar el dinero.
   c. Piensas quedarte en casa.

7. *a.* Prefiero tomar el tren.
   b. Van a andar.
   c. Me acordé de tomar el tren.

8. *a.* María cesa de cantar.
   b. Francisco va a venir.
   c. Yo te invito a venir.

9. *a.* Sí, prefiero salir.
   b. No, voy a quedarme aquí.
   c. No, quiero volver a casa.

10. *a.* Quiero ver una película vieja.
   b. Espero tener el disco.
   c. Te invito a mirarla conmigo.

15
The Present Subjunctive

The subjunctive is a verb form that has almost disappeared from spoken English. It is sometimes heard in expressions such as "if I *were* you" (instead of "I was") and "we insist that she *leave* early" (instead of "she leaves"). In Spanish, however, the subjunctive is still used regularly in the spoken language. In fact, it is almost impossible to avoid in any lengthy conversation.

The Subjunctive After Impersonal Expressions and Certain Verbs

Es necesario salir temprano.	It is necessary to leave early.
Es necesario que yo **salga** temprano.	It is necessary for me to leave (that I leave) early.
Ella quiere aprender el español.	She wants to learn Spanish.
Ella quiere que tú **aprendas** el español.	She wants you to learn Spanish.
Prefiero hablar despacio.	I prefer to speak slowly.
Prefiero que ellos **hablen** despacio.	I prefer that they speak slowly.
Esperamos ir al teatro.	We hope to go to the theater.
Esperamos que Ud. **vaya** al teatro.	We hope that you will go to the theater.

1. The subjunctive form of the verb is generally used after:

   a. *impersonal expressions:* **es necesario que, es posible que, es importante que,** etc.

   b. *verbs of wishing, asking, or telling* (*someone to do something*): **querer, pedir, decir,** etc.

   c. *verbs that express feeling* (*hoping, fearing, being sorry,* etc.): **esperar*, temer, sentir, alegrarse,** etc.

Esperar may also be followed by a verb in the indicative: "Esperamos que Ud. **irá** al teatro."

123

2. In such cases, the subjunctive can be used only if there is a change of subject:

Ella quiere que **yo** aprenda.   *She* wants *me* to learn.

If no change of subject occurs, the infinitive is used: **Ella** quiere **aprender.**

3. A clause that contains a verb in the subjunctive is generally introduced by **que.**

4. A verb in the present subjunctive may have either a present or a future meaning:

Espero que **venga.** $\begin{cases} \text{I hope she is coming.} \\ \text{I hope she will come.} \end{cases}$

Formation of the Present Subjunctive

---

5. To conjugate a verb in the present subjunctive, use the singular and plural forms of the formal command (see chapter 4). The **Ud.** form is the same as the first and third person singular; the **Uds.** form is the same as the third person plural. The other three forms of the subjunctive are obtained by adding the endings **-s, -mos,** and **-is** to the **yo** form of the subjunctive. (For stem-changing verbs, see §7, below.) For example:

Formal Command		*Present Subjunctive*	
poner	**ponga** Ud.	**ponga**	**pongamos**
		pongas	**pongáis**
		ponga	**pongan**
tomar	**tome** Ud.	**tome**	**tomemos**
		tomes	**toméis**
		tome	**tomen**
pensar	**piense** Ud.	**piense**	**pensemos**
		pienses	**penséis**
		piense	**piensen**
volver	**vuelva** Ud.	**vuelva**	**volvamos**
		vuelvas	**volváis**
		vuelva	**vuelvan**

6. Note that the subjunctive forms of verbs with spelling changes (see Appendix VIII) are obtained in the same way:

buscar	**busque** Ud.	**busque**	**busquemos**
		busques	**busquéis**
		busque	**busquen**

7. The **nosotros** and **vosotros** subjunctive forms of *stem-changing* verbs are obtained as follows:

(1) *-AR* AND *-ER* VERBS

If the command form has **ie** or **ue** in its stem, the **nosotros** and **vosotros** forms retain the stem vowel of the infinitive:

piense—pensemos, penséis
vuelva—volvamos, volváis

(2) *-IR* VERBS

a. If the command form has **ie** in its stem, this changes to **i** in the **nosotros** and **vosotros** forms:

(sentir) sienta Ud.   sienta, sientas, sienta, | síntamos, sintáis, | sientan

b. If the command form has **ue** in its stem, this changes to **u** in the **nosotros** and **vosotros** forms:

(dormir) duerma Ud.   duerma, duermas, duerma, | durmamos, durmáis, | duerman

c. If **i** is the stem vowel in the command form, it is the stem vowel in all six forms (including those for **nosotros** and **vosotros**):

(pedir) pida Ud.   pida, pidas, pida, pidamos, pidáis, pidan
(seguir) siga Ud.   siga, sigas, siga, sigamos, sigáis, sigan

8. Verbs that have irregular command forms will have the same irregular forms in the present subjunctive:

dar:	*dé, des, dé, demos, deis, den*
estar:	*esté, estés, esté, estemos, estéis, estén*
ir:	*vaya, vayas, vaya, vayamos, vayáis, vayan*
saber:	*sepa, sepas, sepa, sepamos, sepáis, sepan*
ser:	*sea, seas, sea, seamos, seáis, sean*

Practice A: Write the six forms of the present subjunctive.

EXAMPLE: recibir: *reciba, recibas, reciba, recibamos, recibáis, reciban*

1. necesitar: _____

2. beber: _____

3. escribir: _____

4. hacer: _____

5. ver: _____

6. almorzar: _____

7. perder: _____

8. ser: _____

9. estar: _____

10. decir: _____

11. tocar: _____

12. morir: _____

13. jugar: _____

14. traducir: _____

15. preferir: _____

Practice B: Change the infinitive to the present subjunctive.

EXAMPLE: Queremos bailar esta noche.

Queremos que tú ___*bailes*___ también.

1. Es necesario escribir cartas.

Es necesario que yo _____ una carta.

2. Prefiero comer carne.

Prefiero que Ud. _____ ensalada.

3. Esperan venir esta tarde.

Esperan que nosotras _____ mañana.

4. Temo entrar en esa casa.

Temo que ellos _____ en ese edificio.

5. Es importante empezar ahora.

Es importante que ella _____ en seguida.

Some Impersonal Expressions That Require the Subjunctive in the *QUE* Clause

es dudoso, it is doubtful

es importante, it is important

es lástima, it is a pity

es posible, it is possible

es imposible, it is impossible

es necesario, it is necessary

es probable, it is probable

Practice C: Supply the subjunctive forms as shown in the example.

EXAMPLE: Es posible que ellos___*vengan*___   ___*lean*___   ___*hablen*___
                                   (venir)   (leer)   (hablar)

1. Es lástima que tú no   _____   _____   _____
                              (ir)   (escribir)   (volver)

2. Es dudoso que él   _____   _____   _____
                         (contestar)   (almorzar)   (decir)

3. Es probable que nosotros_____   _____   _____
                              (ser)   (estar)   (saber)

Impersonal Expressions That Are Not Used With the Subjunctive

Es cierto que ellos **vendrán** mañana.

Es verdad que él **tiene** el dinero.

It is certain that they will come tomorrow.

It is true that he has the money.

6. Impersonal expressions that express certainty are not followed by the subjunctive in the **que** clause.

Practice D: Complete the sentences as shown by the examples in italics.

1. It's important for you to study (that you study).   *Es importante que tú estudies.*

   a. It's important for you to be here (that you be here).

      Es importante que tú _____ aquí.

   b. It's important for you to have (that you have) money.

      Es importante que tú _____ dinero.

   c. It's important for you to come on time (that you come on time).

      Es importante que tú _____ a tiempo.

2. It is necessary for me to go.   *Es necesario que yo vaya.*

   a. It is necessary for me to leave.   Es necesario que _____.

   b. It is necessary for me to eat.   Es necesario que _____.

   c. It is necessary for me to run.   Es necesario que _____.

3. It is certain that they will leave.   *Es cierto que ellos saldrán.*

   a. It is certain that they will take the medicine.

      Es cierto que _____ la medicina.

   b. It is certain that they will be doctors.

      Es cierto que _____ médicos.

   c. It is certain that they will win.

      Es cierto que _____.

4. It is possible for me to learn that.   *Es posible que yo aprenda eso.*

   a. It is possible for me to be there early.

      Es posible que _____ allí temprano.

   b. It is possible for me to buy the books.

      Es posible que _____ los libros.

   c. It is possible for me to know the subjunctive.

      Es posible que _____ el subjuntivo.

Verbs That Require the Subjunctive in the *QUE* Clause

A. WISHING

> **querer,** to want   **desear,** to wish   **preferir,** to prefer

Ella **quiere** que yo **vaya** a la fiesta.[1]   She wants me to go (that I go) to the party.

¿**Prefieres** que ella **se quede** en casa?   Do you prefer that she remain at home?

Practice E: Complete the sentences as shown by the examples in italics.

1. He wants us to leave.   *Quiere que salgamos.*

   a. He wants us to go.   Quiere que _____.

   b. He wants us to come early.   Quiere que _____ temprano.

   c. He wants us to work.   Quiere que _____.

2. He wants me to travel.   *Quiere que yo viaje.*

   a. He wants me to win.   Quiere que yo _____.

   b. He wants me to eat.   Quiere que yo _____.

   c. He wants me to run.   Quiere que yo _____.

3. Do they prefer that we eat less?   *¿Prefieren que comamos menos?*

   a. Do they prefer that we drink more?   ¿Prefieren que _____ más?

   b. Do they prefer that we be there?   ¿Prefieren que _____ allí?

   c. Do they prefer that we stay?   ¿Prefieren que _____?

B. TELLING, ASKING, ORDERING, FORBIDDING, PERMITTING

> **decir,** to tell   **mandar,** to order   **prohibir,** to forbid
>
> **pedir,** to ask   **permitir,** to permit

Él dice que **yo venga.** ⎫[2]
Él **me** dice que **venga.** ⎭   He tells me to come.

Pedimos que **ella venga** temprano. ⎫
Le pedimos que **venga** temprano. ⎭   We ask her to come early.

¿Permite Ud. que **ellos fumen?** ⎫
¿**Les** permite Ud. que **fumen?** ⎭   Do you permit them to smoke?

---

[1] A direct translation from English may produce an erroneous equivalent in Spanish. For example, the equivalent of *she wants me to call* is not **ella me quiere llamar,** which means *she wants to call me,* but **ella quiere que yo llame.**

[2] The two sentences do not always have the same meaning. In some cases, omitting the object pronoun may require a different translation. **Él dice que yo venga** may mean "He says that I should come," which does not necessarily imply that he says that *to me.* Similarly, the first sentence of the second pair (**Pedimos que. . .**) may mean "We ask that she come early," which leaves it unclear whether we are asking *her* or someone else (perhaps her parents).

7. The verbs **decir, mandar, pedir, permitir,** and **prohibir** may be used with or without object pronouns. If they are used with object pronouns, the subject pronoun is omitted before the verb in the **que** clause. (The subject pronoun in the **que** clause may be omitted in either case.)

Practice F: Complete the sentences as shown by the examples in italics.

1. They tell us to work.

   Dicen que nosotros trabajemos.
   Nos dicen que trabajemos.

   a. They tell us to study.

   Dicen que _____.

   _____ dicen que _____.

   b. They tell us to rest.

   Dicen que _____.

   _____ dicen que _____.

2. She asks them to get up.

   Ella pide que ellos se levanten.
   Ella les pide que se levanten.

   a. She asks them to sit down.

   Ella pide que _____.

   Ella _____ pide que _____.

   b. She asks them to remain.

   Ella pide que _____.

   Ella _____ pide que _____.

3. The teacher forbids us to drink beer.

   El profesor prohíbe que nosotros bebamos
   cerveza.
   El profesor nos prohíbe que bebamos cerveza.

   a. The teacher forbids us to write the words.

   El profesor prohíbe que _____
   las palabras.

   El profesor _____ prohíbe que

   _____ las palabras.

   b. The teacher forbids us to come late.

   El profesor prohíbe que _____
   tarde.

   El profesor _____ prohíbe que

   _____ tarde.

4. They tell me to speak slowly.

   Dicen que yo hable despacio.
   Me dicen que hable despacio.

   a. They tell me to run fast.

   Dicen que _____ de prisa.

   _____ dicen que _____ de
   prisa.

   b. They tell me to sell my house.

   Dicen que _____ mi casa.

   _____ dicen que _____ mi
   casa.

C. EXPRESSING FEELINGS

alegrarse de, to be glad   **sentir,** to be sorry   **temer,** to fear

esperar, to hope   **tener miedo de,** to be afraid of

Practice G: Complete the sentences as shown in the example.

EXAMPLE:

I'm sorry to be here.   Siento estar aquí.
a. I'm sorry that he is here.   *Siento que él esté aquí.*
b. I'm sorry that he does not have the   *Siento que él no tenga el dinero.*
   money.
c. I'm sorry that he doesn't know the   *Siento que él no sepa la dirección.*
   address.

1. Are you afraid to cross the street?   ¿Tienes miedo de cruzar la calle?

   a. Are you afraid that I will cross the street? ¿Tienes miedo de que _____
                                                       la calle?

   b. Are you afraid that I will go home?   ¿Tienes miedo de que _____
                                                       a casa?

   c. Are you afraid that I will leave?   ¿Tienes miedo de que _____?

2. We hope to see the film.   Esperamos ver la película.

   a. We hope that you will see the film.   Esperamos que _____ la
                                                       película.

   b. We hope that you will take the money.   Esperamos que _____ el
                                                       dinero.

   c. We hope that you will do the work.   Esperamos que _____ el
                                                       trabajo.

3. I'm glad to be here.   Me alegro de estar aquí.

   a. I'm glad that they are here.   Me alegro de que _____ aquí.
   b. I'm glad that they are speaking.   Me alegro de que _____.
   c. I'm glad that they are returning.   Me alegro de que _____.

D. TO DOUBT, DENY, BE UNCERTAIN

   dudar, to doubt   **negar (ie),** to deny   **no estar seguro, -a,** not to be sure

Practice H: Complete the sentences as shown in the example.

EXAMPLE

I doubt that he will listen.   Dudo que él escuche.
a. I doubt that he will go.   Dudo que él *vaya.*
b. I doubt that he will come.   Dudo que él *venga.*
c. I doubt that he will arrive on time.   Dudo que él *llegue* a tiempo.

1. She denies that you are smart.

    a. She denies that you know the truth.

    b. She denies that you work here.

    c. She denies that you want money.

2. We are not sure that they are coming.

    a. We are not sure that they are going.

    b. We are not sure that they speak Spanish.

    c. We are not sure that they hear the music.

Ella niega que tú seas inteligente.

Ella niega que tú _____ la verdad.

Ella niega que tú _____ aquí.

Ella niega que tú _____ dinero.

No estamos seguros de que vengan.

No estamos seguros de que _____.

No estamos seguros de que _____ español.

No estamos seguros de que _____ la música.

8. **Dudar, negar, no estar seguro, -a,** and other expressions of doubt or denial require the subjunctive in the **que** clause. When **dudar** and **negar** are used *negatively*, however, they are followed by the indicative since they express certainty. For the same reason, **estar seguro, -a** is also followed by the indicative.

Practice I: Complete the sentences as shown in the examples.

EXAMPLES:
I doubt that he will run.
I do not doubt that he will run.
He does not deny that you have money.
He denies that you have money.

Dudo que él corra.
No dudo que él *correrá*.
No niega que tú tienes dinero.
Niega que tú *tengas* dinero.

1. She is not sure that we will eat there.

    She is sure that we will eat there.

Ella no está segura de que comamos allí.

Ella está segura de que _____ allí.

2. We doubt that the teacher will give the exam.

    We do not doubt that the teacher will give the exam.

Dudamos que la profesora dé el examen.

No dudamos que la profesora

_____ el examen.

3. The teacher does not deny that Spanish is easy.

    The teacher denies that Spanish is easy.

El profesor no niega que el español es fácil.

El profesor niega que el español

_____ fácil.

EJERCICIOS

A. Repeat the sentence orally, replacing the verb in italics with the appropriate form of the verb in parentheses. (Write the new verb form in the blank at the right.)

EXAMPLE: Quiero que *bailes*. (aprender)
Quiero que aprendas.   _____*aprendas*_____

1. Dudan que *volvamos* temprano. (regresar)   _____

2. Prefiere que *vengas* a casa. (ir)   _____

3. La profesora nos dice que *leamos* mucho. (estudiar) _____

4. Me alegro de que *sepan* la verdad. (decir)   _____

5. Queremos que ellos *vayan* al cine con nosotras. (andar) _____

6. Es lástima que no *comprendan* a ese hombre. (conocer)   _____

7. No están seguros de que *necesitemos* el mapa. (vender)   _____

8. Me piden que *entre en* el cuarto. (salir de)   _____

9. El general quiere que los soldados *luchen*. (ser valientes) _____

10. Niego que Pablo *compre* los artículos. (querer)   _____

B. Complete the sentence with the appropriate form of the verb in italics.

EXAMPLE: Quiero *comprar* los discos pero no puedo. Por eso quiero que tú los _____*compres*_____ .

1. Esperan *traer* los libros y esperan que Ud. los _____ también.

2. Es importante *ahorrar* dinero. Es importante que todo el mundo _____ dinero.

3. Es imposible *mirar* la televisión toda la noche, pero es posible que los niños la _____ todo el día.

4. ¿No prefieres *leer* novelas buenas? No quiero que tú _____ estas novelas malas.

5. Es cierto que Roberto *vendrá* a la fiesta pero es dudoso que María _____ con él.

6. Quiero *ir* al centro mañana y quiero que tú _____ conmigo.

7. Tememos *salir* de casa por la noche y tememos que nuestros hijos _____ .

8. Me alegro de *ver* a mis abuelos y me alegro también de que Uds. los _____ .

9. Ella pide a José que *se siente* allí. También pide a sus hermanos que _____ al lado de ella.

10. Queremos que ellos *se queden* en nuestra casa hoy. Y ellos quieren que nosotros _____ en su casa mañana.

C. Answer with a complete sentence in Spanish:

1. ¿Prefiere Ud. que yo salga de su casa?

_____

2. ¿Quieres que yo traiga la foto?   _____

3. ¿Es necesario que toda la clase hable español?

_____

4. ¿Es lástima que tengamos que asistir a la escuela?

_____

5. ¿Teme Ud. que el profesor (la profesora) dé un examen mañana?

_____

6. ¿Pide su padre que Ud. trabaje los sábados y domingos?

_____

7. ¿Quiere su madre que Ud. vuelva a casa temprano los sábados por la noche?

_____

8. ¿Niega Ud. que su profesora (profesor) de español sea la mejor profesora (el mejor profesor) de la escuela?

_____

9. ¿Esperan sus padres que Ud. llegue a ser médico (médica)?

_____

10. ¿Es importante que nosotros conservemos energía?

_____

D. Form sentences as shown in the example.

EXAMPLE: yo / querer / tú / ir / fiesta
Yo quiero que tú vayas a la fiesta.

1. madre / preferir / nosotros / quedarse / en casa / esta noche

_____

2. ellos / alegrarse / yo / tener / coche nuevo

_____

3. ser / necesario / Ud. / tomar / tren

_____

4. padre / decir / yo / venir / con él / tienda

_____

5. ser importante / todo el mundo / conocer / mujer

_____

E. Translate into Spanish:

1. *a.* It is a pity that he does not have the tickets.

_____

   b. It is important for him to have the money.

_____

2. *a.* Do you (*Ud.*) want to see the program?

_____

   b. Do you want her to see the program?

_____

3. *a.* He does not doubt that you (*tú*) can do it.

_____

   b. He doubts that they will be able to play.

_____

4. *a.* They are telling her to prepare dinner.

_____

   b. They are asking me to serve the salad.

_____

5. *a.* Is it possible to go to the movies tonight?

_____

   b. It is impossible for them to go to the theater.

_____

6. *a.* I'm sorry to hear that (*eso*).

_____

   b. I'm sorry that they will not hear the music.

_____

7. *a.* We hope that you (*Uds.*) will be able to attend the party.

_____

   b. We hope to attend the concert tomorrow evening.

_____

8. *a.* I want you (*tú*) to be here this afternoon.

_____

   b. I want to be there later. _____

9. *a.* They are afraid that he will tell a lie.

_____

b. They are afraid to tell the truth.

_____

10. *a.* It is necessary for me to pay the bill.

_____

b. It is necessary to pay the bills every month.

_____

F. *Listening Comprehension.* Your teacher will read aloud ten questions in Spanish. After each question is read, circle the letter of the most appropriate answer.

1. *a.* Quiero que digas la verdad.
   b. Quiero que digan algo interesante.
   c. No quieres que diga nada.

2. *a.* Sí, vamos a la playa muy temprano.
   b. No, no es posible, porque me gusta el cine.
   c. No es posible porque tengo que quedarme en casa.

3. *a.* No, dudo que haga buen tiempo.
   b. Sí, creo que hará mal tiempo.
   c. No, quiero que haga mal tiempo.

4. *a.* No, preferimos que te sientes allí.
   b. No, preferimos que se sienten allí.
   c. Sí, prefiero que se siente aquí.

5. *a.* Mando que traiga el mensaje.
   b. Manda que traigamos los billetes.
   c. Manda que traigas los documentos.

6. *a.* No, no es necesario visitarla.
   b. No, no es necesario que la visite.
   c. Sí, es necesario que la visites.

7. *a.* No quiero que venga nunca.
   b. Quiero que vengan a las ocho.
   c. Quieres que venga muy temprano.

8. *a.* Sí, pido que contesten.
   b. No, no pedimos que conteste.
   c. No, no pedimos que contesten.

9. *a.* Sí, temo que toquen música clásica.
   b. Sí, temo que toques música popular.
   c. No, no temo que toque música *rock*.

10. *a.* No, no quiero conducir.
   b. No, creo que causarás un accidente.
   c. Sí, quiero que conduzcan ahora mismo.

16
The Imperfect Subjunctive

Es posible que **vengan** más tarde.	It is possible that they will come later.
Era posible que **vinieran (viniesen)** más tarde.	It was possible that they would come later.
Esperan que **vayas** a casa.	They hope that you will go home.
Esperaron que **fueras (fueses)** a casa.	They hoped that you would go home.
Queremos que Uds. **estén** allí temprano.	We want you to be there early.
Queríamos que Uds. **estuvieran (estuviesen)** allí temprano.	We wanted you to be there early.

1. The *present* subjunctive is generally used in the **que** clause when the verb in the main clause is in the present or the future tense. The present subjunctive is often translated by the English future tense (*will*).

2. When the verb in the main clause is in a past tense (that is, in the imperfect or the preterite), the *imperfect* subjunctive is used in the **que** clause. The imperfect subjunctive is often translated with the word *would*.

Formation of the Imperfect Subjunctive

---

3. The imperfect subjunctive is formed from the *third person plural* of the *preterite* tense (see chapters 6 and 7). Remove the **-ron** ending, add **-ra** or **-se** to the preterite stem, and conjugate as follows:

	Preterite, *3rd Person Plural*	*Imperfect Subjunctive*	
		-ra FORM	**-se** FORM
tomar	**toma**ron	toma*ra*	toma*se*
		toma*ras*	toma*ses*
		toma*ra*	toma*se*
		tomá*ramos*	tomá*semos*
		toma*rais*	toma*seis*
		toma*ran*	toma*sen*

decir	**dij**eron	dij**era**	dij**ese**
		dij**eras**	dij**eses**
		dij**era**	dij**ese**
		dij**éramos**	dij**ésemos**
		dij**erais**	dij**eseis**
		dij**eran**	dij**esen**
poner	**pusie**ron	pusi**era**	pusi**ese**
		pusi**eras**	pusi**eses**
		pusi**era**	pusi**ese**
		pusi**éramos**	pusi**ésemos**
		pusi**erais**	pusi**eseis**
		pusi**eran**	pusi**esen**

4. The **-ra** and **-se** forms are interchangeable; that is, either form may be used in most cases. (The exceptions are not treated in this book.)

Practice A: Write the *-ra* and *-se* forms of the imperfect subjunctive.

EXAMPLE:

hablar: (*a*) *hablara, hablaras, hablara, habláramos, hablarais, hablaran*
        (*b*) *hablase, hablases, hablase, hablásemos, hablaseis, hablasen*

1. escribir: (*a*) _____
        (*b*) _____

2. andar: (*a*) _____
        (*b*) _____

3. tener: (*a*) _____
        (*b*) _____

4. conducir: (*a*) _____
        (*b*) _____

5. ser: (*a*) _____
        (*b*) _____

6. querer: (*a*) _____
        (*b*) _____

7. oír: (*a*) _____
        (*b*) _____

8. pedir: (*a*) _____
        (*b*) _____

9. poder: (*a*) _____

       (*b*) _____

10. estar: (*a*) _____

       (*b*) _____

Practice B: Using the verb in parentheses, complete the sentence with the *-ra* form of the imperfect subjunctive. Write the alternate *-se* form in the blank at the right.

EXAMPLE:

(ir) Ella quiso que nosotros __*fuéramos*__ al cine.   ____*fuésemos*____

1. (beber) Ellos preferían que yo _____ poco.   _____

2. (vender) Era necesario que nosotros _____ la casa.   _____

3. (ser) Yo dudaba que ella _____ inteligente.   _____

4. (volver) Pidieron que ellos _____ temprano.   _____

5. (cantar) Yo no quería que tú _____ solo.   _____

6. (saber) Era imposible que Uds. _____ la verdad.   _____

7. (dar) Yo sentí que el profesor _____ el examen.   _____

8. (visitar) Ella nos dijo que _____ a España.   _____

9. (hacer) Se alegraron de que yo _____ eso.   _____

10. (andar) Era importante que tú _____ despacio.   _____

11. (tener) Yo esperaba que vosotras _____ los discos.   _____

12. (poder) Fue dudoso que ella _____ ir con nosotros.   _____

13. (estar) Negaban que nosotras _____ allí.   _____

14. (comer) Era imposible que él _____ tanto.   _____

15. (traer) El jefe mandó que el empleado _____ los papeles.   _____

EJERCICIOS

A. Complete the change in tense by replacing the present subjunctive with the imperfect subjunctive. (Use either the *-se* or the *-ra* form, writing the alternate form in the blank at the right.)

EXAMPLE:

Quiero que Ud. *conteste.*

Quería que Ud. __*contestara*__.   ____*contestase*____

1. Siento mucho que no *tengas* el tiempo.

Sentí mucho que no _____ los documentos.   _____

2. Prefieren que *vayamos* con ellos.

Preferían que _____ con Uds.   _____

3. Ella pide que tú la *acompañes* a la fiesta.

Ella pidió que tú la _____ al restaurante.   _____

4. Espero que Uds. no *sufran* mucho.

Esperaba que Uds. no _____ demasiado.   _____

5. Nos alegramos de que ellos *ganen* el concurso.

Nos alegrábamos de que ellos _____ la
competición.   _____

B. Complete the change in tense by replacing the imperfect subjunctive with the present subjunctive.

    EXAMPLE: Prefería que ellos *vinieran* temprano.

             Prefiero que ellos ___*vengan*___ antes de las seis.

1. ¿Querías que yo *viera* ese programa?

¿Quieres que yo _____ esa película?

2. Dudábamos que *pudieran* jugar al tenis por cuatro horas.

Dudamos que _____ llegar antes de las siete.

3. Nos dijeron que *trajésemos* los discos.

Nos dicen que _____ las cintas.

4. Era dudoso que *robaran* las joyas.

Es dudoso que _____ los diamantes.

5. Esperábamos que Uds. no lo *hicieran* tan pronto.

Esperamos que Uds. lo _____ lo más pronto posible.

C. Combine the two sentences as shown in the examples.

    EXAMPLES: Yo haré el trabajo. Mi padre lo prefiere.
               Mi padre prefiere que yo haga el trabajo.

               Les dimos el dinero. Era necesario.
               Era necesario que les diéramos (diésemos) el dinero.

1. Dijeron la verdad. Yo lo dudaba.

_____

2. Mandaré los paquetes. Mis abuelos lo piden.

_____

3. Corríamos por el parque. Ella lo negaba.

_____

4. Todos los alumnos estudiarán toda la noche. Es dudoso.

_____

5. Fuimos a España el verano pasado. Era importante.

_____

D. Use each group of words to form (_a_) a sentence with a _que_ clause in which the present subjunctive is required, and (_b_) the same sentence in the past tense, in which the imperfect subjunctive is required. (You may add words if necessary.)

EXAMPLE: mamá / no querer / yo / beber / café
      a. Mamá no quiere que yo beba café.
      b. Mamá no quería que yo bebiera (bebiese) café.

1. presidente / pedir / todos / gastar / menos dinero

    _a._ _____

    _b._ _____

2. ser dudoso / chicos / estar allí

    _a._ _____

    _b._ _____

3. yo / esperar / tío / traer / muchos / regalos

    _a._ _____

    _b._ _____

4. ser lástima / profesor / dar / examen / el lunes

    _a._ _____

    _b._ _____

5. Felipe / dudar / nosotros / ir / concierto

    _a._ _____

    _b._ _____

E. Translate into Spanish:

  1. _a._ It was necessary for them to arrive on time.

    _____

    _b._ It is necessary for them to arrive early.

    _____

2. *a.* I doubt that they will go to the shopping center (*centro comercial*).

_____

b. I doubted that they would go downtown.

_____

3. *a.* I'm afraid he won't have the tickets.

_____

b. I was afraid he wouldn't have the money.

_____

4. *a.* It is a pity that we won't see that film.

_____

b. It was a pity that we did not see that program.

_____

5. *a.* They asked me to write them a letter.

_____

b. They ask me to write it (*f.*).

_____

6. *a.* He doesn't want you (*tú*) to come.

_____

b. He didn't want you (*Uds.*) to come.

_____

7. *a.* We were sorry that she wasn't there.

_____

b. We are sorry that she won't be here.

_____

8. *a.* I told them to bring the records.

_____

b. I will tell them to bring the tapes.

_____

9. *a.* I hope he listens to the rock concert (concierto de música *rock*).

_____

b. I hoped he would listen to the music.

_____

10. *a.* It was doubtful that they heard the news.

_____

b. It is doubtful that they will hear the program.

_____

F. *Listening Comprehension.* Your teacher will read aloud ten statements in Spanish. After each statement is read, circle the letter of the most appropriate response.

1. *a.* Era necesario que yo me quedara en tu casa.
   b. Me gustaban esos programas de televisión.
   c. Pero tenía que volver a casa temprano.

2. *a.* Es verdad, porque la profesora insistía.
   b. Sí, todos iban a la fiesta.
   c. No, porque ellos vendieron el coche allí.

3. *a.* Mamá preparaba un plato delicioso.
   b. Íbamos a ver un film interesante.
   c. Me alegraba también, porque ella da muchas tareas.

4. *a.* Buena idea, porque queríamos comer temprano.
   b. Estaba lloviendo toda la noche.
   c. Los partidos siempre son interesantes.

5. *a.* Lo siento mucho; es muy simpático.
   b. Me alegro mucho, porque es muy amable.
   c. Bien, tengo que ir con ella al centro.

6. *a.* Muy bien, papá; tengo que hacer muchas cosas.
   b. Pero yo prefiero salir porque está lloviendo mucho.
   c. Me gusta mucho este teatro.

7. *a.* De acuerdo. Nos encontraremos a las siete.
   b. Gracias, ella se siente mejor ahora.
   c. Gracias, pero no tengo suficiente dinero.

8. *a.* Yo me alegro mucho, porque así cometerá más crímenes.
   b. Todos los profesores de español son criminales.
   c. Es dudoso que lo encuentren, porque nadie puede identificarlo.

9. *a.* Hay que bajar la temperatura en casa durante el invierno.
   b. Bien, vamos a visitarle mañana en la Casa Blanca.
   c. Usaremos los acondicionadores de aire todo el día.

10. *a.* Nos gustaba mucho esa música.
   b. No me interesan esas películas.
   c. El tema era muy interesante.

17
The Imperfect Subjunctive in "If" Clauses

A	*B*
Si estudias, aprenderás.	Si **estudiaras (estudiases), aprenderías.**
If you study, you will learn.	If you studied, you would learn.
Viajaremos si tenemos el dinero.	**Viajaríamos** si **tuviéramos (tuviésemos)** el dinero.
We will travel if we have the money.	We would travel if we had the money.
Si Uds. van a España, ¿cuándo partirán?	Si Uds. **fueran (fuesen)** a España, ¿cuándo **partirían**?
If you go to Spain, when will you leave?	If you went to Spain, when would you leave?

1. In the sentences of column *A*, we indicate what *will* happen if something else occurs. In the sentences of column *B*, we indicate what *would* happen if something occurred or were to occur (now or in the future).

2. In the sentences of column *A*, the "if" clauses state a condition in the present tense. The verb in the main clause is in the future tense.

3. In the sentences of column *B*, the "if" clauses are of two types:

a. They state a condition that is contrary to fact or reality. "We would travel if we had the money" implies that *we don't have the money.*

b. They express a degree of uncertainty. Note the tone of the last sentence ("If you went to Spain, . . ."), which sounds as if the speaker were only "supposing."

In both types, the verb in the "if" clause is in the imperfect subjunctive (either the **-ra** or the **-se** form). The verb in the main clause is in the conditional.

Practice A: Circle the letter of the correct Spanish translation.

1. If they were there, we would see them.
   a. Si estuviesen allí, los veríamos.
   b. Si están allí, los veremos.

2. If she comes, I'll speak with her.
   a. Si viene, hablaré con ella.
   b. Si viniera, hablaría con ella.

3. If I had time, I'd travel.
   a. Si tuviera tiempo, viajaría.
   b. Si tengo tiempo, viajaré.

4. If they went, would they visit their relatives?
   a. Si fuesen, ¿visitarían a sus parientes?
   b. Si van, ¿visitarán a sus parientes?

5. If I ask them, they will go with us.
   a. Si les pidiera, irían con nosotras.
   b. Si les pido, irán con nosotras.

6. If I were rich, I'd buy a yacht.
   a. Si soy rico, compraré un yate.
   b. Si fuera rico, compraría un yate.

Practice B: Complete the Spanish sentences with a verb in the present indicative or the imperfect subjunctive (whichever is appropriate).

1. If I didn't leave now, I would see him.

   Si yo no _____ ahora, lo vería.

2. If he can go, I'll accompany him.

   Si él _____ ir, lo acompañaré.

3. If you went to the party, you would have a good time.

   Si tú _____ a la fiesta, pasarías un buen rato.

4. If I learn the subjunctive, I will be very smart.

   Si _____ el subjuntivo, seré muy inteligente.

5. What would they do if they lost their money?

   ¿Qué harían si _____ su dinero?

EJERCICIOS

A. Answer with a complete sentence in Spanish:

1. ¿Qué haría Ud. si ganara un millón de dólares en la lotería?

_____

2. Si Ud. fuera el profesor (la profesora) de español, ¿daría muchos exámenes?

_____

3. Si tú pudieras viajar a algún país extranjero, ¿qué país escogerías?

_____

4. Si Ud. fuese la directora (el director) de la escuela, ¿qué cambios efectuaría (bring about)?

_____

5. Si Ud. fuera astronauta, ¿adónde le gustaría ir?

_____

6. Si hace buen tiempo el domingo, ¿qué hará su familia?

_____

7. ¿Cómo se sentiría Ud. si tuviera un Rolls Royce?

_____

8. Si una mujer fuera candidata para la presidencia de los Estados Unidos, ¿votaría Ud. por ella?

_____

9. Si vieses a uno de tus profesores en la calle, ¿qué le dirías?

_____

10. Si Ud. no aprende el subjuntivo, ¿estará contento(-a) o triste?

_____

11. Si la televisión no existiera, ¿qué haría su familia para divertirse después de la cena?

_____

12. Si nevara en julio, ¿qué pensaríamos?

_____

13. Si su padre comprara un yate, ¿adónde irían Uds.?

_____

14. Si hay un concierto en el parque mañana, ¿irá Ud.?

_____

15. Si Ud. telefoneara a su profesora (profesor) de español, ¿qué pensaría ella (él)?

_____

B. Change the sentence so that the "if" clause expresses a condition requiring the use of the imperfect subjunctive.

EXAMPLE: Si vienes mañana, hablaré contigo.
Si vinieras mañana, hablaría contigo.

1. Si vas a la fiesta, te acompañaremos.

_____

2. Si estudiamos más, sacaremos buenas notas.

_____

3. Si aprenden el español, podrán conversar con los españoles.

_____

4. Si tengo el coche, daré un paseo por la tarde.

_____

5. Si ella vuelve temprano, ¿podremos verla?

_____

6. Si preparas una buena comida, la comeré.

_____

7. Si nieva mañana, ¿iremos a esquiar?

_____

8. Si te casas conmigo, te daré todo mi amor y mi dinero.

_____

9. Si leo un buen libro en vez de mirar la televisión, ¿seré más inteligente?

_____

10. Si no escuchas música *rock*, ¿morirás de aburrimiento?

_____

C. Translate into Spanish:

1. *a.* If we invite them to the party, will they come?

_____

   b. If we invited them to the theater, would they come?

_____

2. *a.* If you drive the car, I will stay home.

_____

   b. If you drove, I would stay there.

_____

3. *a.* If the teacher gives us a test tomorrow, when will we study?

   _____

   b. If the teacher gave you a test tomorrow, when would you study?

   _____

4. *a.* If I get up early, will I be able to go with you?

   _____

   b. If I got up late, would I be able to go with them?

   _____

5. *a.* If you (*tú*) earn enough money, will you buy the guitar?

   _____

   b. If you earned one hundred dollars, would you buy the radio?

   _____

6. *a.* If we went to the shopping center, what would we buy there?

   _____

   b. If we go to the shopping center, what will we buy?

   _____

7. *a.* If they brought the record, would you (*Uds.*) listen to it?

   _____

   b. If they bring the records, will she listen to them?

   _____

8. *a.* If she goes out, will you (*Ud.*) follow her?

   _____

   b. If she were to go out now, would you (*Uds.*) follow her?

   _____

9. *a.* If I promised you diamonds, would you marry me?

   _____

   b. If he promises her a diamond ring, will she marry him?

   _____

10. *a.* If we go to the restaurant, what will we eat?

   _____

   b. If they went to a concert, where would they sit ("seat themselves")?

   _____

D. *Listening Comprehension.* Your teacher will read aloud ten statements in Spanish. Each statement is a reply to a question. After the statement is read, circle the letter of the question that is being answered.

1. *a.* ¿Cómo se sentirían Uds. si ganaran mucho dinero en la lotería?
   b. ¿Adónde irían Uds. si pudieran viajar?
   c. ¿Qué harían Uds. si tuviesen mucho dinero?

2. *a.* ¿Qué haría Ud. si fuera al cine?
   b. ¿Qué haría Ud. si su profesor (profesora) anunciara que iba a dar un examen difícil?
   c. ¿Cuándo se acostaría Ud. si tuviera sueño?

3. *a.* Si Ud. pudiera aprender una lengua extranjera, ¿cuál preferiría?
   b. Si Ud. pudiese hacer un viaje, ¿qué país visitaría?
   c. Si tú pudieras conducir el coche, ¿adónde irías?

4. *a.* Si Ud. me encontrase en la calle a las tres de la tarde, ¿qué diría?
   b. Si Ud. me llamara por teléfono por la mañana, ¿qué diría?
   c. Si Ud. escribiera al Presidente de los Estados Unidos, ¿cómo empezaría la carta?

5. *a.* ¿Qué estudiarían Uds. si tuvieran un examen difícil?
   b. ¿Qué harían Uds. si no tuviesen dinero?
   c. ¿Qué harían Uds. si sacaran malas notas en todas sus clases?

6. *a.* ¿Saldrían Uds. de casa si su mamá preparara una buena comida?
   b. ¿Qué harían Uds. si alguien gritara «¡Fuego!» en su casa?
   c. ¿Qué dirían Uds. si un buen amigo visitara su casa?

7. *a.* ¿Qué haría Ud. si no tuviese nada de comer en casa?
   b. ¿Adónde iría Ud. para comprar ropa?
   c. ¿A qué hora iría Ud. a la escuela todos los días?

8. *a.* ¿Qué comería Ud. si tuviera hambre?
   b. ¿Qué ocurriría si Ud. saliera para la escuela a las cinco de la mañana?
   c. ¿Por qué iría Ud. a un concierto?

9. *a.* ¿Qué harán Uds. el verano próximo?
   b. ¿Cuándo irán Uds. al campo?
   c. ¿Dónde pasarán Uds. las vacaciones de verano?

10. *a.* ¿Adónde irás tú si quieres nadar?
    b. ¿Cuándo irás a nadar?
    c. ¿Por qué irás a la playa?

PART FOUR

NOUNS, ADJECTIVES, AND ADVERBS

18
Gender; Nouns and Articles in the Singular and Plural; the Contractions *AL* and *DEL*; Using *DE* to Express Possession

GENDER

Singular   *Plural*

MASCULINE NOUNS DENOTING MALES

el muchacho, the boy   **los muchachos,** the boys
el profesor, the teacher   **los profesores,** the teachers
el hombre, the man   **los hombres,** the men

MASCULINE NOUNS DENOTING CONCEPTS OR INANIMATE OBJECTS

el plato, the dish   **los platos,** the dishes
el baile, the dance   **los bailes,** the dances
el placer, the pleasure   **los placeres,** the pleasures
el derecho, the right (to do something)   **los derechos,** the rights

FEMININE NOUNS DENOTING FEMALES

la muchacha, the girl   **las muchachas,** the girls
la profesora, the teacher   **las profesoras,** the teachers
la dama, the lady   **las damas,** the ladies
la madre, the mother   **las madres,** the mothers

FEMININE NOUNS DENOTING CONCEPTS OR INANIMATE OBJECTS

la idea, the idea   **las ideas,** the ideas
la explicación, the explanation   **las explicaciones,** the explanations
la guerra, the war   **las guerras,** the wars
la frase, the sentence   **las frases,** the sentences
la pared, the wall   **las paredes,** the walls

1. All Spanish nouns are either masculine or feminine.

2. A noun that denotes a male is masculine.

3. A noun that denotes a female is feminine.

4. A noun that denotes an idea, a concept, or an inanimate object may be masculine or feminine.

5. All masculine nouns take the definite articles **el** (*sing.*) and **los** (*pl.*).

6. All feminine nouns take the definite articles **la** (*sing.*) and **las** (*pl.*).

7. Many masculine nouns end in **-o.**

8. Many feminine nouns end in **-a, -d,** and **-ión.**

MASCULINE PLURAL NOUNS THAT REFER TO A "MIXED" GROUP OF MALES AND FEMALES

los hermanos, the brothers, the brother(s) and sister(s)
los tíos, the uncles, the aunt(s) and uncle(s)
los padres, the fathers, the father and mother, the parents
los señores Rivera, Mr. and Mrs. Rivera

Practice A: Express in Spanish:

1. the grandmother and grandfather　_____

2. the king and queen　_____

3. her girlfriends and boyfriends　_____

4. his father and mother　_____

5. the sons and daughters　_____

Making Nouns Plural

---

9. Nouns that end in a vowel add **-s** to form the plural:

el cuaderno, the notebook　　　　　los cuaderno**s**, the notebooks
el hombre, the man　　　　　　　　los hombre**s**, the men
la tía, the aunt　　　　　　　　　　las tía**s**, the aunts

10. Nouns that end in a consonant add **-es** to form the plural:

la flor, the flower	las flor**es,** the flowers
el animal, the animal	los animal**es,** the animals
la pared, the wall	las pared**es,** the walls

11. Nouns that end in **-z** change the **-z** to **c** before adding **-es:**

la luz, the light	las lu**c**es, the lights
el lápiz, the pencil	los lápi**c**es, the pencils

12. Nouns ending in **-n** or **-s** that have an accent mark on the last syllable drop the accent in the plural:

la lección, the lesson	las lecciones, the lessons
el francés, the Frenchman	los franceses, the Frenchmen

Exception:

el país, the country	los países, the countries

13. If a noun of more than one syllable ends in **-n** and has no accent mark, it takes an accent mark over the stressed vowel in the plural:

la orden, the order	las órdenes, the orders
el joven, the young man	los jóvenes, the young men, the young people

14. Nouns ending in **-s** in the singular that are stressed on the next-to-last syllable remain the same in the plural:

el **paraguas,** the umbrella	los **paraguas,** the umbrellas
el **lunes,** (on) Monday	los **lunes,** (on) Mondays

Special Cases

MASCULINE NOUNS THAT END IN -A

*el artista, the artist	los **artistas,** the artists
*el atleta, the athlete	los **atletas,** the athletes
el **clima,** the climate	los **climas,** the climates
el **día,** the day	los **días,** the days
el **drama,** the drama	los **dramas,** the dramas
el **mapa,** the map	los **mapas,** the maps
el **problema,** the problem	los **problemas,** the problems
el **programa,** the program	los **programas,** the programs

---

*When referring to women, these nouns have the feminine forms **la** artista (*pl.,* **las** artistas) and **la** atleta (*pl.,* **las** atletas).

FEMININE NOUNS THAT END IN -o

la foto, the photograph

la mano, the hand

la radio, the radio

las fotos, the photographs

las manos, the hands

(*radio sets* = **los** radios)

FEMININE NOUNS THAT TAKE *EL* IN THE SINGULAR BECAUSE OF A STRESSED FIRST SYLLABLE BEGINNING WITH *A-* OR *HA-*

el agua, the water

el alma, the soul

el hacha, the axe

el hambre, the hunger

las aguas, the waters

las almas, the souls

las hachas, the axes

(generally not in the plural)

Practice B: Write the plural forms. (Include the articles.)

1. el primo _____

2. la mujer _____

3. la ciudad _____

4. el cinturón _____

5. la catedral _____

6. el título _____

7. la nación _____

8. la hermana _____

9. la carne _____

10. el examen _____

11. el águila _____

12. el crucigrama _____

13. la amistad _____

14. el jueves _____

15. el interés _____

16. el pez _____

17. el jardín _____

18. la costumbre _____

19. la piel _____

20. el dolor _____

The Indefinite Articles: *Un, Una, Unos, Unas*

---

un sello, a (one) stamp

una manzana, an (one) apple

unos sellos, some stamps

unas manzanas, some apples

15. The indefinite article (**un, una**) means *a, an, one.* The plural forms (**unos, unas**) mean *some, a few.*

Practice C: Express in Spanish.

1. *a.* an idea _____

   b. some ideas _____

2. *a.* a bank _____

   b. some banks _____

3. *a.* a favor _____

   b. some favors _____

4. *a.* one park _____

   b. some parks _____

5. *a.* one page _____

   b. some pages _____

The Contraction AL

Hablo **al** profesor.   I speak to the teacher.
　　　a los profesores.   　　　to the teachers.
　　　a la chica.   　　　to the girl.
　　　a las chicas.   　　　to the girls.

16. When the preposition **a** precedes **el,** the two words combine to form the word **al.** There are no other contractions with **a.**

Practice D: Write the correct form of the definite article with *a.*

1. Mandamos regalos _____ abuelos.

2. ¿Qué das _____ chico?

3. Siempre escribo _____ amigos de mi madre.

4. Debo dar el salario _____ criada.

5. ¿Cuándo vamos _____ cine?

The Contraction DEL

Hablo **del** actor.   I am speaking of the actor.
　　　de los actores.   　　　of the actors.
　　　de la actriz.   　　　of the actress.
　　　de las actrices.   　　　of the actresses.

17. When the preposition **de** precedes **el,** the two words combine to form the word **del.** There are no other contractions with **de.**

Practice E: Write the correct form of *de* plus the definite article.

1. Mi madre sale _____ cocina.

2. Mi hermano viene _____ mercado.

3. Hablamos _____ chicas.

4. ¿Quiénes salen _____ edificios?

5. Es el libro _____ profesor.

Using DE to Express Possession

¿**De** quién es la casa?   Whose house is it?
Es la casa **de** Juan.   It is John's house.
La casa es **de** Juan.   The house is John's.

el cuarto **de** María	Mary's room
la pluma **del** chico	the boy's pen
el maestro **de** los chicos	the boys' teacher
el amigo **de la** tía	the aunt's friend
el amigo **de las** tías	the aunts' friend

18. Possession is expressed in Spanish by **de** or **de** + the definite article. **De** is used before a person's name.

19. In English, the position of the apostrophe—'s or s'—indicates whether the possessor is singular or plural. Note this when translating into Spanish. There is no apostrophe in Spanish.

Practice F: Answer the question in two ways as shown in the example, using the clue in parentheses. Then write the English equivalents.

EXAMPLE:

¿De quién es el libro? (Ana)	*Whose book is it?*
a. *El libro es de Ana.*	*The book is Ann's.*
b. *Es el libro de Ana.*	*It is Ann's book.*

1. ¿De quién es el periódico? (la maestra) _____

a. _____ _____

b. _____ _____

2. ¿De quién son los lápices? (el director) _____

a. _____ _____

b. _____ _____

3. ¿De quiénes son las raquetas de tenis? (los jugadores) _____

a. _____ _____

b. _____ _____

4. ¿De quiénes es la casa? (las muchachas) _____

a. _____ _____

b. _____ _____

5. ¿De quién es la pulsera? (María) _____

a. _____ _____

b. _____ _____

6. ¿De quién son las cintas? (el Presidente) _____

a. _____ _____

b. _____ _____

Using *DE* to Say What Something Is Made Of

¿**De** qué es el reloj?   What is the watch made of?
El reloj es **de** oro.   The watch is made of gold.
Es un reloj **de** oro.   It is a gold watch.
un sombrero **de** paja   a straw hat
un pastel **de** cereza   a cherry pie
la ensalada **de** atún   the tuna fish salad

20. **De** precedes the noun denoting the material or ingredients of which something is made.

Practice G: Continue the pattern shown in the first two items.

1. ¿De qué es la camisa? (seda)   *What is the shirt made of?*
   a. *La camisa es de seda.*   *The shirt is made of silk.*
   b. *Es una camisa de seda.*   *It is a silk shirt.*

2. ¿De qué es el sandwich? (pollo)   *What is the sandwich made with?*
   a. *El sandwich es de pollo.*   *The sandwich is (made with) chicken.*
   b. *Es un sandwich de pollo.*   *It is a chicken sandwich.*

3. ¿De qué es la silla? (madera) _____
   a. _____   _____
   b. _____   _____

4. ¿De qué es el helado? (vainilla) _____
   a. _____   _____
   b. _____   _____

5. ¿De qué son los pantalones? (lana) _____
   a. _____   _____
   b. _____   _____

6. ¿De qué es el pastel? (melocotón) _____
   a. _____   _____
   b. _____   _____

EJERCICIOS

A. Repeat each sentence orally, using the plural forms of the expressions in italics. (Write the plural forms in the blanks.)

1. ¿Qué hacen Uds. *el viernes*?   _____

2. Para subir, tenemos que usar *el ascensor*.   _____

3. Voy a cantar *la canción*.   _____

4. ¿De qué *país* son ellos?   _____

5. Tengo *una pregunta* para ti.   _____

6. Hay *un árbol* en *el jardín*.   _____

                                                                   _____

7. En *la exposición* hablamos *al artista*.   _____

                                                                   _____

8. Roberto tiene *un problema*.   _____

9. ¿Qué tienen en *la mano*?   _____

10. En *el techo* hay *una luz*.   _____

                                                                   _____

11. Hay *un hospital* cerca de *la estación*.   _____

                                                                   _____

12. Hay *un hotel* al lado *del puerto*.   _____

                                                                   _____

13. Después *de la clase* vamos *al cine*, y luego *a la estación*. _____

                                                                   _____

                                                                   _____

14. Quiero comprar *un reloj* y *una pulsera*.   _____

                                                                   _____

15. El precio *del diamante* es muy alto.   _____

B. Write the opposite gender.

1. una madre _____   6. una directora _____

2. el hijo _____   7. los señores _____

3. unos abuelos _____   8. un nieto _____

4. la profesora _____   9. la hermana _____

5. las reinas _____   10. los artistas _____

C. Form sentences as shown in the examples.

EXAMPLES: el lápiz: la profesora   *Es el lápiz de la profesora.*
                  los lápices: el chico   *Son los lápices del chico.*

1. las flores: Elena _____

2. el tocadiscos: el niño _____

3. la raqueta: la jugadora _____

4. los discos: las hermanas _____

5. el zapato: Felipe _____

6. la compañía: el comerciante _____

7. el puesto: los vendedores _____

8. los diccionarios: el profesor _____

9. el perro: Ana _____

10. el laboratorio: los científicos _____

D. Form a sentence with each group of words, as shown in the example.

EXAMPLE: mi hermano / dar / los billetes / el cajero
                Mi hermano da los billetes al cajero.

1. nosotros / dar / la comida / el perro

_____

2. ellos / escribir / las cartas / las primas

_____

3. mi madre / mandar / el dinero / el banco

_____

4. el chico / prometer / un regalo / la madre

_____

5. yo / prestar / diez dólares / Juan

_____

E. Translate into Spanish:

1. *a.* Henry's school _____

    b. Mary's class _____

2. *a.* the boys' team _____

    b. the girls' club _____

3. *a.* the woolen socks _____

   b. the nylon blouse _____

4. *a.* a fish dinner _____

   b. the hamburger lunch _____

5. *a.* the king and queen _____

   b. the husband and wife _____

6. *a.* Mr. and Mrs. Rodríguez _____

   b. the sister and brothers _____

7. *a.* the orders of the general _____

   b. the young men's rights _____

8. *a.* some countries of the north _____

   b. some cities of the south _____

9. *a.* a tennis raquet _____

   b. the baseball gloves _____

10. *a.* the leather shoes _____

    b. the woolen clothing _____

11. *a.* some motorcycles _____

    b. a photograph _____

12. *a.* the iron axes _____

    b. the steel bridge _____

13. *a.* some days _____

    b. some dramas _____

14. *a.* the ladies' voices _____

    b. the men's umbrellas _____

15. *a.* the chocolate ice cream _____

    b. the strawberry pie _____

16. *a.* a pearl necklace _____

    b. a diamond bracelet _____

17. *a.* the problem of the examinations _____

　　b. the climate of the country _____

18. *a.* the solutions to the crossword puzzles _____

　　b. the route to the sea _____

19. *a.* the road from the port to the building _____

　　b. the street from the house to the school _____

20. *a.* the map of the cities _____

　　b. the taste of the water _____

Las Ramblas, Barcelona, España

19
Adjectives: Agreement and Position; Adverbs

Agreement of Adjectives

ADJECTIVES WITH FOUR FORMS

rico:	El comerciante es **rico.**	The merchant is rich.
rica:	La actriz es **rica.**	The actress is rich.
ricos:	Los comerciantes son **ricos.**	The merchants are rich.
ricas:	Las actrices son **ricas.**	The actresses are rich.

1. An adjective that ends in **-o** in the masculine singular has four possible endings, depending on the gender and number of the noun it modifies:*

masculine singular. . . . .**-o**   masculine plural. . . . .**-os**

feminine singular. . . . . .**-a**   feminine plural. . . . . .**-as**

Note: If an adjective modifies two or more nouns of different genders, the masculine plural form is used:

El comerciante y **la actriz** son **ricos.**   The merchant and the actress are rich.

El chico y **la chica** son **buenos.**   The boy and the girl are good.

Practice A: Write the correct form of the adjective.

1. pequeño: Las chicas son _____ .

2. alto: Los edificios son _____ .

3. flaco: La mujer es muy _____ .

4. rojo: El sombrero es _____ .

5. amarillo: Las faldas y los vestidos son _____ .

---

*An adjective is said to modify a noun if it describes the person or thing that the noun refers to: the *smart* girl, a *good* idea, the men are *tall*, etc.

ADJECTIVES WITH TWO FORMS

pobre: El viejo es **pobre**.   The old man is poor.
         La vieja es **pobre**.   The old woman is poor.

pobres: Los viejos son **pobres**.   The old men are poor.
         Las viejas son **pobres**.   The old women are poor.

2. An adjective that does not end in **-o** in the masculine singular generally has only two forms: singular and plural. The masculine and feminine forms are the same.

Practice B: Write the correct form of the adjective.

1. fácil: Los ejercicios no son _____.

2. grande: Mi casa es muy _____.

3. inteligente: Las gatas son _____.

4. popular: José y su hermano son _____.

5. difícil: El crucigrama no es muy _____.

6. feliz:*   Los señores Pereda son _____.

Adjectives of Nationality

Juan es mexicano pero **María** es cubana.   John is Mexican but Mary is Cuban.

3. Adjectives of nationality that end in **-o** in the masculine singular have the usual four forms: mexicano, **-a, -os, -as,** chileno, **-a, -os, -as,** etc.

español—español**a**
francés—frances**a**

Mi tío es **español;** no es **francés**.   My uncle is Spanish; he is not French.
Mi tía es **española;** no es **francesa**.   My aunt is Spanish; she is not French.

4. If an adjective of nationality ends in a consonant in the masculine singular, add **-a** for the feminine singular. If the masculine singular form has an accent mark on the last vowel, the accent mark is omitted in all other forms.

español**es**—español**as**
frances**es**—frances**as**

Mis tíos son español**es;** no son frances**es**.   My uncles (*or* uncle and aunt) are Spanish; they are not French.

Mis tías son español**as;** no son frances**as**.   My aunts are Spanish; they are not French.

---

*As with nouns that end in **-z,** change the **-z** to **-c** before adding **-es.**

5. If an adjective of nationality ends in a consonant in the masculine singular, add **-es** for the masculine plural and **-as** for the feminine plural.*

Practice C: Write the correct form of the adjective.

1. (alemán)   La señora Schmidt es _____.

2. (argentino) Mis amigos son _____.

3. (portugués) Mi primo es _____.

4. (inglés)   Las mujeres son _____.

5. (francés)   Los señores Beaumont son _____.

6. (español)   ¿Es _____ su prima?

Position of Adjectives

ADJECTIVES THAT FOLLOW THEIR NOUNS

Leo una **novela interesante.**	I'm reading an interesting novel.
Mi amigo José es un **hombre rico.**	My friend Joseph is a rich man.
Los **libros extranjeros** son caros.	The foreign books are expensive.
Las **comidas españolas** son deliciosas.	Spanish meals are delicious.

6. In Spanish, descriptive adjectives and adjectives of nationality generally follow the nouns they modify. Compare this with English word order: "the *white house*" = la **casa blanca.**

ADJECTIVES THAT PRECEDE THEIR NOUNS

Tengo **tantos libros** interesantes en mi casa.	I have so many interesting books in my house.
Esa persona estúpida tiene **poca inteligencia.**	That stupid person has little intelligence.
Hay **muchas casas** bonitas en mi calle.	There are many pretty houses on my street.

7. Adjectives of *quantity*, *number*, and *amount* generally precede their nouns, as in English.

---

*Cortés, *courteous*, is not an adjective of nationality and therefore does not follow this rule:

Felipe es **cortés.**	Philip is courteous.
María es **cortés** también.	Mary is courteous too.

Practice D: Place the adjective in the correct blank—before or after the noun. Remember to change the form of the adjective when necessary.

EXAMPLE: mucho: Aquí hay ___*muchas*___ personas _____.

1. inteligente: Los _____ chicos _____ son mis primos.

2. italiano: Mi _____ amigo _____ se llama Roberto.

3. cuánto: ¿_____ muchachos _____ hay en la clase?

4. poco: _____ hombres _____ saben la verdad.

5. verde: Quiero comprar las _____ camisas _____.

Adverbs Ending in -*MENTE*

Los niños están alegres y juegan **alegremente.**	The children are happy and play happily.
La lección es fácil y la aprendemos **fácilmente.**	The lesson is easy and we learn it easily.
El alumno atento escucha **atentamente.**	The attentive pupil listens attentively.

8. English can change some adjectives to adverbs by adding the ending -*ly:* soft—soft*ly*, quick—quick*ly*, etc. The Spanish equivalent of -*ly* is **-mente:** alegre—alegre**mente**, correcto—correcta**mente**, etc. The ending is added to the feminine form of the adjective. If the adjective has an accent mark, the accent mark is retained when **-mente** is added.

Practice E: Complete each sentence by writing the adverbial form of the adjective as shown in the example.

EXAMPLE: Juan es muy rápido y corre *rápidamente.*

1. La gramática no es muy clara, pero la profesora la explica muy _____.

2. Los padres son cariñosos y tratan a sus hijos _____.

3. El alumno es cortés y habla muy _____.

4. Las chicas son inteligentes y hablan muy _____.

5. Las reglas son difíciles y las aprendemos _____.

Note: Some adverbs in Spanish do not end in **-mente:**

bien, well	**despacio,** slowly (synonym of **lentamente**)
mal, badly	**de prisa,** quickly (synonym of **rápidamente**)

EJERCICIOS

A. Change the form of the adjective (where necessary) to agree with the new subject.

EXAMPLE: Los hombres son ingleses.

Las mujeres son ___*inglesas*___.

1. María es muy *inteligente.*

   Alberto es muy _____.

2. Los edificios no son *altos.*

   La casa no es _____.

3. ¿Es *alemana* su amiga?

   ¿Es _____ su tío?

4. ¿*Cuántos* dólares tienes?

   ¿_____ pesetas tienes?

5. Esta lección es muy *difícil.*

   Esos verbos son muy _____.

6. Damos al gato muy *poca* comida.

   Damos a los perros muy _____ huesos.

7. Esa iglesia es muy *antigua.*

   Las casas de Salamanca son muy _____.

8. Estas expresiones son *útiles.*

   Este libro es muy _____.

9. *Todos los* veranos vamos al campo.

   _____ semanas visitamos a nuestros abuelos.

10. Tomás y Elena son *ingleses.*

    Francisca es _____.

B. Write the antonym (opposite) of each adjective in the blank at the right.

EXAMPLE: Mis amigos son *ricos.*   ___*pobres*___

1. La casa del profesor es *vieja.*   _____

2. La biblioteca contiene *muchas* novelas. _____

3. Vivimos en una calle *estrecha.*   _____

4. Mi madre siempre lleva vestidos *negros.* _____

5. Tenemos un coche muy *grande.*   ___ _____

6. Mis abuelos parecen ser muy *jóvenes*. _____

7. Esas tiendas son muy *feas*. _____

8. Los alumnos de mi clase son *malos*. _____

9. ¿Son *débiles* los chicos? _____

10. Dicen que los elefantes son muy *estúpidos*. _____

C. Form sentences with each group of words.

EXAMPLE: pobres / tienen / las / dinero / poco / personas
Las personas pobres tienen poco dinero.

1. célebres / casas / en / grandes / actores / los / viven

_____

2. españoles / visitan / norteamericanas / niños / ciudades / varias / algunos

_____

3. hermoso / felices / las / alegremente / en / parque / el / chicas / juegan

_____

4. inteligente / la / difíciles / explica / conceptos / claramente / muy / profesora / los

_____

5. muy / programa / miembros / club / presentan / varios / interesante / del / un

_____

D. Answer with a complete sentence in Spanish:

1. En su opinión, ¿son inteligentes o estúpidos los gatos?

_____

2. Cuando Ud. saca una nota mala en un examen, ¿están alegres o tristes sus padres?

_____

3. ¿Es fácil o difícil el español?

_____

4. ¿Siempre escucha Ud. atentamente a sus profesores, o habla incesantemente con sus compañeros(-as) de clase?

_____

5. ¿Cuántos libros lleva Ud. a la escuela todos los días?

_____

6. ¿De qué color es la pared de su cuarto?

_____

7. ¿De qué color tiene Ud. los ojos?

Tengo _____

8. ¿Cómo anda Ud. de una clase a otra?

_____

9. Describa Ud. a su mejor amigo (amiga).

_____

10. ¿De qué nacionalidad es su profesora (profesor) de español?

_____

E. Write two Spanish equivalents for each adverb, as shown in the example.

EXAMPLE:

| frequently | *con frecuencia* | *frecuentemente* |

1. sadly _____   _____

2. patiently _____   _____

3. courteously _____   _____

4. affectionately _____   _____

5. carefully _____   _____

6. innocently _____   _____

7. easily _____   _____

8. intelligently _____   _____

9. attentively _____   _____

10. perfectly _____   _____

F. Translate into Spanish:

1. *a.* The sky is blue. _____

   b. The blue sky is beautiful. _____

2. *a.* The bicycles are new. _____

   b. The new bicycles are not cheap. _____

3. *a.* The men are strong. _____

   b. The strong men are handsome. _____

4. *a.* The store is old. _____

   b. The old store is large. _____

5. *a.* The soldiers are English. _____

    b. The English soldiers are not weak. _____

6. *a.* The automobile is French. _____

    b. The French automobile is small. _____

7. *a.* The dinner is delicious. _____

    b. The delicious dinner is expensive. _____

8. *a.* How many children are there (*hay*) in the school? _____

    _____

    b. There are many young students (*estudiantes*). _____

9. *a.* They are very patient. _____

    b. They wait very patiently. _____

10. *a.* His work is dangerous. _____

    b. He lives dangerously. _____

11. *a.* They listen to popular music. _____

    b. They listen attentively. _____

12. *a.* My brother drives very fast. _____

    b. My mother drives very slowly. _____

13. *a.* She is a magnificent singer. _____

    b. She sings magnificently. _____

14. *a.* The teachers are very good. _____

    b. They teach very well. _____

15. *a.* The German players are good athletes. _____

    b. The Frenchmen are famous cooks. _____

G. *Listening Comprehension.* Your teacher will read aloud a short sentence in Spanish followed by the first two or three words of a second sentence. Underline the pair of words that can be used to complete the second sentence.

    EXAMPLE: (Your teacher reads: "María es muy rica. José también. . .")

        a. es rico   *b.* son ricos   *c.* es rica

1. *a.* es alto   *b.* son altas   *c.* es alta

2. *a.* son estúpidos   *b.* es inteligente   *c.* son inteligentes

3. *a.* está enferma   *b.* está bien   *c.* están enfermas

4. *a.* soy alemana   *b.* somos alemanes   *c.* soy portugués

5. *a.* son jóvenes   *b.* es popular   *c.* son populares

H. *Listening Comprehension.* Your teacher will read aloud a question in Spanish. Underline the most appropriate reply.

EXAMPLE: (Your teacher reads: "¿Cómo es su amiga Juana?")

    a. Es alto y hermoso.
    b. <u>Es rica y bonita.</u>
    c. Son altas y bonitas.

1. *a.* Es viejo y generoso.
   b. Son viejos y generosos.
   c. Es pobre y vieja.

2. *a.* películas interesantes
   b. lecciones privadas
   c. programas cortos

3. *a.* Es francesa.
   b. Son portugueses.
   c. Soy española.

4. *a.* bueno   *b.* perfección   *c.* perfectamente

5. *a.* mala   *b.* horribles   *c.* terrible

Juan Carlos, rey de España, y su esposa, la reina Sophia

20
Adjectives With Shortened Forms

uno, a, an, one	*un* hombre, a man, one man
alguno, some	*algún* hombre, some man
ninguno, no	*ningún* hombre, no man
bueno, good	un *buen* hombre, a good man
malo, bad	un *mal* hombre, a bad man
primero, first	el *primer* hombre, the first man
tercero, third	el *tercer* hombre, the third man

1. The shortened forms of these adjectives are used only before a masculine singular noun. Otherwise they have the same endings as other adjectives whose masculine singular forms end in **-o.** Note that the forms **algún** and **ningún** have an accent mark over the **u.**

Bueno, Malo, Primero, Tercero

un **buen** libro
un libro **bueno** ⎬ a good book

un **mal** chico
un chico **malo** ⎬ a bad boy

el **primer** edificio
el edificio **primero** ⎬ the first building

el **tercer** estudiante
el estudiante **tercero** ⎬ the third student

170

2. These four adjectives may precede or follow their nouns. Note all the forms and positions of **bueno:**

el **buen** profesor	el profesor **bueno**
los **buenos** profesores	los profesores **buenos**
la **buena** profesora	la profesora **buena**
las **buenas** profesoras	las profesoras **buenas**

3. These adjectives are usually placed *after* the noun if they are emphasized:

El **mal chico** nunca prestaba atención en la clase.	The bad boy never paid attention in class.

But:

Es un **chico malo;** nunca presta atención.	He is a *bad* boy; he never pays attention.

Lean Uds. la **tercera lección.**	Read the third lesson.

But:

Lean Uds. la **lección tercera,** no la primera.	Read the *third* lesson, not the first (one).

Practice A: Write the correct form of the adjective.

1. *malo:*   Roberto es un _____ jugador de tenis.

2. *ninguno:* No tenemos _____ dinero para pagar la cuenta.

3. *tercero:* Mi _____ clase no es interesante.

4. *primero:* Adán fue el _____ hombre.

5. *bueno:*   Mi madre prepara _____ comidás.

6. *uno:*   El perro es _____ animal doméstico.

7. *alguno:* _____ juegos son muy interesantes.

8. *malo:*   Son _____ muchachos.

9. *tercero:* Vamos a mirar el _____ partido de tenis.

10. *bueno:*   Tú eres un _____ amigo.

11. *alguno:* ¿Puede Ud. recomendar _____ plato?

12. *primero:* Escriban Uds. el ejercicio _____.

13. *uno:*   Ella es _____ persona importante.

14. *bueno:*   Hoy hace _____ tiempo.

15. *ninguno:* No me gusta _____ revista.

Gran, Grande

Jorge Wáshington fue un **gran** hombre.	George Washington was a great man.
La reina Isabel fue una **gran** mujer.	Queen Elizabeth was a great woman.
Don Quijote y *Oliver Twist* son **grandes** novelas.	*Don Quijote* and *Oliver Twist* are great novels.
Ese atleta tiene un cuerpo **grande**.	That athlete has a big (large) body.
Esos atletas tienen los brazos **grandes**.	Those athletes have large arms.

4. The Spanish word for *great* is **gran** before a noun in the singular, **grandes** before a noun in the plural. These forms are the same for both genders.

5. When **grande** follows its noun, it means *big* or *large*.

Practice B: Write the appropriate form of the adjective: *gran*, *grande*, or *grandes*.

1. Los chicos viven en una casa _____.

2. Pablo es un _____ amigo mío.

3. Paca es también mi _____ amiga.

4. Mis hermanos son _____ personas.

5. Ellos viven en casas _____.

6. Mis hermanos no van a caber en tu coche pequeño; son hombres _____.

San, Santo, Santa

San Felipe, Saint Philip   **Santa** María, Saint Mary
San José, Saint Joseph   **Santa** Ana, Saint Anne
          Santo Domingo, Saint Dominick
          Santo Tomás, Saint Thomas

6. The title *Saint* is **San** before the names of male saints. The two exceptions are **Santo Domingo** and **Santo Tomás.** The form **Santa** is used before the names of female saints.

Practice C: Write the Spanish word for *Saint* before each name.

1. _____ Juan   4. _____ Domingo

2. _____ Marta   5. _____ Pedro

3. _____ Bárbara

EJERCICIO

Express in Spanish. In sentences **1, 2, 3,** and **8,** translate the italicized words in two ways.

1. Mr. Smith is *a good teacher.* _____

_____

2. Peter and Philip are *bad players.* _____

_____

3. Do you have *the first record*? _____

_____

4. *a.* Some lessons are very interesting. _____

   b. No lesson is interesting. _____

5. *a.* Saint Francis was very religious. _____

   b. St. Joseph's Day is March 19. ("The day of St. Joseph. . .") _____

_____

6. *a.* He is a great president. _____

   b. Is he a big man? _____

7. *a.* I want some money. _____

   b. They want some milk. _____

8. *The third building* on the right is my house. _____

_____

9. *a.* No man is perfect. _____

   b. No person can enter. _____

10. *a.* I am spending one day in Madrid. (*to spend* [*time*] = **pasar**) _____

_____

   b. They are spending an afternoon in Barcelona. _____

_____

21
Comparison of Adjectives

Expressing Equality

---

tan. . .como

Los chicos son altos.	The boys are tall.
Las chicas son altas también.	The girls are tall too.
Los chicos son **tan** altos **como** las chicas.	The boys are as tall as the girls.
Las chicas son **tan** altas **como** los chicos.	The girls are as tall as the boys.

1. **Tan** + *adjective* + **como** means *as. . .as*, and is used like its English equivalent to express equality between persons or things.

Practice A: Change the two sentences to one sentence expressing an equality.

EXAMPLE: La profesora es inteligente. Los estudiantes son inteligentes también.

> *La profesora es tan inteligente como los estudiantes.*
> Or: *Los estudiantes son tan inteligentes como la profesora.*

1. Mi tío es viejo. Mi padre es viejo también.

_____

2. Esta lección es fácil. La otra lección es fácil también.

_____

3. Gilberto es simpático. Rosa es simpática también.

_____

Practice B: Express a new equality by reversing the order of comparison.

EXAMPLE: María es tan rica como Felipe.
> *Felipe es tan rico como María.*

1. Mi papá es tan inteligente como mi mamá.

_____

2. Los edificios rojos son tan modernos como las casas nuevas.

_____

3. Su abuela es tan generosa como su abuelo.

_____

tanto(-a). . .como*

Tengo **tanto** dinero **como** tú.   I have as much money as you.

Ella recibe **tantas** cartas **como** María. She receives as many letters as Mary.

2. To express *as much. . .as* in Spanish, use **tanto(-a)** + *noun* + **como;** to express *as many. . .as,* use **tantos(-as)** + *noun* + **como.**

Practice C: Write the correct form—*tanto, tanta, tantos,* or *tantas.*

1. Yo leo _____ libros como Ud.

2. José no hace _____ trabajo como Enrique.

3. Pedro bebe _____ leche como su hermana.

4. Vemos _____ películas como tú.

Expressing Inequality

THE COMPARATIVE DEGREE

Juan y Ana son altos, pero Juan es **más** alto **que** Ana.

Algunos dicen que los perros son **más** inteligentes **que** los gatos (. . .que los gatos son **menos** inteligentes **que** los perros).

John and Ann are tall, but John is taller than Ann.

Some say that dogs are more intelligent than cats (. . .that cats are less intelligent than dogs).

3. To express comparison between persons or things, we use **más** + *adjective* + **que** (*more. . . than*) or **menos** + *adjective* + **que** (*less. . .than*).

4. In English, many inequalities are expressed by attaching the suffix *-er* to an adjective: small—smaller, tall—taller, warm—warmer, etc. In Spanish, *smaller* becomes "more small," *taller* becomes "more tall," etc.

Practice D: Change each sentence as shown in the example.

EXAMPLE: Los niños y las niñas son altos.
    Los niños son más altos que las niñas.

1. Paco y Carlos son bajos.

_____

---

*Although this expression is used in comparing *nouns,* it is included in this chapter because of its similarity to **tan. . .como.**

2. Mi casa y su casa son grandes.

_____

3. Ramón y yo estamos tristes.

_____

4. Mi madre y mi tía son bonitas.

_____

5. Mi padre y mi hermano están cansados.

_____

COMPARISON OF NUMBER OR QUANTITY

Tengo **más** libros **que** tú.	I have more books than you.
Tengo **más de** seis libros.	I have more than six books.
Hay **menos** alumnos en esta clase **que** en esa clase.	There are fewer pupils in this class than in that class.
Hay **menos de** veinte alumnos en esta clase.	There are fewer than twenty pupils in this class.

5. The words **más** and **menos** may precede _nouns_ as well as adjectives. Before a number, Spanish uses **de** rather than **que** for English _than_.

Practice E: Complete the sentence with _que_ or _de_.

1. Enrique tiene más _____ cuatro televisores en su casa.

2. Yo tengo más dinero _____ mi amiga Elena.

3. Hay menos _____ diez miembros en este club.

4. Mi prima me manda más cartas _____ mi primo.

5. Tú eres menos fuerte _____ yo.

THE SUPERLATIVE DEGREE

¿Quién es **el alumno más alto de** la clase?	Who is the tallest pupil in the class?
Dolores es **la más alta de** la clase.	Dolores is the tallest in the class.
¿Cuál es **el disco más popular de** la colección?	Which is the most popular record in the collection?
Este disco es **el más popular de** la colección.	This record is the most popular in the collection.

6. The superlative degree (English _the. . .-est_ or _the most. . ._) is expressed in Spanish by **el (la, los, las) más. . . .** The definite article agrees with its noun in gender and number even if the noun is not expressed: "es **la** más alt**a** de la clase," _she is the tallest in the class_ (the noun **alumna** or **chica** is understood).

7. Note how the superlative degree is expressed when a noun is used: *the richest man* becomes "the man most rich" (**el hombre más rico**); *the smartest woman* becomes "the woman most smart" (**la mujer más inteligente**).

8. After a superlative, the word *in* is expressed by **de** in Spanish:

el cuarto más pequeño **de** la casa   the smallest room *in* the house

Practice F: Complete the Spanish expressions.

EXAMPLE: the largest book in the library

el libro _____*más grande de la*_____ biblioteca

1. the prettiest flower in the garden

   la flor _____ jardín

2. the most difficult lessons in the book

   las lecciones _____ libro

3. the most interesting story in the magazine.

   el cuento _____ la revista

4. the strongest athlete in the school

   el atleta _____ escuela

5. the least handsome boy in the group (least = *menos*)

   el muchacho _____ grupo

Special Adjectives of Comparison

Paco, Ana y Felipe son tres jugadores de béisbol.   Frank, Ann, and Philip are three baseball players.

Paco es muy bueno.   Frank is very good.

Ana es **mejor que** Paco.   Ann is better than Frank.

Felipe es **el mejor del** grupo.   Philip is the best in the group.

9. Mejor (*pl.*, **mejores**), *better, best,* is one of four adjectives that do not use **más.** (Compare English *good, better, best.*) The following adjectives have irregular comparative forms:

bueno, -a buenos, -as	good	mejor mejores	better	el (la) mejor los (las) mejores	the best
malo, -a malos, -as	bad	peor peores	worse	el (la) peor los (las) peores	the worst

| joven / jóvenes } young | menor / menores } younger* | el (la) menor / los (las) menores } the youngest* |
| viejo, -a / viejos, -as } old | mayor / mayores } older* | el (la) mayor / los (las) mayores } the oldest* |

Practice G: Supply the correct form of the comparative or superlative.

EXAMPLE: Yo soy malo, pero ellos son ____*peores*____ que yo.

1. María es muy buena, pero Luis es _____ que ella.

2. Juanita y Roberto son malos, pero Rosa y Alberto son _____ _____ de la clase.

3. Mi hermana tiene quince años. Yo tengo trece años. Yo soy _____ que mi hermana.

4. Mi padre tiene cuarenta y seis años. Mi madre tiene cuarenta y cuatro años. Mi abuelo tiene setenta y mi abuela tiene sesenta y cinco. Mis abuelos son _____ _____ de la familia.

Summary

A. EXPRESSING EQUALITY: **tan. . .como; tanto(-a). . .como**

María y Juana son **tan** ricas **como** Antonio.   Mary and Joan are as rich as Anthony.
Tengo **tantas** revistas **como** ellos.   I have as many magazines as they (do).

B. EXPRESSING INEQUALITY

(1) *Comparative Degree:* **más. . .que** or **menos. . .que**

Ellos son **más** pobres **que** nosotros.   They are poorer than we (are).
Esta botella tiene **menos** leche **que** ésa.   This bottle has less milk than that one.

(2) *Superlative Degree:* **el / la / los / las** } **más (menos). . .de**

la muchacha **más** inteligente **de** la clase   the smartest girl in the class

C. IRREGULAR FORMS

The adjectives **bueno(-a)**, **malo(-a)**, and **joven** have irregular comparative forms: **mejor (peor) que**, *better (worse) than*; **mayor (menor) que**, *older (younger) than*. These have the superlative forms **el (la) mejor**, *the best*, **el (la) mayor**, *the oldest*, etc.

---

*These may also be expressed by the regular forms:

| younger { más joven / más jóvenes | youngest { el (la) más joven / los (las) más jóvenes |
| older { más viejo, -a / más viejos, -as | oldest { el (la) más viejo(-a) / los (las) más viejos(-as) |

EJERCICIOS

A. Use the given sentence to write three kinds of comparison, as shown in the example.

EXAMPLE: En la familia de Jorge, el abuelo y la abuela son amables.
     a. *La abuela es tan amable como el abuelo.*
     b. *La abuela es más amable que el abuelo.*
     c. *La abuela es la más amable de la familia.*

1. En la cesta de frutas, las manzanas y las uvas son buenas.

    a. _____

    b. _____

    c. _____

2. En la clase, Francisca y Elena son hermosas.

    a. _____

    b. _____

    c. _____

3. En la escuela, Fernando y Enrique son fuertes.

    a. _____

    b. _____

    c. _____

4. En la lista de postres, el pastel y el dulce son malos.

    a. _____

    b. _____

    c. _____

5. En el club, el chico y yo somos jóvenes.

    a. _____

    b. _____

    c. _____

B. Express the same idea by starting the sentence with the words in italics.

EXAMPLES: Mi padre es mayor que *mi madre.*
            Mi madre es menor que mi padre.

            Los leones son más feroces que *los tigres.*
            Los tigres son menos feroces que los leones.

1. Yo tengo menos dinero que *mis amigos*.

_____

2. El calor es peor que *el frío*.

_____

3. ¿Es Juana más inteligente que *Dorotea*?

_____

4. Los diamantes son más caros que *las perlas*.

_____

5. Estos panecillos viejos son mejores que *ese pan duro*.

_____

C. Begin the sentence with the words in italics, using an adjective of opposite meaning.

EXAMPLE: El perro es más débil que *el lobo*.
El lobo es más fuerte que el perro.

1. Mi casa es más pequeña que *su casa*.

_____

2. El señor López es más rico que *la señora González*.

_____

3. Ella tiene más amigos que *nosotros*.

_____

4. Tu escuela es más antigua que *mi casa*.

_____

5. Marta está más triste que *Guillermo*.

_____

D. Answer with a complete sentence in Spanish:

1. ¿Es el español tan importante como el inglés?

_____

2. ¿Quién es el estudiante más alto de la clase?

_____

3. ¿Es Ud. mayor que su padre?

_____

4. ¿Quién es su mejor amigo (amiga)?

_____

5. ¿Es su clase de español la más interesante de la escuela?

_____

6. ¿Quién es el menor (la menor) de su familia?

_____

7. ¿Es marzo más corto que febrero?

_____

8. ¿Es su profesor (profesora) más inteligente que Ud.?

_____

9. ¿Ve Ud. tantos programas de televisión como su hermano (hermana)?

_____

10. En su opinión, ¿quién fue el peor presidente de los Estados Unidos? ¿Y quién fue el mejor?

_____

E. Translate into Spanish as shown by the examples in italics:

1. I am as tall as you.   _Yo soy tan alto como Ud._

   _a._ I am as intelligent as you. _____

   _b._ She is as lazy as he. _____

   _c._ They are as bad as she. _____

   _d._ We are as good as they. _____

2. Is he lazier than his brother?   _¿Es él más perezoso que su hermano?_

   _a._ Is he smarter than his sister? _____

   _b._ Are you younger than your cousin? _____
   (two ways)

   _____

   _c._ Are they more beautiful than Mary? _____

   _d._ Are we better than the teacher? _____

3. Joan is the prettiest girl in the class.   _Juana es la muchacha más bonita de la clase._

   _a._ It is the largest school in the neighborhood. _____

   _____

   _b._ They are the tallest boys in the club. _____

   _____

   _c._ He is the richest man in the city. _____

   _____

   _d._ I live in the smallest building on the street. _____

   _____

4. Ann is the smartest in the class.   *Ana es la más inteligente de la clase.*

    a. Louise is the tallest in the family. _____

    b. I am the oldest in the group. _____

    c. He is the worst in the school. _____

    d. They are the most studious in the class. _____

    _____

5. *a.* John is as rich as Mary. _____

    b. Mary is as rich as John. _____

    c. Mary is richer than Louis. _____

    d. Charles is the richest in the group. _____

    _____

    e. Helen is the least rich in the club. _____

    _____

    f. We have less than you. _____

    g. They read as many books as we. _____

    h. She has more than ten dollars. _____

    i. I have fewer than fifteen records. _____

F. *Listening Comprehension.* Your teacher will read to the class ten statements in Spanish. In each case, circle the letter of the statement that is logically consistent or has the same meaning.

1. *a.* Yo tengo veinte años y Ud. tiene diez y ocho años.
    b. Yo tengo diez y ocho años y Ud. tiene veinte años.
    c. Tengo más años que Ud.

2. *a.* Él tiene ocho libros y ella tiene nueve.
    b. Ella tiene diez libros y él tiene diez también.
    c. Ella tiene más de ocho libros y él tiene menos de ocho.

3. *a.* Hay veinte chicas y diez y siete chicos.
    b. Hay veinte y dos chicas y veinte chicos.
    c. Hay cincuenta y cinco alumnos.

4. *a.* Los jóvenes tienen más inteligencia.
    b. Los jóvenes no saben tanto como los viejos.
    c. Los jóvenes son menos inteligentes.

5. *a.* Jorge tiene más dinero que Pablo.
    b. Pablo tiene menos dinero que Jorge.
    c. Pablo tiene más dinero que Jorge.

6. *a.* Yo tengo más dinero que tú.
    b. Tú tienes más dinero que yo.
    c. Yo tengo menos dinero que tú.

7. *a.* Ella es peor que él.
   b. Él es peor que ella.
   c. Él es mejor que ella.

8. *a.* Paco tiene tantos años como Paula.
   b. Paula es menor que Paco.
   c. Paula es mayor que Paco.

9. *a.* David es el más fuerte de los tres.
   b. David es menos fuerte que Roberto.
   c. Roberto es más fuerte que Tomás.

10. *a.* Roberta es menos gorda que Juanita.
    b. Gilda es la menos gorda de las tres.
    c. Juanita es la más gorda de las tres.

SUPPLEMENT: The Absolute Superlative
(-ísimo)

una casa **grandísima**	a very large house
unos gatitos **pequeñísimos**	some very small kittens

10. The absolute superlative is a special form of the adjective that ends in **-ísimo(-s)** or **-ísima(-s)**. The suffix means *very, extremely, unusually.* It can also mean *very much* or *very many:*

Te quiero **muchísimo.**	I love you very much.
Ella tiene **muchísimas** amigas.	She has very many friends (*f.*).

11. Some adjectives undergo a spelling change before the **-ísimo** suffix is added:

La vieja tenía el pelo **blanquísimo.**   The old woman had very white hair.
(The **c** in **blanco** changes to **qu** to retain the hard *k* sound before **i.**)

Los discursos fueron **larguísimos.**   The speeches were very long.
(The **g** in **largo** changes to **gu** to retain the hard *g* sound before **i.**)

Eran ocasiones **felicísimas.**   They were very happy occasions.
(The **z** in **feliz** changes to **c** before **i.**)

Practice H: Complete the Spanish expressions with the *-ísimo* form of the adjective.

1. the very wide avenue

   la avenida _____

2. a very happy marriage

   un matrimonio _____

3. the extremely dry climate

   el clima _____

4. a very bitter taste (bitter = *amargo, -a*)

   un sabor _____

5. some very beautiful churches (Use *bello, -a.*)

   unas iglesias _____

6. The news pleased them very much.

   La noticia les gustó _____.

7. They worked very hard ("much") and earned very little.

   Trabajaron _____

   y ganaron _____.

22
Demonstrative Adjectives and Pronouns

Demonstrative Adjectives

THIS	THESE
este lápiz, this pencil	**estos** lápices, these pencils
esta revista, this magazine	**estas** revistas, these magazines

THAT	THOSE
ese hombre, that man	**esos** hombres, those men
esa mujer, that woman	**esas** mujeres, those women

THAT (OVER THERE)	THOSE (OVER THERE)
aquel edificio, that building	**aquellos** edificios, those buildings
aquella casa, that house	**aquellas** casas, those houses

1. *This* and *these* are expressed in Spanish as follows:

> **este** + masculine singular noun
> **esta** + feminine singular noun
> **estos** + masculine plural noun
> **estas** + feminine plural noun

2. *That* and *those* are expressed in Spanish as follows:

> **ese** + masculine singular noun
> **esa** + feminine singular noun
> **esos** + masculine plural noun
> **esas** + feminine plural noun

3. *That* and *those* are also expressed by the forms **aquel, aquella, aquellos, aquellas,** but these forms are used to point out persons or objects that are at some distance from both the speaker and the person spoken to.

Practice A: Write the Spanish word for *this* or *these.*

1. _____ sala

2. _____ hombres

3. _____ mesas

4. _____ mes

Practice B: Write the Spanish word for *that* or *those*, using the forms *ese, esa*, etc.

1. _____ mujeres

2. _____ sombrero

3. _____ caja

4. _____ lápices

Practice C: Write the Spanish word for *that* or *those*, using the forms *aquel, aquella*, etc.

1. _____ muchachos

2. _____ lecciones

3. _____ silla

4. _____ casa

Practice D: Write the appropriate form of the Spanish adjective.

1. _____ casas
   (these)

2. _____ chico
   (that)

3. _____ mujer
   (this)

4. _____ escuela
   (that, over there)

5. _____ chicas
   (those)

6. _____ relojes
   (those, over there)

7. _____ edificio
   (this)

8. _____ pueblos
   (these)

9. _____ profesores
   (those)

10. _____ ciudad
    (that)

Demonstrative Pronouns

Me gusta **este** periódico pero no me gusta **ése.**

I like *this* newspaper but I don't like *that one.*

Esa flor es más bonita que **ésta.**

That flower is prettier than *this one.*

Estos niños son más grandes que **aquéllos.**

These children are bigger than *those* (at a distance).

4. The demonstrative adjective must be followed by a noun. The adjective and its noun can be replaced by a demonstrative pronoun, which is used to avoid repetition:

estos niños y **aquéllos** = estos niños y **aquellos niños**

esa casa y **ésta**= esa casa y **esta casa**

5. Unlike the adjective forms, the demonstrative pronouns have an accent mark on the stressed vowel: éste, ése, aquél, aquélla, etc.

Practice E: Write the pronoun that can be used in place of the given expression.

EXAMPLE: esta casa ___*ésta*___

1. esas chicas _____   5. estas ideas _____

2. este cuarto _____   6. aquel edificio _____

3. aquella vista _____   7. estos billetes _____

4. ese coche _____

Practice F: Write a phrase consisting of a demonstrative adjective and a noun that could be replaced by the given pronoun.

EXAMPLE: aquél   *aquel hombre (aquel chico, aquel libro, etc.)*

1. ésos _____

2. ésta _____

3. ésa _____

4. aquéllas _____

5. éstos _____

Neuter Demonstrative Forms

Esto es horrible.   This is horrible.
Eso no me gusta.   I do not like that.
¿Qué es **aquello**?   What is that?

6. **Esto, eso,** and **aquello** are neuter forms and refer to an idea or a preceding statement.

7. The neuter forms are also used to refer to an object that cannot be immediately identified. Once the identification is made, the neuter form can be replaced by a demonstrative pronoun that indicates gender and number:

—¿Qué son **esto** y **eso**?
—Son plantas.
—No me gusta esta planta, pero me gusta **ésa**.

—**Eso** es feo. ¿Qué es?
—Es un edificio.
—No me gusta ese edificio, pero me gusta **éste**.

EJERCICIOS

A. Replace the noun in italics with the noun in parentheses, and make a corresponding change in the form of the demonstrative adjective. (Write the new phrase in the blank.)

EXAMPLE: Quiero comprar esa *blusa.*
(vestido) _____ *ese vestido* _____

1. Vamos a aquella *tienda.* (supermercado) _____

2. Estos *coches* son grandes. (plantas) _____

3. Mi madre quiere comprar ese *escritorio.*
(sillas) _____

4. Mañana visitamos esos *museos.* (ciudad) _____

5. Andan por esa *calle.* (paseos) _____

6. ¿Dónde está *aquel* teatro? (casa) _____

7. Necesito esta *corbata.* (sombrero) _____

8. Uds. deben tomar este *vino.* (bebidas) _____

9. Vamos a pedir esos *postres.* (sopa) _____

10. Aquellos *hombres* son inteligentes.
(mujeres) _____

B. Answer the questions as shown in the example.

EXAMPLE: ¿Quiere Ud. tener este libro?
(that one) *No, pero quiero tener ése.*

1. ¿Quieren Uds. comer estas frutas?

(those) _____

2. ¿Va Ud. a ver esos programas?

(these) _____

3. ¿Desea Ud. comprar este vestido?

(that one [over there]) _____

4. ¿Vas a cantar esa canción?

(this one) _____

5. ¿Tocas estos discos?

(those) _____

6. ¿Comen Uds. estos pasteles?

(those) _____

7. ¿Escribes tú con ese lápiz?

(this one) _____

8. ¿Juega ella con esta raqueta?

(that one [over there]) _____

9. ¿Ves aquel edificio?

(this one) _____

10. ¿Consultan ellos este mapa?

(that one) _____

C. Translate into Spanish:*

1. *a.* This bicycle and that one are expensive.

_____

b. That bicycle and this one are cheap.

_____

2. *a.* That bus and this one are new.

_____

b. This bus and that one are old.

_____

3. *a.* These handkerchiefs and those are pretty.

_____

b. Those handkerchiefs and these are small.

_____

4. *a.* I want to buy those shoes and these.

_____

b. These shoes and those are comfortable.

_____

5. *a.* That drink and this one are delicious.

_____

b. This drink and that one are sweet.

_____

---

*Keep in mind: Adjectives must agree in gender and number with the nouns they modify.

6. *a.* We go to that café and this one.

_____

   b. Those cafés and these are old.

_____

7. *a.* I want those potatoes and these.

_____

   b. Do you want this potato or that one?

_____

8. *a.* I'm buying these films and those (over there).

_____

   b. That film (over there) and this one are good.

_____

9. *a.* That magazine and this one are interesting.

_____

   b. Let's buy these magazines and those.

_____

10. *a.* I want to read this article and that one.

_____

   b. These articles and those are not interesting.

_____

11. *a.* I believe this. _____

    b. I do not believe that. _____

12. *a.* What is that (over there)? _____

    b. What is this? _____

23
Possessive Adjectives and Pronouns

Possessive Adjectives

MY

mi amigo, my friend
mi revista, my magazine

mis amigos, my friends
mis revistas, my magazines

YOUR (familiar singular)

tu abrigo, your coat
tu clase, your class

tus abrigos, your coats
tus clases, your classes

YOUR, HIS, HER, THEIR

su coche $\left\{\begin{array}{l}\text{your}\\\text{his}\\\text{her}\\\text{their}\end{array}\right\}$ car
(su casa) (house)

sus coches $\left\{\begin{array}{l}\text{your}\\\text{his}\\\text{her}\\\text{their}\end{array}\right\}$ cars
(sus casas) (houses)

1. The forms **mi, tu,** and **su** are the same for masculine and feminine nouns. The plural forms **mis, tus,** and **sus** are used when the thing possessed is in the plural.

Practice A: Write the possessive adjective.

1. _____ profesor
     (their)

2. _____ escuela
     (my)

3. _____ padre
     (her)

4. _____ libros
     (my)

5. _____ raquetas
     (his)

6. _____ discos
     (your, fam. sing.)

SU(-S) AND ITS SUBSTITUTES

2. **Su(-s)** has several meanings: *your*, *his*, *her*, *its*, *their*. For greater clarity, **su(-s)** may be replaced by expressions like the following:

his book: **el libro de él**   your book: **el libro de Ud. (Uds.)**
his books: **los libros de él**   your books: **los libros de Ud. (Uds.)**

her book: **el libro de ella**   their book: **el libro de ellos (ellas)**
her books: **los libros de ella**   their books: **los libros de ellos (ellas)**

Practice B: Replace the given expression with a phrase that clarifies the intended meaning of *su(-s)*, as indicated in parentheses.

EXAMPLE: (your) sus libros   *los libros de Ud.*

1. (her) su casa   _____

2. (their) sus cuadernos   _____

3. (his) su hermano   _____

4. (your, *pl.*) su problema   _____

5. (their) sus padres   _____

OUR

nuestro tío, our uncle   **nuestros** tíos, our uncles
nuestra tía, our aunt   **nuestras** tías, our aunts

YOUR (FAMILIAR PLURAL)

vuestro pueblo, your town   **vuestros** pueblos, your towns
vuestra ciudad, your city   **vuestras** ciudades, your cities

3. **Nuestro** and **vuestro** have four possible endings (**-o, -a, -os, -as**) depending on whether the person or thing possessed is masculine or feminine, singular or plural.

Practice C: Write the possessive adjective. ("your" = *fam. pl.*)

1. _____ cocina
         (our)

2. _____ equipo
         (your)

3. _____ cuartos
         (our)

4. _____ casa
         (your)

5. _____ automóvil
         (our)

Practice D: Write the possessive adjective in the form required by the noun at the right.

1. su hermano   _____ hermana

2. mis zapatos   _____ chaqueta

3. tu radio   _____ televisores

4. nuestro teatro   _____ cines

5. vuestras amigas   _____ sobrino

Possessive Pronouns

Yo tengo **mi** periódico y ella tiene **el suyo.**   I have *my* newspaper and she has *hers.*
Él tiene **su** cartera y yo tengo **la mía.**   He has *his* wallet and I have *mine.*

4. The possessive adjective is always followed by a noun. The adjective and its noun can be replaced by a possessive pronoun, which is used to avoid repetition:

mi periódico y **el suyo** = mi periódico y **su periódico**

Possessive Adjective	*Possessive Pronoun*
mi abuelo, my grandfather	**el mío**
mi abuela, my grandmother	**la mía**
mis hermanos, my brothers	**los míos** } mine
mis plantas, my plants	**las mías**
tu sombrero, your hat	**el tuyo**
tu corbata, your tie	**la tuya**
tus sobrinos, your nephews	**los tuyos** } yours
tus lámparas, your lamps	**las tuyas**
nuestro sofá, our sofa	**el nuestro**
nuestra criada, our maid	**la nuestra**
nuestros perros, our dogs	**los nuestros** } ours
nuestras clases, our classes	**las nuestras**
vuestro sillón, your armchair	**el vuestro**
vuestra casa, your house	**la vuestra**
vuestros gatos, your cats	**los vuestros** } yours
vuestras maletas, your suitcases	**las vuestras**

su edificio { your / his / her / their } building   **el suyo**

su biblioteca { your / his / her / their } library   **la suya**

} yours, his, hers, theirs

sus maestros $\begin{Bmatrix} \text{your} \\ \text{his} \\ \text{her} \\ \text{their} \end{Bmatrix}$ teachers

los suyos $\Big\}$

las suyas $\Big\}$ yours, his, hers, theirs

sus tierras $\begin{Bmatrix} \text{your} \\ \text{his} \\ \text{her} \\ \text{their} \end{Bmatrix}$ lands

Practice E: Change each expression to a pronoun.

EXAMPLE: mis lecciones   *las mías*

1. su casa   _____

2. nuestros libros   _____

3. sus problemas   _____

4. tu cartera   _____

5. vuestras tías   _____

Practice F: Write an expression consisting of a possessive adjective and a noun that could be replaced by the given possessive pronoun. Use any suitable noun.

EXAMPLE: los míos   *mis tíos (mis libros, mis maestros, etc.)*

1. las nuestras _____

2. la suya   _____

3. el mío   _____

4. los suyos _____

5. el tuyo   _____

EL SUYO AND ITS SUBSTITUTES

—Aquí está el libro de María. ¿Lo quiere Ud.?

"Here is Mary's book. Do you want it?"

—No, ya tengo **el suyo.**

"No, I already have ---."

—¿El mío?

"Mine?"

—No, **el de ella.**

"No, *hers.*"

5. Each of the forms **el suyo, la suya, los suyos,** and **las suyas** has several meanings: *yours, his, hers, its,* or *theirs.* For greater clarity, they can be replaced by expressions like the following:

mi libro y **el suyo**	my book and yours, his, hers, theirs
el de Ud(s).	yours
el de él	his
el de ella	hers
el de ellos (ellas)	theirs

nuestras flores y **las suyas**	our flowers and yours, his, hers, theirs
las de Ud(s).	yours
las de él	his
las de ella	hers
las de ellos (ellas)	theirs

6. *Keep in mind:* These forms agree in gender and number with *the person or thing possessed,* not with the possessor.

Practice G: Use a clarifying phrase instead of the possessive pronoun.

EXAMPLE: Yo tengo mi pelota y ____*la de él*____.
                                                    (his)

1. Como mi postre y _____.
                                        (hers)

2. Buscamos nuestras cartas y _____.
                                                    (yours [Uds.])

3. Me gustan mis juegos y _____.
                                            (his)

4. Quiero tener estos diamantes y _____.
                                                        (yours [Ud.])

5. Visitamos tu ciudad y _____.
                                        (theirs)

SER + Possessive Pronoun

El gato es **mío.**	The cat is mine.
Estas revistas son **tuyas.**	These magazines are yours.

7. If a possessive pronoun is the object of the verb **ser,** the article (**el** mío, **las** suyas, etc.) is dropped.

Practice H: Complete the Spanish sentences.

EXAMPLE: The skirt is hers.

La falda ____*es suya*____.

1. This necktie is his.

   Esta corbata _____.

2. These books are mine.

   Estos libros _____.

3. This notebook isn't yours (*familiar sing.*)

   Este cuaderno no _____.

4. The chairs are ours.

   Las sillas _____.

5. Here are some pencils; aren't they yours (*formal sing.*)?

   Aquí están unos lápices; ¿no _____?

6. "Gentlemen, this car is yours, isn't it?" "No, it is not ours."

   —Señores, este coche _____, ¿verdad?

   —No, no _____.

In 7–10, use a clarifying phrase instead of a form of *suyo*.

> EXAMPLES: The skirt is hers.   The books are yours (*sing.*)
>
>   La falda ____*es de ella*____.   Los libros ____*son de Ud.*____.

7. These neckties are not his.

   Estas corbatas no _____.

8. The house is theirs (*f.*).

   La casa _____.

9. This table is yours (*pl.*).

   Esta mesa _____.

10. "These magazines are mine; those are yours (*sing.*), aren't they?" "No, those are theirs (*m.*)."

    —Estas revistas son mías; ésas _____, ¿no?

    —No, ésas _____.

Possessive Pronouns Used as Adjectives

Juana es una amiga **mía.**	Joan is a friend *of mine.*
Ellos son vecinos **nuestros.**	They are neighbors *of ours.*

8. A possessive adjective may *follow* the noun it modifies, in which case the adjective is replaced by the pronoun form: **mi** amiga—una amiga **mía; sus** cosas—unas cosas **suyas,** etc. Possessive pronouns used in this way are expressed in English by *of* + a possessive: *of mine, of yours, of hers,* etc.

Practice I: Write in Spanish.

1. three books of hers   _____

2. some money of ours   _____

3. some pens of his   _____

4. a watch of mine   _____

5. four diamonds of yours (*familiar sing.*)   _____

EJERCICIOS

A. Write the form of the possessive adjective that corresponds to the subject of the sentence.

EXAMPLE: Yo tengo ____*mis*____ libros.

1. ¿Toca ella _____ discos hoy?

2. No queremos conducir _____ coche.

3. Escribimos a _____ amigos en Puerto Rico.

4. Tú no tienes _____ tarea.

5. Ellos hablan con _____ profesor de ciencia.

6. ¿Tenéis _____ maletas?

7. Hablo con _____ primas por teléfono.

8. ¿Trae Ud. _____ guitarra a la fiesta?

9. Vemos _____ programas favoritos.

10. ¿Escribes a _____ parientes en Venezuela?

B. Each of the following statements is a reply to a question. Write the question, using a possessive adjective.

EXAMPLE: Sí, tengo mis libros. {
¿Tienes tus libros?
or
¿Tiene Ud. sus libros?
}

1. No, no visitamos a nuestros abuelos. _____

2. Sí, voy a buscar mi ropa. _____

3. No, ellos no tienen su dinero. _____

4. No, tú no puedes jugar con tus amigos. _____

5. Sí, vemos nuestros programas. _____

6. Sí, vamos a nuestra casa. _____

7. No, no queremos nuestro dinero. _____

8. Sí, él llega con su hermano. _____

9. Sí, salgo con mis padres. _____

10. No, Uds. no merecen sus notas. _____

C. Complete the sentence with a possessive pronoun, as shown in the example.

EXAMPLE: Tú tienes tu comida y yo tengo _____la mía_____.

1. Ellos van a su casa y nosotros vamos a _____.

2. Pedro toca su piano y Elena toca _____.

3. Nosotros leemos nuestros periódicos y José lee _____.

4. Mis padres son viejos; Clara dice que _____ son jóvenes.

5. Ellos juegan con sus amigos y yo juego con _____.

6. Diana va con su familia y Juan va con _____.

7. Ellos van a su escuela y tú vas a _____.

8. Los hombres tienen sus problemas y las mujeres tienen _____.

9. Tú dices que tus notas son buenas y yo digo que _____ son buenas también.

10. Ellos llegan en su coche y nosotros llegamos en _____.

D. Answer with a complete sentence, using a possessive pronoun.

EXAMPLE: ¿Qué abrigo llevas esta noche?   *Llevo el mío.*

1. ¿Con qué lápiz escribes? _____

2. ¿Qué ropa llevan ellos? _____

3. ¿Qué libros tiene Ud.? _____

4. ¿A qué cuarto van Uds.? _____

5. ¿De qué clase viene él? _____

6. ¿Qué bicicleta usa Felipe? _____

7. ¿Qué novelas lee el autor? _____

8. ¿En qué habitación duermes tú? _____

9. ¿Con qué dinero pagan Uds. la cuenta? _____

10. ¿A qué calle llegan ellos? _____

E. Answer with a complete sentence, using the clue in parentheses.

EXAMPLE: ¿De quién es esta caja? (*his*)
       Esta caja es suya.

1. ¿De quiénes son estas camisas? (*mine*)

_____

2. ¿De quién son estos vestidos? (*hers*)

_____

3. ¿De quiénes es esa casa? (*ours*)

_____

4. ¿De quiénes son estos coches? (*theirs*)

_____

5. ¿De quién son estos libros? (*yours*, familiar sing.)

_____

F.   Rewrite the sentence in two ways by replacing *de* + noun with (*a*) *su*(*-s*), (*b*) *de* + pronoun.

EXAMPLE: El libro de Ana es interesante.
   a. Su libro es interesante.
   b. El libro de ella es interesante.

1. Las corbatas de Antonio son de muchos colores.

   a. _____

   b. _____

2. ¿Dónde está el tocadiscos de Flora?

   a. _____

   b. _____

3. ¿Tienes la llave del profesor?

   a. _____

   b. _____

4. Llevamos a la fiesta los discos de Paquita.

   a. _____

   b. _____

5. Me gusta la escuela de Ramón y Marta.

   a. _____

   b. _____

G.   Rewrite the sentence in two ways by using (*a*) a form of *suyo*, (*b*) a substitute for *suyo* that is more specific.

EXAMPLE: Los zapatos de José son bonitos.
   a. Los suyos son bonitos.
   b. Los de él son bonitos.

1. La pulsera de Lola es cara.

   a. _____

   b. _____

2. El reloj de la abuela es viejo.

　　a. _____

　　b. _____

3. Las camisas del hombre son bonitas.

　　a. _____

　　b. _____

4. El coche de los primos es nuevo.

　　a. _____

　　b. _____

5. Las joyas de mi madre son raras.

　　a. _____

　　b. _____

H. Translate into Spanish:

1. *a.* I have his gloves and mine. _____

　　b. He has my gloves and his. _____

2. *a.* Our street and yours (*familiar sing.*) are wide. _____

　　_____

　　b. Your street and ours are narrow. _____

3. *a.* Their store and his are big. _____

　　b. His store and theirs are small. _____

4. *a.* Where are her relatives and yours (*formal pl.*)? _____

　　_____

　　b. Your relatives and hers are going to the party. _____

　　_____

5. *a.* Our rugs and his are red. _____

　　b. His rugs and ours are beautiful. _____

6. *a.* My apartment and hers are modern. _____

　　b. Her apartment and mine are not large. _____

7. *a.* Two friends (*f.*) of his are coming tonight. _____

　　_____

    b. Some friends (*m.*) of mine are leaving for Spain. _____

_____

8. *a.* Some neighbors (*m.*) of ours are in the country. _____

_____

    b. Some neighbors (*f.*) of yours (*formal sing.*) are here. _____

_____

9. *a.* A watch of hers is there. _____

    b. Three watches of hers are on the table. _____

10. *a.* Some shirts of his are very old. _____

    b. Do you have a shirt of mine? _____

I. *Listening Comprehension.* Your teacher will read aloud ten questions in Spanish. In each case, underline the most appropriate reply.

1. *a.* Es mío.
  b. Son mías.
  c. Son tuyos.

2. *a.* Es nuestra.
  b. Es mía.
  c. Son suyas.

3. *a.* Sí, voy a las mías.
  b. No, voy a la mía.
  c. No, voy a la de él.

4. *a.* No, no tengo la tuya.
  b. Sí, tengo los suyos.
  c. Sí, tengo el tuyo.

5. *a.* Sí, salgo con la suya.
  b. Sí, salgo con la de ella.
  c. Sí, salgo con el suyo.

6. *a.* los de ella
  b. el de ellos
  c. la de él

7. *a.* las tuyas
  b. los tuyos
  c. la suya

8. *a.* los nuestros
  b. la nuestra
  c. el de Ud.

9. *a.* el suyo
  b. los tuyos
  c. la suya

10. *a.* No, es un amigo mío.
  b. Sí, es un amigo nuestro.
  c. Sí, es un amigo mío.

PART FIVE

PRONOUNS

24
The Personal *A*;
Direct Object Pronouns
LO, LA, LOS, LAS

The Personal *A*

A	*B*
REFERRING TO THINGS	REFERRING TO PEOPLE
¿Qué?	*¿A quién? ¿A quiénes?*
¿Qué ven Uds.?	¿A quién ven Uds.?
What do you see?	Whom do you see?
Vemos la mesa.	Vemos **a** la chica (**a** Juana).
We see the table.	We see the girl (Jane).
Vemos los edificios.	¿A quiénes ven Uds.?
We see the buildings.	Vemos **a** los chicos.
	We see the boys.
	Vemos **a** las chicas (**a** María y Elena).
	We see the girls (Mary and Helen).

1. The direct object may be a thing (column *A*) or a person (column *B*). In Spanish, if the direct object refers to persons, it is preceded by **a.** This preposition, called the personal **a,** has no meaning in English.

2. The personal **a** is usually not used with **tener. (Tengo una hermana.)**

In chapters 24–27, object pronouns are used only with verbs in the present tense in order to focus on constructions in which object pronouns precede the verb. Their position in relation to other verb forms is presented in chapter 28.

3. The personal **a** is generally used before the names of places or countries:*

Ella ama **a** Madrid.   She loves Madrid.
Visitan **a** Inglaterra.   They are visiting England.

Practice A: Write the personal *a* in the blank if it is required. (Remember: *a + el = al.*)

1. ¿Comprendes _____ la palabra?

2. No veo _____ mi padre.

3. Vamos a visitar _____ ese país.

4. ¿Quién conoce _____ el hombre?

5. Siempre ayudamos _____ nuestra madre.

6. No oímos _____ la música.

7. Tiene _____ cuatro hermanos.

8. Esta noche invitamos _____ María.

9. No recuerdo _____ las mujeres.

10. El profesor describe _____ Venezuela.

Direct Object Pronouns

A. **lo,** him, it (*m.*)   **los,** them (*m.* or "mixed" genders)
   la, her, it (*f.*)   **las,** them (*f.*)

Yo tengo **el libro.**   Yo **lo** tengo.
I have *the book*.   I have *it*.

Vemos **al muchacho.**   **Lo** vemos.
We see *the boy*.   We see *him*.

Ven **la casa.**   **La** ven.
They see *the house*.   They see *it*.

¿Oyes a **Rosa?**   ¿**La** oyes?
Do you hear *Rose*?   Do you hear *her*?

¿Leen Uds. **los periódicos?**   ¿**Los** leen Uds.?
Do you read *the newspapers*?   Do you read *them*?

Ella no conoce a **mis amigos.**   Ella no **los** conoce.
She does not know *my friends*.   She does not know *them*.

---

*It is omitted, however, if the definite article is part of the name: **Ama la Habana,** *She loves Havana;* **Visitan los Estados Unidos.** *They are visiting the United States.*

No escribimos **las cartas.**
We're not writing *the letters.*

No **las** escribimos.
We're not writing *them.*

¿No invitas a **las chicas?**
Aren't you inviting *the girls?*

¿No **las** invitas?
Aren't you inviting *them?*

4. The direct object pronouns **lo, la, los, las** may refer to things or persons.

5. The direct object pronouns directly precede the conjugated form of the verb.

B. lo
   la } *you,* formal sing.   los
                               las } *you,* plural

No **lo** comprendo, señor. Hable Ud. más despacio, por favor.

I don't understand you, sir. Please speak more slowly.

Ellos dicen que **las** conocen, señoras. ¿Los conocen Uds.?

They say they know you, ladies. Do you know them?

6. As object pronouns meaning *you,* **lo** and **la** are used only when speaking to someone addressed as **usted.** The plural forms, however, are both formal and familiar (except in Spain—see chapter 25):

¿Dónde están Uds., niños? No **los** veo.

Where are you, children? I don't see you.

7. *Caution:* In English, the pronoun *you* may be either subject ("*you* see Mary") or object ("Mary sees *you*"). As subject, *you* = **usted** ("**Ud.** ve a María"); as direct object, *you* = **lo, la, los,** or **las** ("María **lo [la,** etc.] ve").

Practice B: Express in Spanish, using the correct equivalent of *you:* **Ud., Uds., lo, la, los,** or **las.**

1. (you, *f. pl.*)

   a. Do you know them (*m.*)?

   b. Do they know you?

   _____   _____

2. (you, *m. sing.*)

   a. She sees you.

   b. You see her.

   _____   _____

3. (you, *f. sing.*)

   a. Does she understand you?

   b. Do you understand her?

   _____   _____

4. (you, *m. pl.*; they/them = las profesoras)

    a. They greet you.

    b. You listen to them.

_____

_____

Summary

lo,* you (*m. sing.*), him, it (*m.*)
la, you (*f. sing.*), her, it (*f.*)

los, you (*m. pl.*), them (*m.* or "mixed" genders)
las, you (*f. pl.*), them (*f.*)

Practice C: Rewrite the sentence to include the Spanish equivalent of the object pronoun in parentheses.

    EXAMPLE: (them, *f.*) ¿No ve ella?   *¿No las ve ella?*

  1. (her)   No comprenden bien. _____

  2. (it, *f.*)   ¿Dices tú siempre? _____

  3. (you, *m. sing.*) Nosotros vemos claramente. _____

  4. (them, *f.*)   Vendemos todos los días. _____

  5. (it, *m.*)   ¿No quiere Ud.? _____

  6. (you, *f. pl.*)   No entendemos bien. _____

  7. (her)   ¿Visitan Uds. mañana? _____

  8. (it, *m.*)   Escribimos todas las semanas. _____

  9. (him)   ¿Oyes tú bien? _____

10. (them, *m.* & *f.*) Yo no compro con frecuencia. _____

Clarifying the Meanings of Pronouns *LO, LOS, LA, LAS*

8. Since each of the pronouns **lo, los, la,** and **las** may have several meanings, the intended meaning may be clarified or emphasized by adding as follows:

Yo **lo** veo.   I see it.
Yo **lo** veo *a él.*   I see him.
Yo **lo** veo *a Ud.*   I see you.

¿**La** comprende él?   Does he understand it?
¿**La** comprende él *a ella*? Does he understand her?
¿**La** comprende él *a Ud.*?   Does he understand you (*f.*)?

_____

*In Spain, the form **le** is used for persons, **lo** for things.

No **los** oímos.	We don't hear them (*ref. to things*).
No **los** oímos *a ellos.*	We don't hear them (*ref. to persons*).
No **los** oímos *a Uds.*	We don't hear you.
Las ve.	He sees them (*ref. to things*).
Las ve *a ellas.*	He sees them (*ref. to persons*).
Las ve *a Uds.*	He sees you.

EJERCICIOS

A. Rewrite the sentence, changing the underlined words to object pronouns.

EXAMPLE: ¿Tiene Ud. el diccionario?   *¿Lo tiene Ud.?*

1. Los alumnos leen la novela.   _____

2. ¿Dónde compramos las verduras?   _____

3. No conozco a ese hombre.   _____

4. Ellos ven a sus primos.   _____

5. ¿Necesitas el mapa?   _____

6. Mañana recibimos los paquetes.   _____

7. Escuchamos a la profesora.   _____

8. ¿Quién vende los coches?   _____

9. ¿Mira Ud. a Luisa?   _____

10. ¿Dónde construyen la escuela?   _____

B. Answer in Spanish, using the same object pronoun.

EXAMPLE: Allí está el museo. ¿Lo visitan Uds.?
Sí, *lo visitamos.* Or: No, *no lo visitamos.*

1. Es una buena bicicleta. ¿La compras?

   Sí, _____

2. Necesitamos pan. ¿Lo vende Ud.?

   No, _____

3. Estos hombres hablan mal. ¿Los entiendes?

   No, _____

4. Ella tiene mis discos. ¿Los escucha?

   Sí, _____

5. Hay buenos programas esta noche en la televisión. ¿Los ven ellos?

   Sí, _____

6. Tus hermanos son simpáticos. ¿Los amas?

No, _____

7. El Presidente va a estar en nuestra ciudad. ¿Lo invitan Uds. a su casa?

Sí, _____

8. Mi tía vive en el segundo piso. ¿La conoce Ud.?

No, _____

9. Me gustan estos *blue-jeans*. ¿Los compras en aquella tienda?

Sí, _____

10. Este tocadiscos está roto. ¿Lo reparan Uds. aquí?

No, _____

C. Write a question for each statement, as shown in the examples.

EXAMPLES: Sí, lo vemos.   *¿Lo ven Uds.?*

No, no las compro.   *{ ¿Las compras tú?*
                          { ¿Las compra Ud.?

Lo venden allí.   *¿Dónde lo venden?*

La estudian por la tarde.   *¿Cuándo la estudian?*

1. No, no lo deseamos. _____

2. La escucho en la sala. _____

3. Sí, los tengo. _____

4. Ellos los practican en el gimnasio. _____

5. Las vende en la esquina. _____

6. La oímos todas las mañanas. _____

7. Ella no lo quiere porque no es importante. _____

8. Lo comemos con mantequilla. _____

9. No, no las compramos hoy. _____

10. Yo la abro; él no. _____

D. Repeat exercise C, but this time use an appropriate noun instead of a pronoun.

EXAMPLE: Sí, lo vemos.   *{ ¿Ven Uds. el coche?*
                                or
                                { ¿Ven Uds. al profesor?

1. _____   **2.** _____

3. _____   **4.** _____

5. _____   **6.** _____

7. _____   8. _____

9. _____   10. _____

E. Translate into Spanish:

1. *a.* Are you visiting the city? _____

   b. Yes, I am visiting it. _____

   c. Is he visiting it too? _____

2. *a.* Is she studying Spanish? _____

   b. No, she isn't studying it. _____

   c. Is she studying it? _____

3. *a.* Are they reading the novels? _____

   b. Yes, they are reading them. _____

   c. Are you (*tú*) reading them too? _____

4. *a.* Who is listening to the teacher (*f.*)? _____

   b. I am listening to her. _____

   c. Who is listening to her too? _____

5. *a.* I don't know you, sir. _____

   b. Does he know you, madam? _____

   c. She does not know you, ladies. _____

6. *a.* We understand you well, sir. _____

   b. Do they understand you, gentlemen? _____

   c. Does Philip understand you, Mr. Gómez? _____

7. *a.* I'm inviting my cousin Henry. _____

   b. I'm also inviting my friend Anne. _____

   c. I'm inviting them tonight. _____

8. *a.* Are you (*Uds.*) watching television? _____

   b. Yes, we're watching it now. _____

   c. Who is watching it this afternoon? _____

9. *a.* My father is buying that car. _____

   b. He's buying it this week. _____

   c. Where is he buying it? _____

10. *a.* I hear him well. _____

    b. I don't hear you, Mr. López. _____

    c. Do you hear him? _____

F. *Listening Comprehension.* Your teacher will read aloud ten questions in Spanish. After each question is read, circle the letter of the most appropriate reply.

1. *a.* Yo lo conozco a él.
    b. Ramón la conoce.
    c. Eva lo conoce a Ud.

2. *a.* Sí, la escucho a ella.
    b. No, no la escucho.
    c. Sí, lo escucho ahora.

3. *a.* No, no los leemos.
    b. Sí, la leemos siempre.
    c. No, no las leemos ahora.

4. *a.* Los chicos la ven.
    b. Los hombres lo ven.
    c. Mis padres las ven.

5. *a.* Visito a mis abuelos.
    b. Visito la ciudad.
    c. Visito a mi amigo.

6. *a.* Sí, lo traigo.
    b. Sí, los traigo.
    c. No, no las traigo.

7. *a.* Yo lo entiendo.
    b. Juan la entiende.
    c. Carlota los entiende.

8. *a.* Lo compramos en la ciudad.
    b. La compramos en esa tienda.
    c. Las compramos en el centro.

9. *a.* No, no los oigo claramente.
    b. No, no lo oigo bien.
    c. Sí, las oigo perfectamente.

10. *a.* No, no las tomo nunca.
    b. Sí, la tomo todas las noches.
    c. Sí, lo tomo siempre.

Dos mujeres policías de Madrid, España

25
Indirect Object Pronouns *LE* and *LES*; Object Pronouns *ME, TE, NOS, OS*

A. le, (*to*) *him,* (*to*) *her*
    les, (*to*) *them*

Hablamos **a Enrique (a Marta).**	**Le** hablamos.
We speak to Henry (to Martha).	We speak to him (her).
¿Quién escribe **a las mujeres (a los hombres)?**	¿Quién **les** escribe?
Who writes to the women (to the men)?	Who writes to them?

B. le, (*to*) *you,* formal singular
    les, (*to*) *you,* plural

Él **le** trae el periódico, señor (señorita).	{ He is bringing you the newspaper, sir (miss). { He is bringing the newspaper to you, sir (miss).
Les decimos la verdad.	We are telling you the truth.

1. The indirect object answers the question *to whom*? For example, "le hablamos" (we speak to him) answers the question "¿a **quién** hablamos?" (*to whom* do we speak?); "**les** trae la carta" (he is bringing them the letter) answers the question "¿**a quiénes** trae la carta?" (*to whom* is he bringing the letter?).

2. Since **le** and **les** have several meanings, the intended meaning may be clarified or emphasized by adding one of the following phrases: **a Ud., a Uds., a él, a ella, a ellos, a ellas.**

210

—¿No **le** escribe *a Ud.*?

"Doesn't she write to *you*?"

—No, ella **le** escribe *a él.*

"No, she writes to *him*."

Les escriben *a Uds.;* nunca **les** escriben *a ellos.*

They write to *you* (*pl.*); they never write to *them.*

3. As we have seen, **le** and **les** are substituted for phrases of the type **a** + *noun:* **a Marta, a los hombres.** For example, "trae la carta **a Marta**" (he brings Martha the letter) can be replaced by "**le** trae la carta" (he brings her the letter). Often, however, both the phrase and its pronoun substitute are used, rather than one *or* the other:

Yo **le** doy el libro **a Juan.**

I give John the book.

¿**Les** presta dinero **a sus hermanos**?

Does she lend money to her brothers?

In this construction—very common in spoken Spanish—**le** or **les** does not affect the meaning of the sentence. Note the similarity between this type of sentence and the use of clarifying phrases:

yo **le** doy el libro **a él**

I give him the book

yo **le** doy el libro **a Juana**

I give Joan the book

4. *Caution:* The English pronouns *you, him, her,* and *them* may be direct or indirect objects, depending upon how they are used:

(direct object)   I see *her* = yo **la** veo
(indirect object)   I write *her* a letter = yo **le** escribo una carta

(direct object)   we see *you* = **los** vemos
(indirect object)   we send *you* the packages = **les** mandamos los paquetes

Practice A: Express in Spanish as shown by the examples in italics.

1. I speak to him.   *Yo le hablo a él.*

   a. I speak to her. _____

   b. I speak to them. _____

   c. I speak to you (*sing.*). _____

2. Do they write to you often?   *¿Le escriben a Ud. a menudo?*

   a. Do they write to him often? _____

   b. Do they write to them (*m.*) often? _____

   c. Do they write to you (*pl.*) often? _____

3. What is she giving you?   *¿Qué le da ella a Ud.?*

   a. What is she giving him? _____

   b. What is she giving her? _____

   c. What is she giving her brother? _____

4. We aren't speaking to her.   *No le hablamos a ella.*

   a. We aren't speaking to you (*pl.*). _____

   b. We aren't speaking to you (*sing.*). _____

   c. We aren't speaking to our friends. _____

5. John is lending her money.   *Juan le presta dinero a ella.*

   a. John is lending him money. _____

   b. John is lending them money. _____

   c. John is lending you (*sing.*) money. _____

Practice B: Direct and Indirect Object Pronouns. Complete the Spanish sentences with the correct object pronoun, choosing among the following:

direct objects: *lo, la, los, las*   indirect objects: *le, les*

1. you, *f. pl.*

   a. I see you.   b. I write to you.

   Yo _____ veo.   Yo _____ escribo.

2. them, *m.*

   a. We send them a letter.   b. We invite them to the house.

   _____ enviamos una carta.   _____ invitamos a la casa.

3. a. I show her the card.   b. I meet her in class.

   _____ muestro la tarjeta.   _____ encuentro en la clase.

4. you, *m. sing.*

   a. They don't hear you.   b. They tell you the truth.

   Ellos no _____ oyen.   _____ dicen la verdad.

5. a. She brings him a gift.   b. She looks at him.

   _____ trae un regalo.   _____ mira.

6. you, *f. sing.*

   a. Do they sell you a ticket?   b. Do they know you?

   ¿_____ venden un billete?   ¿_____ conocen?

7. them, *f.*

   a. I rarely visit them.   b. I don't listen to them.

   Yo rara vez _____ visito.   No _____ escucho.

   c. She greets them and gives them the tickets.

   Ella _____ saluda y _____ da los billetes.

ME, TE, NOS, OS

Ellos **me** ven.	Ellos **me** hablan.
They see me.	They speak to me.
¿**Te** oyen ellos?	¿**Te** escriben ellos?
Do they hear you?	Do they write to you?
No **nos** comprenden.	No **nos** dan dinero.
They don't understand us.	They don't give us money. (They don't give money to us.)
Os veo bien.	**Os** presto los libros.
I see you well.	I lend you the books. (I lend the books to you.)

5. The pronouns **me, te, nos,** and **os** are both direct and indirect objects.*

6. Os, the object-pronoun form of **vosotros,** is used only in Spain. In Spanish America, the familiar plural as object pronoun is expressed by the forms corresponding to **ustedes,** that is, by **los, las,** or **les.**

Practice C: Express in Spanish as shown by the examples in italics. (In this exercise, "you" = *te* or *os*.)

1. Do they see you (*sing.*)?   *¿Te ven?*

   a. Do they see us? _____

   b. Do they see me? _____

   c. Do they see you (*pl.*)? _____

2. He is sending us the records.   *Nos manda los discos.*

   a. He's sending you the records. _____

   b. He's sending me the records. _____

   c. He's sending you (*pl.*) the records. _____

3. Isn't she telling you the truth?   *¿No os dice ella la verdad?*

   a. Isn't she telling you (*sing.*) the truth? _____

   b. Isn't she telling us the truth? _____

   c. Isn't she telling me the truth? _____

---

*Since each of these pronouns has only one meaning, they never require clarifying phrases like those often used with **le** and **les** (see §2.) For *emphasis,* however, one of the following phrases may be added: **a mí, a ti, a nosotros(-as), a vosotros(-as):**

Ella **me** llama *a mí,* no a ellos.	She is calling *me,* not them.
No **nos** escriben *a nosotros*; te escriben *a ti.*	They do not write to *us*; they write to *you.*

EJERCICIOS

A. Complete the answers to the questions.

EXAMPLES:

¿Quién me habla?   Yo *te hablo.*

¿Quién nos oye?   { Ella *os oye.*
                                 { Ella *los oye a Uds.*

1. ¿Quiénes nos saludan?   { Los jefes _____.
                                 { Los jefes _____.

2. ¿Quién te quiere?   Mi novio (novia) _____.

3. ¿Quién me llama?   La profesora _____.

4. ¿Quiénes os traen los juguetes?   Los abuelos _____.

5. ¿Quiénes me odian?   Nosotras _____.

6. ¿Quién nos sirve la comida?*   { El camarero _____.
                                   { El camarero _____.

B. Write the question that is answered by the given statement, as shown in the examples.

EXAMPLES:

Sí, ellos te ven.   *¿Me ven ellos?*

Sí, me paga el dinero.   *a. ¿Te paga el dinero?*
                               b. ¿Le paga el dinero a Ud.?

1. Sí, nos lee el cuento.   a. _____

                               b. _____

2. No, no les explicamos a Uds. la gramática.   _____

3. No, no te digo una mentira.   _____

4. Sí, ellas me dan los discos.   a. _____

                                   b. _____

5. Sí, él nos escribe una carta.   a. _____

                                    b. _____

Hint: In this question, **nos** is an indirect object.

C. Answer with a complete sentence in Spanish, using the clue in parentheses.

EXAMPLE: ¿Qué le* da Ud. a José? (los billetes)
Yo le doy los billetes.

1. ¿Qué le presta Ud. a su amigo? (diez dólares)

_____

2. ¿Qué les dan Uds. a sus padres? (dos regalos)

_____

3. ¿Qué me mandas tú? (una tarjeta postal)

_____

4. ¿Qué le escribes al Presidente? (una carta larga)

_____

5. ¿Qué nos lee papá? (una revista interesante)

_____

6. ¿Qué les sirve Ud. a sus amigos? (pasteles y helado)

_____

7. ¿Qué te cuenta María? (lo que pasa en su casa)

_____

8. ¿Qué le trae Ud. a su novia (novio)? (una caja de dulces)

_____

9. ¿Qué le pregunta a Ud. el hombre? (qué hora es)

_____

10. ¿Qué les contestan a Uds. sus padres? (que están bien)

_____

D. Translate into Spanish:

1. *a.* Who is serving us dinner tonight?

_____

   b. My cousin is serving you (*formal pl.*) dinner.

_____

2. *a.* Is your friend sending you (*familiar sing.*) the stamps?

_____

---

*See page 211, §3.

b. No, he is not sending me the stamps.

_____

3. *a.* What are they telling her?

_____

   b. They're telling her a lie.

_____

4. *a.* When are you (*Ud.*) giving them the money?

_____

   b. I'm giving them the money next week.

_____

5. *a.* Who is lending you (*familiar sing.*) the racquet?

_____

   b. My friend is lending me the racquet.

_____

6. *a.* When does she write to you (*formal sing.*)?

_____

   b. She writes to me every week.

_____

7. *a.* What is the teacher reading to us?

_____

   b. She's reading us *Don Quijote*.

_____

8. *a.* Are you (*tú*) speaking to *them* on the phone?

_____

   b. No, I'm speaking to *her*.

_____

9. *a.* What are you (*vosotros*) asking me?

_____

   b. I'm asking you (*familiar pl.*) how you are.

_____

10. *a.* What are they bringing him later?

_____

b. They're bringing him some magazines and some newspapers.

_____

E. *Listening Comprehension.* Your teacher will read aloud ten questions in Spanish. After each question is read, circle the letter of the most appropriate answer.

1. *a.* Te doy un regalo.
   b. Le doy un libro a ella.
   c. Nos dan dinero.

2. *a.* Sí, te mandamos los billetes.
   b. Sí, les mandamos los billetes.
   c. No, no le mandamos los billetes.

3. *a.* Les digo la verdad.
   b. Le digo un secreto.
   c. Me dice una mentira.

4. *a.* Sí, te leo un cuento.
   b. No, no les leo nada.
   c. Sí, me lees un cuento.

5. *a.* Nos escribe una carta.
   b. No te escribe nada.
   c. Les escribo una tarjeta postal.

6. *a.* No, no nos quieren.
   b. Sí, los quieren mucho.
   c. Sí, me quieren mucho.

7. *a.* Nos pregunta qué tiempo hace.
   b. Le pregunta cómo está.
   c. Me pregunta qué hora es.

8. *a.* Sí, me presta el coche.
   b. Sí, le presto el coche.
   c. No, no le presto el coche a ella.

9. *a.* Les contestan a Uds. por teléfono.
   b. Le contestan con un telegrama.
   c. Me contestan por correo aéreo.

10. *a.* Les paso la sal a ellos.
   b. Nos pasa la sal a nosotros.
   c. Le paso la sal a Ud.

Una pirámide maya o tolteca en Chichén Itzá, Yucatán, México

26
Double Object Pronouns

Using *ME*, *TE*, *NOS*, *OS* With Direct Object Pronouns

Juan **me** manda **el paquete.**
John sends me the package.

Juan **me lo** manda.
John sends it to me.

¿**Te** muestra ella **la foto**?
Does she show you the photo?

¿**Te la** muestra ella?
Does she show it to you?

Nos dan **los libros.**
They give us the books.

Nos los dan.
They give them to us. (They give us them.)

No **os** sirven **las comidas.**
They are not serving you the meals.

No **os las** sirven.
They are not serving them to you. (. . .are not serving you them.)

1. When a direct and an indirect object pronoun are used together, the indirect object (usually a person) precedes the direct object (usually a thing).

SOME DOUBLE-OBJECT COMBINATIONS

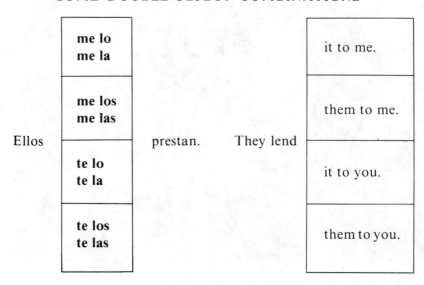

Ellos	me lo / me la	prestan.	They lend	it to me.
	me los / me las			them to me.
	te lo / te la			it to you.
	te los / te las			them to you.

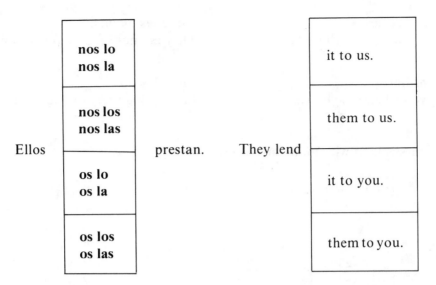

nos lo / nos la	it to us.
nos los / nos las	them to us.
Ellos · os lo / os la · prestan.	They lend · it to you.
os los / os las	them to you.

Practice A: Repeat each sentence, substituting the indicated expressions.

EXAMPLE:
No te los *doy*.

traemos	*No te los traemos.*
prestan	*No te los prestan.*
ofrecen	*No te los ofrecen.*

1. ¿Nos la *escriben*?

   dan   _____

   manda él   _____

   prometes tú   _____

2. ¿Me las *das tú*?

   trae él   _____

   venden Uds.   _____

   presta Ud.   _____

3. Ellos te lo *venden.*

   mandan   _____

   traen   _____

   escriben   _____

LE and LES Become SE Before a Direct Object Pronoun

¿**Le** traen ellos **el billete**?
Are they bringing you (him, her) the ticket?

¿**Se lo** traen ellos?
Are they bringing it to you (him, her)?

Les mostramos **la pintura.**
We show you (them) the painting.

Se la mostramos.
We show it to you (them).

No **le** mandan **las cartas.**
They are not sending you (him, her) the
   letters.

No **se las** mandan.
They are not sending them to you (him, her).

Yo **les** doy **los libros.**
I am giving you (them) the books.

Yo **se los** doy.
I am giving them to you (them).

2. When **le** or **les** is used with **lo, la, los,** or **las,** it changes to **se.**

SOME DOUBLE-OBJECT COMBINATIONS WITH *SE*

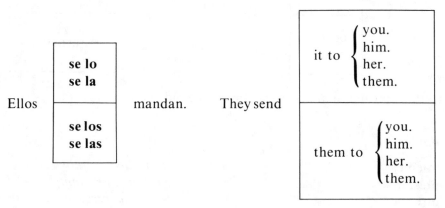

3. Since **se lo, se la,** etc. may have several meanings, the intended meaning can be clarified by adding **a Ud., a Uds., a él, a ella, a ellos,** or **a ellas:**

Se lo mandamos *a ella.*

We send it to *her.*

¿Se los prestan *a Ud.?*

Are they lending them to *you?*

Practice B: Repeat each sentence, substituting the indicated verbs.

EXAMPLE:
Se lo *prometo.*

    doy   *Se lo doy.*

    ofrecen   *Se lo ofrecen.*

    contamos   *Se lo contamos.*

1. Se la *decimos.*

    digo   _____

    dan   _____

    manda   _____

2. Ellos se lo *venden* a él.

    escriben   _____

    explican   _____

    dan   _____

3. ¿Se los *presta* Ud. a ellos?

escribe _____

vende _____

da _____

EJERCICIOS

A. Rewrite the sentence, changing the noun object to a direct object pronoun.

EXAMPLE: Ella me da el dinero.   *Ella me lo da.*

1. Yo te traigo las flores. _____
2. Ellos nos dicen la verdad. _____
3. ¿Le manda él los discos a ella? _____
4. No les damos los billetes a Uds. _____
5. ¿Cuándo me prestas diez dólares? _____
6. Juanita les escribe la tarjeta. _____
7. ¿Quién te lee los cuentos? _____
8. ¿Nos vende Ud. la casa? _____
9. Mamá os sirve la comida. _____
10. La profesora les explica el concepto a ellos. _____

B. In your answers to the following questions, change the noun objects to object pronouns.

EXAMPLE: ¿Dan Uds. el dinero al comerciante?

Sí, *se lo damos.*   Or: No, *no se lo damos.*

1. ¿Llevas tú las flores a tu novia?

No, _____

2. ¿Escriben los alumnos la carta al alcalde?

Sí, _____

3. ¿Dices siempre la verdad a tus padres?

Sí, _____

4. ¿Dan Uds. dinero al dependiente?

Sí, _____

5. ¿Manda él los sellos a sus amigos?

No, _____

6. ¿Me explicas el problema?

No, _____

7. ¿Te vende la bicicleta?

Sí, _____

8. ¿Le lee el profesor el cuento a Ud.?

Sí, _____

9. ¿Nos cuentan ellos la anécdota?

No, _____

10. ¿Les presta él la caja a Uds.?

Sí, _____

C. Write the question that is answered by the given statement, as shown in the examples.

EXAMPLES: Sí, se lo doy.   *¿Se lo da Ud. a ella?*

No, no te los traigo.   *¿Me los traes?*

1. Sí, nos los traen.   _____

2. No, ella no me la explica.   _____

3. Sí, te lo presto.   _____

4. No, no se los damos a Uds.   _____

5. Sí, ellos se las venden a él.   _____

D. Repeat exercise C, but this time use an appropriate noun instead of the direct object pronoun.

EXAMPLE: Sí, se lo doy.   *¿Le da Ud. el libro a ella?*

1. _____   **4.** _____

2. _____   **5.** _____

3. _____

E. Translate into Spanish:

1. *a.* They are sending them (*f.*) to us.

_____

b. Are they sending them (*m.*) to us?

_____

c. They are not sending them (*m.*) to us.

_____

2. *a.* I am lending it (*f.*) to you (*familiar sing.*).

   _____

   b. I am lending her them (*m.*).

   _____

   c. I am lending it (*m.*) to them.

   _____

3. *a.* Are you (*tú*) bringing them (*m.*) to me?

   _____

   b. Are you bringing them to her?

   _____

   c. Are you bringing it (*f.*) to us?

   _____

4. *a.* We don't tell it (*m.*) to you (*formal sing.*).

   _____

   b. We don't give it (*m.*) to you (*formal pl.*).

   _____

   c. We are not selling it (*f.*) to you (*formal sing.*).

   _____

5. *a.* Is he reading it (*m.*) to her?

   _____

   b. He is reading it to her. _____

   c. He is not reading it to her. _____

6. *a.* He's writing it (*f.*) to me.

   _____

   b. He's writing it to us. _____

   c. He's writing it (*m.*) to her. _____

7. *a.* Are they giving them (*m.*) to you (*formal pl.*)?

   _____

   b. Are they giving them (*f.*) to him?

   _____

   c. Are they giving them (*f.*) to us?

   _____

8. *a.* The teacher explains it (*m.*) to me.

_____

   b. Does the teacher explain it to me?

_____

   c. The teacher does not explain it to me.

_____

9. *a.* The waiter serves it (*f.*) to us.

_____

   b. The waiter serves it (*m.*) to her.

_____

   c. The waiter serves it (*f.*) to you (*familiar pl.*).

_____

10. *a.* I'm taking them (*m.*) to them. (Use the verb *llevar.*)

_____

   b. I'm taking them to her.

_____

   c. I'm taking them (*f.*) to you (*familiar sing.*).

_____

F. *Listening Comprehension.* Your teacher will read aloud ten questions in Spanish. After each question is read, circle the letter of the most appropriate answer.

1. *a.* Sí, te los doy.
   b. Sí, me los das.
   c. Sí, os los doy.

2. *a.* Sí, se lo traigo a Ud.
   b. No, no te lo traemos.
   c. No, no se lo traemos a Uds.

3. *a.* Sí, tú nos la escribes.
   b. Sí, tú te la escribes.
   c. Sí, tú me la escribes.

4. *a.* Sí, se los mandan.
   b. Sí, nos los mandan.
   c. No, no me los mandan.

5. *a.* Sí, me lo muestra.
   b. No, no me la muestra.
   c. No, no te la muestra.

6. *a.* Sí, nos la da.
   b. Sí, se la da a él.
   c. Sí, te la da.

7. *a.* Sí, nos la enseña.
   b. Sí, nos las enseña.
   c. Sí, nos lo enseña.

8. *a.* No, no te la dice.
   b. No, no me la dice.
   c. No, no me lo dice.

9. *a.* Sí, me lo lee.
   b. Sí, te lo lee.
   c. Sí, se lo lee.

10. *a.* Sí, te los presto.
   b. Sí, te lo presto.
   c. No, no se lo presto a ella.

27
Reflexive Pronouns

me, myself   **nos,** ourselves

te, yourself   **os,** yourselves

se, (*sing.*) yourself, himself, herself, itself;
    (*pl.*) yourselves, themselves

1. A reflexive pronoun refers to the same person as the subject of the verb:

yo me lavo   *I* wash *myself*

2. Like all other object pronouns, the reflexive pronoun directly precedes the conjugated verb form.

Reflexive Verbs

---

vestirse (i), to dress oneself
I dress myself, get dressed, etc.

yo	*me*	visto
tú	*te*	vistes
Ud. él ella	*se*	viste
nosotros nosotras	*nos*	vestimos
vosotros vosotras	*os*	vestís
Uds. ellos ellas	*se*	visten

enojarse, to get angry, annoyed
I get angry (annoyed), etc.

yo	*me*	enojo
tú	*te*	enojas
Ud. él ella	*se*	enoja
nosotros nosotras	*nos*	enojamos
vosotros vosotras	*os*	enojáis
Uds. ellos ellas	*se*	enojan

3. A reflexive verb is a verb that is used most often with a reflexive pronoun (see the list below), but almost any verb that can take a direct object may have a reflexive pronoun as its object:

Ellos **se** preparan para la prueba.   They are preparing (themselves) for the test.

Some Common Reflexive Verbs

acordarse (ue) de, to remember
   Me acuerdo de la película.

I remember the film.

acostarse (ue), to go to bed, lie down
   Se acuestan a las once.

They go to bed at eleven o'clock.

alegrarse (de), to be glad (to, of)
   Nos alegramos de verle.

We are glad to see you.

asustarse, to become frightened
   No **se asuste** Ud.; ese perro no muerde.

Don't be frightened; that dog doesn't bite.

bañarse, to bathe (oneself)
   Yo me baño todas las mañanas.

I bathe every morning.

callarse, to become silent, stop talking
   Él nunca **se calla.**

He never stops talking.

desayunarse, to have breakfast
   Nos desayunamos a las ocho.

We have breakfast at eight o'clock.

despertarse (ie), to wake up
   Se despierta cuando suena el despertador.

She wakes up when the alarm clock rings.

dirigirse (a), to direct oneself (to), go (toward)
   Si Uds. **se dirigen** al gerente, obtendrán los informes que necesitan.

If you go to the manager, you will get the information you need.

dormirse (ue), to fall asleep
   Siempre **me duermo** en su clase.

I always fall asleep in his class.

encontrarse (ue), to be (situated), find oneself
   Ahora **se encuentran** en Madrid.

They are now in Madrid.

enfadarse
enojarse } to get angry
   ¿**Se enfada (Se enoja)** su maestra si no hacen sus tareas?

Does your teacher get angry if you don't do your homework?

equivocarse, to be mistaken
   El meteorologista **se equivoca;** no lloverá hoy.

The weatherman is mistaken; it will not rain today.

irse
marcharse } to go away, leave

Se fueron (Se marcharon) la semana pasada.   They left last week.

levantarse, to rise, get up ("raise oneself")
¿A qué hora **te levantas?**   At what time do you get up?

llamarse, to be called ("call oneself"), named
¿Cómo **se llama** ese hombre?   What's that man's name?

moverse (ue), to move (oneself)
No **te muevas;** voy a sacar tu foto.   Don't move; I'm going to take your picture.

pasearse, to take a walk, stroll, ride
Vamos a **pasearnos** por la avenida.   Let's stroll along the avenue.
Las muchachas **se pasean** en bicicleta por el   The girls are riding their bicycles through the
  parque.   park.

peinarse, to comb one's hair
¿Por qué no **te peinas?**   Why don't you comb your hair?

ponerse, to put on (an article of clothing); to become
Me pongo el sombrero.   I put on my hat.
Se pone enferma.   She is becoming ill (getting sick).

quedarse, to stay, remain
Nos quedamos en casa.   We are staying home.

quejarse (de), to complain (about)
Se quejan de la comida.   They're complaining about the food.

quitarse, to remove, take off (clothing)
Me quito el abrigo.   I take off my coat.

sentarse (ie), to sit down ("seat oneself")
¿Dónde **te sientas** en la clase de español?   Where do you sit in Spanish class?

4. Note that many reflexive verbs (**irse, quedarse,** etc.) do not have a reflexive meaning in English.

Position of the Reflexive Pronoun in Questions and Negative Clauses

¿**Te quitas** tú los guantes?   Are you taking off your gloves?

Ella **no se marcha** esta tarde.   She isn't leaving this afternoon.

5. In questions and negative clauses, reflexive pronouns have the same position as other object pronouns: *pronoun first, conjugated verb second.* (For their position with verb forms other than those of the present tense, see chapter 28.)

Practice A: Write the indicated form of the verb in the present tense.

1. yo   _____   _____   _____
            desayunarse   sentarse   quejarse

2. Ud.   _____   _____   _____
            encontrarse   irse   enfadarse

3. ella _____   _____   _____
            moverse   peinarse   alegrarse

5. nosotros _____   _____   _____
            ponerse   bañarse   acostarse

5. tú   _____   _____   _____
            irse   llamarse   dirigirse

Practice B: Change the sentence to a question.

EXAMPLE: José se lava la cara.   *¿Se lava José la cara?*

1. Ellas se peinan ahora.   _____

2. Tú te equivocas siempre.   _____

3. Su padre se despierta temprano todos
   los días.   _____

Practice C: Make the sentence negative.

EXAMPLE: Juan se queda en casa.   *Juan no se queda en casa.*

1. Mi madre se llama Beatriz.   _____

2. Yo me quejo del maestro.   _____

3. Los chicos se levantan tarde.   _____

Reflexive Verbs Used With Garments and Parts of the Body

Se lavan la cara y **las manos.**   They wash their faces and hands.

Nos ponemos los zapatos y **el sombrero.** We put on our shoes and hats.

6. a. When the object of a reflexive verb is a garment or a part of the body, the definite article (**el, la, los, las**) is used instead of the possessive adjective (**mi, tu, su,** etc.).

b. If the subject of the verb is in the plural, the garment or part of the body remains in the singular—unless it normally "comes in two's":

Ellos se quitan el sombrero.   They remove their hats.
Nos lavamos la cara.   We wash our faces.

                But:

Nos ponemos los guantes.   We put on our gloves.

Practice D: Complete the Spanish sentences.

1. They are taking off their gloves.   Se quitan _____.

2. We are washing our hands.   Nos lavamos _____.

3. She is putting on her blouse.   Ella se pone _____.

4. I am taking off my shoes.   Me quito _____.

5. Are you washing your faces?   ¿Se lavan Uds. _____?

EJERCICIOS

A. Repeat the sentence orally, replacing the verb in italics with the corresponding form of the verb in parentheses. (Write the new verb form in the blank at the right.)

EXAMPLE: Yo *me baño* todos los días. (peinarse)
          Yo me peino todos los días.   _____*me peino*_____

1. Los atletas *se ponen* el uniforme. (quitarse)   _____

2. ¿A qué hora *te marchas* mañana? (irse)   _____

3. *Se levantan* temprano todos los días. (acostarse)   _____

4. *Me despierto* tarde los sábados. (dormirse)   _____

5. Mis padres *se enfadan* cuando vuelvo a casa tarde.
   (enojarse)   _____

6. Hoy no *nos desayunamos* en casa. (quedarse)   _____

7. ¿Por qué *se asusta* Ud.? (callarse)   _____

8. Yo *me dirijo* por esa calle. (pasearse)   _____

9. ¿*Te alegras* de leer las noticias? (acordarse)   _____

10. ¿Dónde *se encuentran* ellas hoy? (sentarse)   _____

B. Answer with a complete sentence in Spanish:

1. ¿En qué parte de la casa se desayunan Uds.?

   _____

2. ¿Cuándo se quita Ud. el abrigo?

   _____

3. ¿Se acuerda el profesor (la profesora) de dar muchos exámenes a la clase?

   _____

4. ¿Cómo se llaman sus mejores amigos?

   _____

5. ¿De qué se quejan los alumnos generalmente?

_____

6. ¿Qué se pone Ud. cuando hace mucho frío?

_____

7. ¿Dónde se lavan Uds. la cara?

_____

8. ¿Cuándo se enoja la profesora (el profesor) de español?

_____

9. ¿Con qué se peina Ud.?

_____

10. ¿Cuántas veces por semana (por mes) se baña Ud.?

_____

C. Write the question that is answered by the given statement.

EXAMPLE: Me lavo con agua y jabón.   _¿Con qué se lava Ud.?_

1. Nos vamos porque estamos cansados. _____

2. Me acuesto a las once. _____

3. Se quejan porque tienen que trabajar mucho. _____

4. Se mueven de aquí porque no están cómodos. _____

5. Me peino después del desayuno. _____

6. Nos quedamos aquí tres horas. _____

7. Se desayuna en la cocina. _____

8. Me llamo Felipe Rodríguez. _____

9. Se ponen el sombrero cuando tienen frío. _____

10. Los niños se asustan del perro grande. _____

D. Translate into Spanish:

1. _a._ At what time does she get up? _____

   _b._ She gets up at 6:30. _____

2. _a._ Are they putting on their hats? _____

   _b._ No, they are putting on their coats. _____

3. _a._ Are you (_tú_) going away tomorrow morning? _____

   _b._ No, I'm going away this evening. _____

4. *a.* Where (*Por dónde*) are they taking a walk? _____

   b. They're taking a walk downtown. _____

5. *a.* Who is getting angry? _____

   b. We are getting angry. _____

6. *a.* When are you (*tú*) going to bed? _____

   b. I'm going to bed at 10:30. _____

7. *a.* Is she washing her hands? _____

   b. No, she's washing her hair. _____

8. *a.* Where are you (*Uds.*) sitting ("seating yourselves")? _____

   b. We're sitting ("seating ourselves") in the living room. _____

9. *a.* What is his name? _____

   b. His name is Peter López. _____

10. *a.* When are they having breakfast? _____

   b. They're having breakfast at 7:15. _____

E. *Listening Comprehension.* Your teacher will read aloud ten questions in Spanish. After each question is read, circle the letter of the most appropriate answer.

1. *a.* No, me baño por la noche.
   b. Sí, nos bañamos por la mañana.
   c. Sí, se bañan todos los días.

2. *a.* Sí, me voy a las siete.
   b. No, no se van.
   c. Sí, nos vamos muy temprano.

3. *a.* Sí, te pones los guantes.
   b. No, no me pongo los guantes.
   c. No, nos ponemos los zapatos.

4. *a.* Sí, se acuerda bien de la película.
   b. Sí, se acuerdan de esa película.
   c. No, no me acuerdo de la película.

5. *a.* Te levantas a las ocho.
   b. Nos levantamos a las cinco y media.
   c. Se levantan a las seis.

6. *a.* Me encuentro en la ciudad.
   b. Se encuentran lejos del cine.
   c. Se encuentra cerca de la iglesia.

7. *a.* Me paseo por la plaza.
   b. Nos paseamos por el parque.
   c. Te paseas por la avenida.

8. *a.* Sí, se duerme rápidamente.
   b. Sí, me duermo en diez minutos.
   c. No, no nos dormimos pronto.

9. *a.* Se queda en la calle.
   b. Nos quedamos en la escuela.
   c. Me quedo en casa.

10. *a.* Me quejo de mi profesor de español.
   b. Se queja de sus padres.
   c. Nos quejamos de nuestros amigos.

28
Position of Object Pronouns

In All Tenses

PRESENT:
    Le escribo una carta.   I'm writing him a letter.

PRETERITE:
    Me la vendieron ayer.   They sold it to me yesterday.

IMPERFECT:
    Yo siempre **me** levantaba a las seis.   I always used to get up at six o'clock.

FUTURE:
    Los pondremos en la mesa.   We shall put them on the table.

CONDITIONAL:
    ¿**Nos lo** darías tú?   Would you give it to us?

PRESENT PERFECT:
    Lo hemos visto.   We have seen him.

PLUPERFECT:
    ¿Cuándo **se lo** habían enviado ellos?   When had they sent it to you?

PROGRESSIVE TENSES (*see chapter 12*):
    Estamos esperándo**la.** ⎫
    La estamos esperando. ⎭   We are waiting for her.

1. Object pronouns precede the conjugated form of a verb in any tense.

2. In the compound tenses (the present perfect and pluperfect), object pronouns precede the conjugated form of **haber.**

Practice A: Insert the object pronouns to form a sentence as shown in the example.

EXAMPLE:

(te lo) han dado tres veces   *Te lo han dado tres veces.*

1. (me) prestarán los libros mañana   _____

2. (se) ellos miraron en el espejo   _____

3. (se los) ¿dieron ellos ayer?   _____

4. (te) veremos más tarde   _____

5. (nos la) tú no habías dicho   _____

As Objects of Infinitives

Ellos quieren sentar**se** allí. }
Ellos **se** quieren sentar allí. }

They want to sit there.

Yo no podía hacer**lo.** }
Yo no **lo** podía hacer. }

I could not (was not able to) do it.

Voy a decír**selo.** }
Se lo voy a decir. }

I'm going to tell it to her.

Ellos desearán prestár**melo.** }
Ellos **me lo** desearán prestar. }

They will wish to lend it to me.

3. If a pronoun is the object of an infinitive, it is either attached to the infinitive (quieren sentar**se**) or placed directly before the conjugated verb form that precedes the infinitive (**se** quieren sentar). When double object pronouns are attached to an infinitive, an accent mark is placed on the last vowel of the infinitive (desean prestár**melo**).

Practice B: Form a sentence in two ways by inserting the object pronouns.

EXAMPLE: (se las) voy a mostrar　　*Voy a mostrárselas.*

Se las voy a mostrar.

1. (les) no quieren hablar　　_____

　　_____

2. (nos) nosotros vamos a levantar　　_____

　　_____

3. (me lo) pueden escribir　　_____

　　_____

4. (las) van a aprender　　_____

　　_____

5. (se lo) ¿deseas mandar?　　_____

　　_____

As Objects of Present Participles in the Progressive Tenses

Ella está haciéndo**lo.** }
Ella **lo** está haciendo. }

She is doing it.

Estamos sentándo**nos.** }
Nos estamos sentando. }

We are sitting down.

¿Estabas entregándo**selo?** }
¿**Se lo** estabas entregando? }

Were you handing it to her?

Yo estoy diciéndo**telo.** }
Yo **te lo** estoy diciendo. }

I'm telling it to you.

4. If a pronoun is the object of a present participle, it is either attached to the participle (están esperándo**la**) or placed directly before the form of **estar** that precedes the participle (**la** están esperando). When object pronouns are attached to the participle, an accent mark is placed on the stressed vowel.

Practice C: Form a sentence in two ways by inserting the object pronouns.

EXAMPLE: (me los) estaban mandando

Estaban mandándomelos.
Me los estaban mandando.

1. (nos) estamos lavando

_____

_____

2. (te) estoy mirando

_____

_____

3. (se la) estaba vendiendo

_____

_____

4. (la) ellos están aprendiendo

_____

_____

5. (se lo) ¿estás dando?

_____

_____

As Objects of Commands

Affirmative	*Negative*
Quéde**se** Ud. aquí.	No **se** quede Ud. aquí.
Remain here.	Don't remain here.
Escríba**me** Ud. una nota.	No **me** escriba Ud. una nota.
Write me a note.	Don't write me a note.
Díganse**lo** Uds. ahora.	No **se lo** digan Uds. ahora.
Tell it to her now.	Don't tell it to her now.
Préste**noslos** Ud., por favor.	No **nos los** preste Ud., por favor.
Lend them to us, please.	Don't lend them to us, please.

5. Pronoun objects of an affirmative command are attached to the verb—in which case, an accent mark is placed on the stressed vowel. As objects of a negative command, the pronouns are placed between the word **no** and the verb.

Practice D: Include the indicated object pronouns in the given commands.

EXAMPLE:

(le) Hable Ud. _____*Háblele Ud.*_____ ; No hable Ud. _____*No le hable Ud.*_____

1. (se) Levante Ud. _____; No levante Ud. _____

2. (me) Canten Uds. _____; No canten Uds. _____

3. (se las) Escriba Ud. _____ ;

   No escriba Ud. _____

4. (me lo) Cuenten Uds. _____ ;

   No cuenten Uds. _____

5. (se) Miren Uds. _____ ; No miren Uds. _____

6. (nos la) Diga Ud. _____ ;

   No diga Ud. _____

7. (se lo) Muestre Ud. _____ ;

   No muestre Ud. _____

In your answers to items 3, 4, 6, and 7, replace the direct object pronoun with a suitable noun phrase that it could "stand for."

EXAMPLE: Préstesela.   No se la preste.
         Préstele la revista.   *No le preste la revista.*

8. _____   _____
9. _____   _____
10. _____   _____
11. _____   _____

Summary

1. Object pronouns *precede* the conjugated verb form.

PRESENT:
ellos **me lo mandan**   they are sending it to me

PRETERITE:
  te la mandaron   sent it to you

IMPERFECT:
  se los mandaban   were sending (used to send) them to you (her, them, etc.)

FUTURE:
  nos lo mandarán   will send it to us

CONDITIONAL:
  os lo mandarían   would send it to you

PRESENT PERFECT
AND PLUPERFECT:
  se lo han ⎫
  se lo habían ⎬ mandado   have sent it to (you, etc.)
                                          had sent it to (you, etc.)

PROGRESSIVE TENSES:
  me lo están ⎫
  te la estaban ⎬ mandando   are sending it to me
  se los estarán ⎭   were sending it to you
                                          will be sending it to you (him, them, etc.)

2. The pronoun objects of an infinitive are either attached to the infinitive or placed before the conjugated verb form that precedes the infinitive.

No quieren mostrár**noslas.**
        or
No **nos las** quieren mostrar.
⎱

They don't want to show them to us.

3. In the progressive tenses, the pronoun objects of the present participle are either attached to the present participle or precede the form of **estar.**

Están escribiéndo**sela.**
        or
Se la están escribiendo.
⎱

They are writing it to you (him, her, them).

4. The pronoun objects of a command are attached to the verb in affirmative commands and precede the verb in negative commands.

Muéstre**melos** Ud.   No **me los** muestre Ud.
Show them to me.   Do not show them to me.

EJERCICIOS

A. Form a sentence by inserting the pronouns in parentheses. (In items **1, 8, 12,** and **13,** form two sentences that differ only in word order.)

EXAMPLES:

(lo)   ella vio   *Ella lo vio.*
(te las) han prestado   *Te las han prestado.*

1. (me)   no quiere hablar   _____

_____

2. (las)   ¿compraste tú ayer?   _____

3. (te)   ¿habían oído ellos?   _____

4. (le)   no lea Ud. el cuento _____

5. (se)   no miraron en el espejo _____

6. (os)   ¿levantáis vosotros? _____

7. (se)   no vaya Ud.   _____

8. (los)   ¿están Uds. comiendo? _____

_____

9. (nos)   ella no vería   _____

10. (lo)   aprendan Uds. ahora   _____

11. (nos la) escriba Ud.   _____

12. (se lo) estábamos diciendo   _____

_____

13. (me los) ¿pueden mandar? _____

_____

14. (te los)   ellos no darán _____

15. (se las)   digan Uds. más tarde _____

16. (nos los) mande Ud., por favor _____

17. (me la)   no den Uds. _____

18. (os lo)   nosotros hemos dicho _____

19. (te lo)   ¿contaron ellos? _____

20. (se los)   ¿quién dijo? _____

B. Change the sentence from affirmative to negative or vice versa.

EXAMPLES:
Déle Ud. el libro.   *No le dé Ud. el libro.*
No me la escriba.   *Escríbamela.*

1. Dígale la verdad a ella. _____

2. No me cuente esa historia. _____

3. Lávense Uds. las manos. _____

4. No lo haga Ud. ahora. _____

5. Póngalos en el sofá. _____

6. No nos los mande Ud. _____

7. Llévenselo Uds. a él. _____

8. No se las preste Ud. a ellos. _____

9. Véndamelo Ud., por favor. _____

10. No se lo lean Uds. a ella. _____

C. Repeat the sentence, substituting object pronouns for the underlined words.

EXAMPLES: ¿Ven Uds. el programa?

¿Lo ven Uds.?

Van a mostrar la foto al maestro.

a. Van a mostrársela.   b. Se la van a mostrar.

1. ¿Han terminado ellos la tarea?

_____

2. Empiecen Uds. el trabajo.

_____

3. Debes estudiar las lecciones.

a. _____   *b.* _____

4. Estamos mirando <u>la televisión</u>.

a. _____   b. _____

5. ¿Cuándo construyeron <u>esos edificios</u>?

_____

6. ¿Vas a mandar <u>el telegrama a tus padres</u>?

a. _____   b. _____

7. Los niños no dijeron <u>la verdad a su padre</u>.

_____

8. No vendan Uds. <u>el coche a esa señora</u>.

_____

9. ¿Puede Ud. darme <u>cinco dólares</u>?

a. _____   b. _____

10. El banco nos prestó <u>el dinero</u>.

_____

D. Write questions that are answered by the given statements, using suitable nouns in place of the pronouns in italics. (*Note:* In some items, the question may contain both an object pronoun and the noun it "stands for"; see page 211, §3, and the second example below.)

EXAMPLES:

Sí, puedo leer*lo*.   *¿Puedes leer el mapa (el libro, etc.)?*

No, no *se las* mostramos.   *¿**Le** mostraron Uds. las fotos a **Susana**?*

1. Sí, *los* vi ayer. _____

2. No, no *le* escribí. _____

3. Sí, ellos deben hacer*lo* ahora. _____

4. No, no estoy bebiéndo*la*. _____

5. Sí, ella *les* habló anoche. _____

6. No, no pudimos explicár*selo*. _____

7. Sí, nos *las* han dado. _____

8. No, no me *la* estaban diciendo. _____

9. Sí, *se los* quiero regalar. _____

10. No, yo no te *lo* traje. _____

E. Repeat the sentence, substituting an object pronoun for the words in italics. (In items **3, 6,** and **7,** repeat the sentence in two ways.)

EXAMPLE:

Yo le vendí *el disco*.   _____*Yo se lo vendí.*_____

1. Mi mamá nos sirvió *la cena.* _____

2. No me cuente Ud. *la misma historia.* _____

3. ¿Pueden Uds. prestarle *el dinero?* _____

   _____

4. ¿Te han dado *el periódico?* _____

5. Llévele Ud. *los papeles.* _____

6. El profesor estaba explicándonos *el concepto.* _____

   _____

7. No le quieren traer *los juguetes.* _____

   _____

8. Los padres la dieron *a sus hijas.* _____

9. Mándenlo *a su abuela.* _____

10. La madre lo leerá *a su hijo.* _____

F. Translate into Spanish. (Express items **3** and **13** in two ways. In **4, 7,** and **15,** use the progressive tenses—*estar* + present participle—and translate in two ways.)

1. *a.* I saw him last night. _____

   b. I sent it (*m.*) to him yesterday. _____

2. *a.* Tell her the truth. _____

   b. Tell it to her. _____

3. *a.* Can they see you (*familiar sing.*)?

   (1) _____

   (2) _____

   b. Can they give it (*f.*) to you (*familiar sing.*)?

   (1) _____

   (2) _____

4. *a.* He is speaking to them in Spanish.

   (1) _____

   (2) _____

b. They were speaking to him.

(1) _____

(2) _____

5. *a.* Don't write to me yet. _____

b. Don't write it (*f.*) to me yet. _____

6. *a.* Will you (*tú*) pay us tomorrow? _____

b. Will you pay us for it (*m.*) next week? (Do not translate *for.*)

_____

7. *a.* I am not bringing you the package.

(1) _____

(2) _____

b. I am not bringing it to you.

(1) _____

(2) _____

8. *a.* Was she lending them to her brother? (Use the imperfect tense.)

_____

b. Was she lending him them? _____

9. *a.* Pass me the salt and pepper. _____

b. Pass them to me. _____

10. *a.* When did they sell you (*formal pl.*) the skates? _____

b. When did they sell them to you? _____

11. *a.* Sit here, please. (Use *Ud.*) _____

b. Don't sit there. _____

12. *a.* Put on your hat. (Use *Uds.*) _____

b. Don't put on your coat. _____

13. *a.* I don't want to take off my shoes.

   (1) _____

   (2) _____

   b. We cannot stay here today.

   (1) _____

   (2) _____

14. *a.* At what time did you (*tú*) wake up? _____

   b. I woke up at a quarter past six. _____

15. *a.* The students were complaining about the exam.

   (1) _____

   (2) _____

   b. They are complaining of the heat.

   (1) _____

   (2) _____

G. *Listening Comprehension.* Your teacher will read aloud ten questions in Spanish. After each question is read, circle the letter of the most appropriate answer.

1. *a.* Sí, lo voy a ver.
   b. Sí, voy a verlos.
   c. No, no la voy a ver.

2. *a.* Se levantaron a las siete y media.
   b. Nos levantamos a las diez.
   c. Me levanté a las ocho y cuarto.

3. *a.* Sí, estoy mirándola.
   b. Sí, lo estoy mirando.
   c. Sí, estoy mirándolas.

4. *a.* No, no la queremos comprar.
   b. No, no queremos comprarlo.
   c. Sí, queremos comprarla.

5. *a.* Sí, las vi ayer.
   b. No, no lo vi.
   c. No, no la vi.

6. *a.* Sí, se los di.
   b. Sí, se lo di.
   c. No, no se la di.

7. *a.* Sí, estamos diciéndoselos.
   b. No, no se la estamos diciendo.
   c. No, no se las estamos diciendo.

8. *a.* Sí, puedo prestárselo.
   b. No, no se los puedo prestar.
   c. No, no puedo prestársela.

9. *a.* No, no puedo mostrárselo.
   b. No, no se la puedo mostrar.
   c. No, no puedo mostrártelos.

10. *a.* Sí, te lo venderé.
    b. Sí, te la venderé.
    c. Sí, se lo venderé a Ud.

29
GUSTAR and Other Verbs Used With Indirect Object Pronouns

GUSTAR	

Me **gusta el disco.**	I like the record.
Me **gustan los discos.**	I like the records.
Me **gusta cantar.**	I like to sing.
Le **gusta la casa.**	$\left\{ \begin{array}{l}\text{You (\textit{sing.}) like} \\ \text{He (She) likes}\end{array} \right\}$ the house.
¿Le **gustan las casas**?	$\left\{ \begin{array}{l}\text{Do you like} \\ \text{Does he (she) like}\end{array} \right\}$ the houses?
Nos **gusta el fútbol.**	We like soccer.
Nos **gustan los deportes.**	We like sports.
Nos **gusta jugar** al tenis.	We like to play tennis.
No les **gusta el programa.**	$\left\{ \begin{array}{l}\text{You (\textit{pl.})} \\ \text{They}\end{array} \right\}$ do not like the program.
¿No les **gustan los programas**?	Don't $\left\{ \begin{array}{l}\text{you (\textit{pl.})} \\ \text{they}\end{array} \right\}$ like the programs?

1. *To like* is expressed in Spanish by using the verb **gustar,** *to please.* Thus, *I like the house* becomes, "The house is pleasing to me": **La casa me gusta.** Note that the subject often *follows* the verb: **Me gusta la casa.**

2. In constructions with the verb **gustar,** the object of the verb "to like" becomes the subject of **gustar.** The subject of "to like" becomes the indirect object of **gustar:**

	SUBJECT	VERB	OBJECT
English	I	like	the record.
	INDIRECT OBJECT	VERB (agrees with subject)	SUBJECT
Spanish	**me**	**gusta**	**el disco.**

	SUBJECT	VERB	OBJECT
English	I	like	the records.
	INDIRECT OBJECT	VERB (agrees with subject)	SUBJECT
Spanish	**me**	**gustan**	**los discos.**

3. **Gustar** is used in the third person singular (**gusta**) if what is liked is in the singular or expressed by an infinitive. It is used in the third person plural (**gustan**) if what is liked is in the plural.

4. **Gusta** and **gustan** are regularly preceded by an indirect object pronoun, that is, by **me, te, le, nos, os,** or **les.**

5. When **gustar** is used, a statement can be changed to a question without changing the word order:

Le gusta comer.   He likes to eat.
¿Le gusta comer?   Does he like to eat?

Practice A: Change the verb from singular to plural or vice versa.

1. Nos gusta el juguete.   _____ los juguetes.
2. No les gustan los gatos.   _____ el gato.
3. ¿Te gusta la comida?   _____ las comidas?
4. No me gustan las frutas.   _____ la fruta.
5. ¿Le gusta estudiar?   _____ las lecciones?

Using *GUSTAR* When the Subject of "to Like" Is a Noun

A Roberto le gusta la película.   Robert likes the film.

¿A los chicos les gusta correr?   Do the boys like to run?

A la niña no le gustan los dulces.   The child (*f.*) does not like the candy.

6. a. When the subject of *to like* is a noun—for example, the name of a person—the equivalent Spanish expression has the form **a** + *person* + **le** or **les** + **gusta(n)** + *the thing liked:*

A Juan le gustan <u>los zapatos nuevos.</u>
                        the thing liked

b. The phrase **a** + *person* may also *follow* the verb:

Le gustan **a Juan** los zapatos nuevos.

c. The thing liked may be expressed by an infinitive:

A Juan le gusta **trabajar.**

Practice B: In each pair of expressions, the first refers to persons, the second, to what they like. Express this idea in a sentence.

EXAMPLE: Juana, la casa   *A Juana le gusta la casa.*

1. mis amigos, jugar _____

2. la chica, los discos _____

3. Roberto, el equipo _____

4. los profesores, la clase _____

5. el padre, mirar la televisión _____

In items 6–8, the second expression refers to what is *not* liked.

EXAMPLE: Juana, la casa   *A Juana no le gusta la casa.*

6. los alumnos, el examen _____

7. mis amigos, trabajar _____

8. Elena, las novelas _____

In items 9 and 10, form questions.

EXAMPLE: Juana, la casa   *¿A Juana le gusta la casa?*
                    or
          ¿Le gusta a Juana la casa?

9. el muchacho, estudiar _____

10. tus amigas, el tenis _____

Clarifying the Meanings of *LE* and *LES*

Le gusta el perro.	You like the dog.	**A Ud.** le gusta el perro.
	He likes the dog.	**A él** le gusta el perro.
	She likes the dog.	**A ella** le gusta el perro.
¿No **les** gusta?	Don't you (*pl.*) like it?	¿**A Uds.** no les gusta?
	Don't they (*m.*) like it?	¿**A ellos** no les gusta?
	Don't they (*f.*) like it?	¿**A ellas** no les gusta?

7. Since **le** and **les** have several possible meanings, the intended meaning can be clarified by adding one of the following phrases:

for **le:**	for **les:**
a Ud., a él, a ella	**a Uds., a ellos, a ellas**

Practice C: Add the correct phrase to clarify the meaning of the Spanish pronoun.

1. They (*f.*) do not like the work.

   _____ no les gusta el trabajo.

2. Do you (*sing.*) like to eat?

   ¿_____ le gusta comer?

3. She likes the flowers.

   _____ le gustan las flores.

4. Don't you (*pl.*) like the gift?

   ¿_____ no les gusta el regalo?

5. He does not like the tapes.

   _____ no le gustan las cintas.

The clarifying phrase may either precede or follow the verb. Continue as before:

6. She likes the books.

   Le gustan _____ los libros.

7. Doesn't he like to swim?

   ¿No le gusta _____ nadar?

8. They (*m.*) like the new house.

   Les gusta _____ la casa nueva.

Using *GUSTAR* When "To Like" Has the Object "It" or "Them"

—¿Te gusta mi traje?　　　　　　"Do you like my suit?"
—Sí, me gusta.　　　　　　　　 "Yes, I like it."

—¿A él le gustan las corbatas?　 "Does he like the ties?"
—No, no le gustan.　　　　　　　"No, he does not like them."

8. In Spanish, *I like it* becomes "it pleases me," *she likes them* becomes "they please her," etc. Thus, the object pronouns *it* and *them* would be expressed by *subject* pronouns in Spanish. Since the subject of **gustar** is not expressed if it is a pronoun, no equivalent of *it* or *them* appears in the Spanish translation:

we like it = <u>nos　gusta</u>
us　it pleases

Practice D: Express in Spanish.

1. We do not like it.   _____

2. I do not like them.   _____

3. Do they like it?   _____

4. She does not like them.   _____

5. Don't you (*familiar sing.*) like them?   _____

GUSTAR in All Tenses

Singular	*Plural*
PRESENT:	
Me **gusta** el programa.	Me **gustan** los programas.
I like the program.	I like the programs.
PRETERITE:	
¿No te **gustó** el espectáculo?	¿No te **gustaron** los espectáculos?
Didn't you like the show?	Didn't you like the shows?
IMPERFECT:	
Siempre le **gustaba** el español.	Siempre le **gustaban** sus clases.
He always liked Spanish.	He always liked his classes.
FUTURE:	
Le **gustará** el vestido.	No le **gustarán** los zapatos.
She will like the dress.	She will not like the shoes.
CONDITIONAL:	
Les **gustaría** salir.	Les **gustarían** estos regalos.
They would like to leave.	They would like these gifts.
PRESENT PERFECT:	
Nos **ha gustado** la pieza.	No nos **han gustado** los libros.
We have liked the play.	We have not liked the books.
PLUPERFECT:	
Le **había gustado** la cinta.	Le **habían gustado** las cintas.
He had liked the tape.	He had liked the tapes.

9. In all tenses, **gustar** is used only in the third person singular and plural.*

Practice E: Complete the Spanish sentences.

1. They used to like tennis.   _____ el tenis.

2. Has he liked the gifts?   ¿_____ los regalos?

---

*There are exceptions to this rule, but they are beyond the scope of this book.

3. She will not like the program. _____ el programa.

4. Did you (*familiar sing.*) like the ice cream? ¿_____ el helado?

5. We would like to play. _____ jugar.

6. They had not liked the new house. _____ la casa nueva.

Other Verbs Used Like *GUSTAR*

faltar, to be lacking (to) [*to need*]
    Nos falta dinero.   We need money. ("Money is lacking to us.")

importar, to be important (to) [*to care, to matter*]

No **me importan** los precios.   { I don't care about the prices.
                               { The prices don't matter (are not important) to me.

¿Qué **te importa**?   { What do you care?
                               { What does it matter to you?

interesar, to interest (someone) [*to be interested in*]
    ¿**Les interesaba** a Uds. la música?   Were you interested in the music?
                                    ("Did the music interest you?")

parecer, to seem [*to think, be of the opinion*]
    Me parece que no vienen.   I think (It seems to me) that they are not coming.

    —¿Qué **les pareció** la pieza?   "What did you think of the play?"
    —**Nos pareció** muy interesante.   "We thought it was very interesting."

quedar, to be left (to someone), to have left
    Nos quedaron diez dólares.   We had ten dollars left.

tocar, to be someone's turn
    A Juanito **le tocará** jugar más tarde.   It will be Johnny's turn to play later.

10. The verbs **faltar, importar, interesar, parecer, quedar,** and **tocar** are used like **gustar;** that is, the forms of the third person singular and plural are always preceded by an indirect object pronoun (**me, te, le, nos, os,** or **les**):

A las chicas **les quedó** sólo un billete.   The girls had only one ticket left.

Practice F: Complete the sentence by changing the verb from the singular to the plural or vice versa.

1. Nos faltaban amigos.

    Nos _____ un amigo.

2. No me interesa la pieza.

    No me _____ las piezas.

3. ¿Qué te parecían los discos?

¿Qué te _____ el disco?

4. ¿No les importa el dinero?

¿No les _____ los conciertos?

5. ¿Cuántos dólares le quedaban al maestro?

¿Cuánto tiempo le _____?

EJERCICIOS

A. Repeat the sentence, changing its tense to the tense indicated by letter in accordance with the following code:

a = the present	*e* = the conditional
b = the preterite	*f* = the present perfect
c = the imperfect	*g* = the pluperfect
d = the future	

EXAMPLE: Me gusta la novela.
      b. Me gustó la novela.
      e. Me gustaría la novela.
      g. Me había gustado la novela.

1. No nos importan esos problemas.

  b. _____   *e.* _____

  c. _____   *f.* _____

2. ¿Te quedó bastante dinero?

  a. _____   *f.* _____

  d. _____   *g.* _____

3. Le había tocado a María pagar la cuenta.

  a. _____   *d.* _____

  b. _____   *e.* _____

4. ¿Le gustaron las películas?

  c. _____   *f.* _____

  d. _____   *g.* _____

5. ¿Qué os han parecido las nuevas modas?

  a. _____   *c.* _____

  b. _____   *e.* _____

B. Answer with a complete sentence in Spanish:

1. ¿Le gustan a Ud. las películas extranjeras?

_____

2. ¿Te gusta pasar los domingos leyendo o jugando?

_____

3. ¿Cuándo les gusta a Uds. ir a la playa?

_____

4. ¿Te parece interesante este libro?

_____

5. ¿Le importa a su abuela mirar la televisión?

_____

6. ¿Qué le gusta a su padre hacer por la noche?

_____

7. ¿Cuántas veces por semana les gusta a sus amigos ir al cine?

_____

8. ¿Cuánto dinero te queda al fin de la semana?

_____

9. ¿A quién le tocó lavar los platos anoche en su casa?

_____

10. ¿Te ha interesado este ejercicio?

_____

C. Write the question that is answered by the given statement.

EXAMPLE: No, me gusta leer revistas.
       ¿Le gusta leer libros?

1. No, no nos gustaría viajar este verano.

_____

2. Sí, me interesan estos discos.

_____

3. Les gustaba escuchar la radio.

_____

4. No, no le gustan a María.

_____

5. Te tocará mañana.

_____

D. Repeat the sentence orally, replacing the verb with the corresponding form of the verb in parentheses. (Write the new verb form in the blank at the right.)

EXAMPLE: Me quedan tres dólares. (faltar)   *faltan*
    Me faltan tres dólares.

1. No nos gusta hacerlo. (importar)   _____

2. ¿Te tocó escribir en la pizarra? (gustar) _____

3. No me importaban esas cosas. (interesar) _____

4. ¿Les gustaría salir temprano? (importar) _____

5. No me interesarían sus chistes. (gustar) _____

E. Arrange the words to form a sentence.

1. ¿ / ellos / les / a / gustaba / cartas / escribir / no / ?

_____

2. parque / los / me / andar / domingos / el / por / gusta

_____

3. ¿ / cuaderno / quedan / el / cuántos / te / papeles / en / ?

_____

4. novelas / de / no / interesan / Hemingway / esas / nos

_____

5. ¿ / noche / te / ir / una / conmigo / esta / discoteca / a / gustaría / ?

_____

F. Translate into Spanish:

1. *a.* I do not like these programs. _____

 b. I do not like this program. _____

2. *a.* Do they like to play baseball? _____

 b. Does she like to play tennis? _____

3. *a.* We like those paintings. _____

 b. My father likes those paintings too. _____

4. *a.* He needs ("lacks") twenty dollars. _____

 b. I need fifteen pesetas. _____

5. *a.* It doesn't matter to us. (We don't care.) _____

 b. It did not matter to Mary. (Mary didn't care.) _____

6. *a.* Who likes to see foreign films? (¿*A quién le. . .?*) _____

_____

b. Who is interested in Spanish films? _____

7. *a.* Does he like them a lot? _____

b. No, he doesn't like them. _____

8. *a.* Would she like to go to the movies with me? _____

_____

b. Would they like to go downtown with us? _____

_____

9. *a.* It's your turn to play now. (Use the familiar sing.) _____

_____

b. It's not my turn to drive tonight. _____

10. *a.* What do you (*pl.*) think of the show? (Use *parecer.*) _____

_____

b. We think it's very bad. _____

G. *Listening Comprehension.* Your teacher will read aloud ten questions in Spanish. After each question is read, circle the letter of the most appropriate answer.

1. *a.* Sí, me gustan mucho.
   b. No, no te gustan.
   c. No, no me gusta.

2. *a.* No, no le gustaba.
   b. Sí, le gustan.
   c. No, le gusta jugar al béisbol.

3. *a.* No, prefiero ir a un restaurante.
   b. Sí, nos gustaría mucho.
   c. Sí, le gustaría.

4. *a.* Sí, me interesa mucho.
   b. No, prefieren la televisión.
   c. No, no les interesaba.

5. *a.* Me parecen malas.
   b. Nos parece muy buena.
   c. No me parece interesante.

6. *a.* Nos gustaría quedarnos en casa.
   b. Me gustaría ir a la Florida.
   c. Me ha gustado viajar por España.

7. *a.* Le quedan veinte dólares.
   b. Te quedan diez centavos.
   c. Les queda un peso.

8. *a.* Me tocó anoche.
   b. Nos tocará más tarde.
   c. Me tocará mañana.

9. *a.* No, no le gustan.
   b. No, le gusta salir a la calle.
   c. No, les gusta jugar en la calle.

10. *a.* Les interesan las discotecas.
   b. Le interesa la música *rock*.
   c. Me interesan los deportes.

30
Prepositional Pronouns

Prepositions

COMMON ONE-WORD PREPOSITIONS

a, to, at
con, with
de, of, from, about
para, for

por, through, by, for
sin, without
sobre, on, about

COMMON TWO-WORD PREPOSITIONS

acerca de, about, concerning
antes de, before
cerca de, near
delante de, in front of

después de, after
detrás de, behind, in back of
lejos de, far from

Pronouns That Follow Prepositions

El regalo es **para mí.**	The gift is for me.
Hablaban **de ti.**	They were talking about you.
Vamos **con Ud. (Uds.)**	We are going with you.
Estoy **cerca de él.**	I am near him.
Salen **sin ella.**	They are leaving without her.
El edificio está **delante de nosotros(-as).**	The building is in front of us.
El sótano está **debajo de vosotros(-as).**	The cellar is under you.
Estoy **lejos de ellos(-as).**	I am far from them.

1. Prepositional pronouns are the same as the subject pronouns except for **yo,** which becomes **mí,** and **tú,** which becomes **ti.**

2. Note these special forms:

      conmigo, with me   **contigo,** with you (*familiar sing.*)

Practice A: Write in Spanish.

1. for us   _____

2. near you (*familiar sing.*)   _____

3. in front of me   _____

4. without them (*m.*)   _____

5. after her   _____

6. with me   _____

Spanish Equivalents of "It" and "Them" as Objects of Prepositions

Vienen **del parque.**
They're coming from the park.

Voy **a la escuela.**
I'm going to school.

Sabe mucho **acerca de los nuevos programas.**
She knows a great deal about the new programs.

No tengo sellos **para las cartas.**
I don't have (any) stamps for the letters.

Vienen **de él.**
They're coming from it.

Voy **a ella.**
I'm going to it.

Sabe mucho **acerca de ellos.**
She knows a great deal about them.

No tengo sellos **para ellas.**
I don't have (any) stamps for them.

3. As object of a preposition, *it* is expressed as either **él** or **ella,** depending on the gender of the noun it replaces. Similarly, the plural form *them* becomes either **ellos** or **ellas,** depending on whether the replaced noun is masculine or feminine.

Practice B: Replace the underlined phrase with an equivalent phrase containing a prepositional pronoun.

    EXAMPLE: La iglesia está cerca de la casa.   *cerca de ella*

1. Nuestra escuela está lejos del parque.   _____

2. Vamos al cine.   _____

3. Hay un túnel debajo de la iglesia.   _____

4. Los pájaros vuelan sobre la ciudad.   _____

5. No puedo ver nada por las ventanas sucias. _____

The Pronoun *Sí*

Juan compró el libro **para sí**.	John bought the book for himself.
Ellas hablan **acerca de sí**.	They're talking about themselves.
Llevan su ropa **consigo**.	They're taking their clothes with them.
	(They're taking along their clothes.)
Juana habla **consigo**.	Jane talks to herself.

4. As object of a preposition, **sí** means *yourself*, *yourselves*, *himself*, *herself*, or *themselves*. Note the special form **consigo** (= **con** + **sí**).

Practice C: Underline the expression that completes the sentence correctly.

1. Joseph goes with him.
   José va (con él, consigo).

2. Frank takes his book with him.
   Pancho trae sus libros (con él, consigo).

3. The books are for her.
   Los libros son (para ella, para sí).

4. The men talk about themselves.
   Los hombres hablan (de ellos, de sí).

5. Are you bringing the candy with you?
   ¿Trae Ud. los dulces (con Ud., consigo)?

6. Are they going with you?
   ¿Van (con Ud., consigo)?

Objects of Verbs and Objects of Prepositions

Les escribo.	I write to them.
Tengo una carta para **ellos**.	I have a letter for them.

5. Do not confuse the kinds of pronouns presented in chapters 24–28 with the type of pronoun discussed in this chapter. The terms "direct object" and "indirect object" refer to objects of *verbs*, whereas prepositional pronouns are the objects of *prepositions*:

DIRECT OBJECT	INDIRECT OBJECT	OBJECT OF PREPOSITION
yo **la** veo	yo **le** doy el libro	yo voy con **ella**
I see *her*	I give *her* the book	I go with *her*

When a clarifying phrase is added (see page 210, §2), note that **a** is followed by prepositional pronouns: "yo le doy el libro a **Ud.** (a **él**, a **ella**)."

Practice D: Underline the phrase or pronoun that completes the sentence correctly.

1. Nosotros (les, a ellos) escribimos.

2. Yo hablo con (la, ella).

3. (Me, Mí) dicen cosas interesantes.

4. La silla está detrás de (te, ti, tú).

5. ¿(Lo, a Ud.) ven ellos?

6. Nunca les hablamos a (los, ellos) porque ellos nunca nos hablan a (nos, nosotros).

EJERCICIOS

A. Repeat the sentence orally, substituting a pronoun for the words following the preposition in the underlined expression. (Write the new expression in the blank at the right.)

EXAMPLE: Hablamos <u>con la hermana de Alberto</u>.
Hablamos con ella.   *con ella*
_____

1. Estos discos son <u>para mi amigo Juan</u>. _____

2. Vivo cerca <u>de mis primas</u>. _____

3. <u>Sin los profesores</u> no sabríamos nada. _____

4. Nuestra escuela está situada <u>delante de la iglesia</u>. _____

5. ¿Qué hay <u>detrás de ese edificio</u>? _____

6. Fuimos al cine <u>con Ana y Elena</u>. _____

7. No quiero ir a una universidad <u>lejos de mis padres</u>. _____

8. Siempre pensamos <u>en nuestras familias</u>. _____

9. Entre <u>después de Juan</u>. _____

10. Hemos traído unos libros <u>para la profesora</u>. _____

B. Answer with a complete sentence in Spanish. (In **3** and **4,** use the familiar singular in your reply.)

1. ¿Es para Ud. el libro?   Sí, _____.

2. ¿Podemos ir al museo contigo?   No, _____.

3. ¿Hablas de mí?   Sí, _____.

4. ¿Vas al baile sin mí?   Sí, _____.

5. ¿Viven ellos lejos de Uds.?   No, _____.

C. Translate into Spanish:

1. Who is traveling with you (*familiar sing.*) next summer?

_____

2. Without him we can't finish our work.

_____

3. What is on the sofa? The coats are on it.

_____

4. Do you (*Ud.*) want to go to the tennis match with me?

_____

5. They are buying the food for themselves.

_____

6. Who is in front of you (*familiar sing.*)?

_____

7. Nobody is in front of me. _____

8. Are you talking about us? _____

9. No, we are talking about them (*f.*).

_____

10. I'm sending the package to him. (Include a clarifying phrase—see page 210, §2.)

_____

D. *Listening Comprehension.* Your teacher will read aloud ten questions in Spanish. After each question is read, circle the letter of the most appropriate answer.

1. *a.* Nadie va contigo.
  b. Carmen va conmigo.
  c. José va con ella.

2. *a.* Hay un árbol detrás de ti.
  b. Hay una mesa detrás de mí.
  c. Hay un edificio detrás de ella.

3. *a.* Nuestros padres hablan acerca de nosotros.
  b. Nosotros hablamos acerca de ti.
  c. Mis amigos hablan acerca de mí.

4. *a.* Alfonso vive cerca de nosotros.
  b. Mi vecino Roberto vive cerca de mí.
  c. La familia López vive cerca de ellos.

5. *a.* No, no es para ti.
  b. Sí, es para Uds.
  c. Sí, es para Ud.

6. *a.* No, no voy a ella.
  b. No, no voy a él.
  c. Sí, voy a ellas.

7. *a.* No, no vengo con ella.
  b. No, no vengo contigo.
  c. Sí, vengo con vosotros.

8. *a.* Traen un pastel consigo.
  b. Traemos los libros con nosotras.
  c. Traigo un cuaderno conmigo.

9. *a.* Felipe entró antes de ti.
  b. Ella entró antes de mí.
  c. Elena entró antes de ella.

10. *a.* Hay muchos pisos en ellos.
  b. Hay muchos apartamentos en él.
  c. Hay oficinas en ella.

31
The Passive *SE* and
the Indefinite *SE*

The Passive *SE*

¿Qué **se vende** en esa tienda?
What is sold in that store?

Se vende pan.   **Se venden** corbatas.
Bread is sold.   Neckties are sold.

¿Qué **se compra** allí?
What is bought there?

Se compra cerveza.   **Se compran** bebidas.
Beer is bought.   Drinks are bought.

¿Qué **se ve** en la televisión?
What is seen on television?

Se ve un programa bueno.   **Se ven** muchos programas.
A good program is seen.   Many programs are seen.

---

1. **Se** + a third-person verb form is often equivalent to a third-person form of *to be* + a past participle: bread *is sold*, the programs *are seen*, the food *was eaten*. In this construction, the pronoun **se** is called the passive **se**. The verb is third person singular if the subject is in the singular, third person plural if the subject is in the plural.*

2. When the passive **se** is used, the sentence may be translated into English in several ways:

$$\text{Se venden zapatos en una zapatería.} \begin{cases} \text{Shoes are sold} \\ \text{One sells shoes} \\ \left.\begin{cases} \text{You} \\ \text{They} \\ \text{People} \end{cases}\right\} \text{sell shoes} \end{cases} \text{in a shoe store.}$$

---

*In other words, the verb is used reflexively: see chapter 27. When **se** is passive, note that the subject usually *follows* the verb:

(reflexive **se**) **Los niños** se lavan.   The children wash themselves.
(passive **se**)   Se lavan **los platos**.   The dishes are being washed.

Practice A: Complete the answers to each question.

EXAMPLE: ¿Qué se compra en esa tienda?

a. ___*Se compra*___ ropa.

b. ___*Se compran*___ cigarrillos.

1. ¿Qué se aprende en nuestra escuela?

a. _____ el español.

b. _____ tres lenguas.

c. _____ matemáticas.

d. _____ biología.

2. ¿Qué se oye en la radio?

a. _____ música.

b. _____ noticias.

c. _____ una novela radiofónica (soap opera).

d. _____ los partidos de fútbol.

3. ¿Qué se come en este restaurante?

a. _____ postres buenos.

b. _____ arroz con pollo.

c. _____ biftec.

d. _____ muchas variedades de pescado.

3. The passive **se** is also used when the subject is an infinitive phrase:

No **se permite** <u>fumar en la escuela</u>.
                          subject

Smoking is not permitted in school.
("To-smoke-in-school is not permitted.")

Se puede <u>viajar allí por autobús</u>.
                    subject

You (One, People) can travel there by bus.

Se debe <u>ayudar a los pobres</u>.
                  subject

The poor should be helped.

Practice B: Complete the Spanish sentence with an expression containing *se.*

1. One should study in order to learn. (Use the verb *deber.*)

_____ para aprender.

2. Where is smoking forbidden?

¿Dónde _____?

3. You can't read without light.

No _____ sin luz.

The Indefinite *SE*

Se dice que es inteligente.   It is said that he is intelligent.

No **se sabe** mucho acerca de ellos.

$$\left.\begin{array}{l}\text{Not much is known} \\ \text{One doesn't know much} \\ \left.\begin{array}{l}\text{We} \\ \text{People}\end{array}\right\} \text{don't know much}\end{array}\right\} \text{about them.}$$

En la sala de recreo **se juega** a las cartas o **se lee.**

$$\left.\begin{array}{l}\text{In the recreation room,} \\ \text{one plays cards or reads.} \\ \left.\begin{array}{l}\text{you} \\ \text{we} \\ \text{they} \\ \text{people}\end{array}\right\} \text{play cards or read.}\end{array}\right.$$

No **se duerme** en las clases de ella.

$$\left.\begin{array}{l}\text{One doesn't sleep} \\ \left.\begin{array}{l}\text{You} \\ \text{We} \\ \text{They} \\ \text{People}\end{array}\right\} \text{don't sleep in } her \text{ classes.}\end{array}\right.$$

4. Se is used with the third person singular form of the verb if the verb does not have a definite subject. This construction can be translated in several ways: **se dice** = *it is said, one says, you say, we (they) say, people say.*

Practice C: Complete the Spanish sentences with expressions containing *se.*

1. We pay before entering.

   _____ antes de entrar.

2. How do you say *cine* in English?

   ¿Cómo _____ *cine* en inglés?

3. You say *movies.*

   _____ *movies.*

4. What do people do here on Sundays?

   ¿Qué _____ aquí los domingos?

5. They play tennis or they swim in the pool.

   _____ al tenis o _____ en la piscina.

Using the Passive *SE*

A. IN VARIOUS TENSES

Singular   *Plural*

PRESENT:
Se abre la puerta.   **Se abren** las puertas.
The door is opened.   The doors are opened.

PRETERITE:
Se abrió la puerta.   **Se abrieron** las puertas.
The door was opened.   The doors were opened.

IMPERFECT:
Se abría la puerta.   **Se abrían** las puertas.
The door was being opened.   The doors were being opened.

FUTURE:
Se abrirá la puerta.   **Se abrirán** las puertas.
The door will be opened.   The doors will be opened.

CONDITIONAL:
Se abriría la puerta.   **Se abrirían** las puertas.
The door would be opened.   The doors would be opened.

PRESENT PERFECT:
Se ha abierto la puerta.   **Se han abierto** las puertas.
The door has been opened.   The doors have been opened.

PLUPERFECT:
Se había abierto la puerta.   **Se habían abierto** las puertas.
The door had been opened.   The doors had been opened.

B. WITH INFINITIVES AND PRESENT PARTICIPLES

INFINITIVE:
Se puede abrir la puerta.   **Se pueden** abrir las puertas.
The door can be opened.   The doors can be opened.

PRESENT PARTICIPLE:
{ **Se está abriendo** la puerta. }   { **Se están abriendo** las puertas. }
{ **Está abriéndose** la puerta. }   { **Están abriéndose** las puertas. }
The door is being opened.   The doors are being opened.

Practice D: Change the verb form from the singular to the plural or vice versa.

1. Mañana *se verán* buenos programas en la televisión.

   Esta noche _____ un programa especial.

2. Esta tarde *se ha encontrado* dinero en la calle.

   Esta mañana _____ veinte dólares.

3. *Se sabía* la causa del accidente.

   _____ muchas cosas acerca de ellos.

4. En la clase de inglés *se leyeron* seis novelas.

   En la clase de español _____ una novela el semestre pasado.

5. *Se está lavando* la ropa.

   _____ los platos.

6. *Se han vendido* las joyas.

   _____ el coche.

Practice E: Change to the indicated tense.

1. Se prohíbe comer en esta clase.

   (imperfect) _____ comer en la clase.

2. No se permitirá fumar allí.

   (conditional) No _____ jugar allí.

3. Se debe ir a la escuela.

   (present perfect) _____ volver a casa.

4. Se necesitaba aprender la lengua.

   (present) _____ estudiar mucho.

5. Se ha podido tomar el autobús.

   (future) _____ tomar el tren.

Using the Indefinite *SE* in Various Tenses

PRESENT:
   Se dice, it is said, one says, you say, they say, people say

PRETERITE:
   se dijo, it was said, one said, you said, they said, people said

IMPERFECT:
   se decía, it was being said, people were saying, etc.

FUTURE:
   se dirá, it will be said, people will say, etc.

CONDITIONAL:
   se diría, it would be said, people would say, etc.

PRESENT PERFECT:
   se ha dicho, it has been said, people have said, etc.

PLUPERFECT:

se había dicho, it had been said, people had been saying, etc.

WITH INFINITIVES AND PRESENT PARTICIPLES:

se puede decir } it can be said, one can say, etc.
puede decirse

se está diciendo } it is being said, people are saying, etc.
está diciéndose

Practice F: Change to the indicated tense.

1. Se decía que eran tontos.

   (present) _____ que son inteligentes.

2. Se sabe que vienen mañana.

   (present perfect) _____ que van al cine.

3. Se jugaba al béisbol en el verano.

   (future) _____ al tenis si hace buen tiempo.

4. ¿Qué se hacía allí?

   (pluperfect) ¿Qué _____ antes?

5. Se está insistiendo en que el informe es falso.

   (imperfect) _____ en que la historia era verdadera.

EJERCICIOS

A. Repeat the sentence orally, replacing the underlined verb with the corresponding form of the verb in parentheses. (Write the new verb form in the blank at the right.)

EXAMPLE: Se enseñan cuatro lenguas. (aprender)
     Se aprenden cuatro lenguas.   *Se aprenden* _____

1. ¿A qué hora se toma café en su casa? (beber) _____

2. En ese restaurante se sirven buenas comidas. (preparar) _____

3. ¿A qué hora se abrirá el cine? (cerrar) _____

4. ¿Dónde se compraron esos zapatos baratos? (vender) _____

5. ¿En qué estación se esperaba el tren? (tomar) _____

6. Se visitarán muchas ciudades en el viaje. (ver) _____

7. Para ir de un piso a otro se baja la escalera. (subir) _____

8. En nuestra clase se discuten muchas cosas. (decir) _____

9. ¿Qué se sabía acerca de ese autor? (escribir) _____

10. En el concierto se escucharon muchas canciones. (oír) _____

B. Change the verb to the indicated tense.

EXAMPLE: Se ve que son inteligentes.
(imperfect) *Se veía* que eran inteligentes.

1. Se sabe que es un buen profesor.

(future) _____ que es un buen jugador.

2. No se permite comprar cerveza antes del mediodía.

(preterite) No _____ comprar cerveza ayer.

3. Se cree que la guerra es inevitable.

(imperfect) _____ que la guerra era horrible.

4. Se prohíbe cruzar la calle con la luz roja.

(present perfect) _____ cruzar ese puente.

5. No se paga para entrar en la biblioteca.

(conditional) No _____ para entrar en el zoo.

C. Answer with a complete sentence in Spanish:

1. ¿Cuántas lenguas se enseñan en su escuela?

_____

2. ¿Se permite fumar en ciertos cines?

_____

3. ¿A qué hora se abren las puertas de su tienda favorita mañana?

_____

4. ¿Dónde se puede oír buena música *rock*?

_____

5. ¿Por dónde se entra en su escuela?

_____

6. ¿Qué se sabía acerca del Presidente Washington?

_____

7. ¿Qué cosas se observan en una calle de la ciudad?

_____

8. ¿Dónde se puede bailar por la noche?

_____

9. ¿Qué se compra para leer las noticias?

_____

10. ¿Se hicieron viajes a la luna desde su ciudad el año pasado?

_____

D. Write the question that is answered by the given statement.

EXAMPLE: Se ven en el cine.
        ¿Dónde se ven películas?

1. Se permitía comer sólo en la cafetería.

_____

2. Se sirven tres comidas al día.

_____

3. Se compraron carne, pollo, pescado y otros comestibles.

_____

4. Se comen huevos fritos con pan y mantequilla.

_____

5. Se llamó a la camarera.

_____

6. Se corta con un cuchillo.

_____

7. Se podría nadar en la piscina municipal.

_____

8. Se vieron películas buenas.

_____

9. En mi casa se toma a mediodía.

_____

10. Se bailará, se cantará y se tomarán refrescos.

_____

E. Translate into Spanish, using the pronoun _se:_

1. _a._ What is being read in class today? _____

   _b._ What will be read tomorrow? _____

   _c._ What was read yesterday? _____

2. *a.* How many programs are seen on television? _____

_____

   b. How many films were seen on television last night? _____

_____

   c. How many shows would be seen on Sunday? _____

_____

3. *a.* *Good meals are served in that restaurant. _____

_____

   b. *Lunch has already been served in the cafeteria. _____

_____

   c. What was being served for dinner? _____

4. *a.* What is being said? _____

   b. What would be said? _____

   c. What was said last night? _____

5. *a.* Many cars are driven through the streets. _____

_____

   b. Many trucks have been driven. _____

   c. Many buses will be driven. _____

6. *a.* The television is turned off at eleven o'clock. _____

_____

   b. The radio used to be turned off at ten o'clock. _____

_____

   c. The lights will be turned off at midnight. _____

_____

7. *a.* People know a lot about that person. _____

_____

   b. People used to know a lot about those people. _____

_____

   c. What has been known about that girl? _____

_____

_____

*For word order, see the footnote on page 257.

8. *a.* How much money is given to the poor? _____

_____

b. How much will be given for education? _____

_____

c. How much was given for sports? _____

9. *a.* A lot of noise is made in the cafeteria. _____

_____

b. Little noise was made this morning. _____

c. How much noise had been made? _____

10. *a.* The doors are closed at 9:00 P.M.* _____

b. The school will be opened at 7:30 A.M.* _____

_____

c. The theater has already been opened. _____

_____

F. *Listening Comprehension.* Your teacher will read aloud ten questions in Spanish. After each question is read, circle the letter of the most appropriate answer.

1. *a.* Se ven pinturas famosas.
   b. Se veían cuadros interesantes.
   c. Se oye música clásica.

2. *a.* Se compraba pan.
   b. Se compran corbatas, camisas y zapatos.
   c. Se compraban trajes, vestidos y sombreros.

3. *a.* Se venden en una librería.
   b. Se vende en una librería.
   c. Se venden en la biblioteca.

4. *a.* Sí, se sabían los verbos.
   b. No, se sabía muy poco.
   c. Sí, la lección se sabía bien.

5. *a.* Se saldrá por la puerta principal.
   b. Se saldría por la tarde.
   c. Se saldrá a las tres.

6. *a.* Se aprende a hablar, a escribir y a leer.
   b. Se aprende a jugar al tenis.
   c. Se aprende a tomar cerveza y vino.

7. *a.* Cuando se está bien.
   b. Cuando se está enfermo.
   c. Cuando se sabe la lección.

8. *a.* Se estudiaron las lecturas.
   b. Se estudiarán los verbos, el vocabulario y la gramática.
   c. Se estudiará biología.

9. *a.* Se permite en ciertos lugares.
   b. Se permite en la sala de clase.
   c. Se permitía en el teatro.

10. *a.* Se miraba para saber qué hora era.
   b. Se mira para dormir.
   c. Se mira para saber la hora.

*Write the time in Spanish words.

PART SIX

OTHER GRAMMAR TOPICS

32
Using *HACE* and *HACÍA* to Express the Passage of Time

¿Cuánto tiempo hace?

¿Cuánto tiempo hace que **vives** aquí?

How long have you been living here? ("How much time does-it-make that you are living here?")

Hace dos años que **vivo** aquí.

I have been living here for two years. ("It makes two years that I am living here.")

1. The sentences above express an action or situation that began in the past and continues into the present. To construct sentences like these, use the following formulas:

To form a question: **cuánto tiempo hace que** + *present tense*
To form a statement: **hace** + *time* + **que** + *present tense*

Practice A: Complete the Spanish sentences.

1. How long have they been working there?

   ¿Cuánto tiempo hace que _____ allí?

2. We have been studying Spanish for three years.

   Hace tres años que _____ el español.

3. How long have you been waiting for the report?

   ¿_____ que esperas el informe?

4. Rachel has been reading that novel for two weeks.

   _____ que Raquel lee esa novela.

5. The boys have been playing baseball for several years.

   Hace varios años que los muchachos _____ al béisbol.

6. How long has she been ill?

   ¿Cuánto tiempo hace que ella _____ enferma?

7. I haven't had lunch with them for several days.

   _____ que no tomo el almuerzo con ellos.

¿Cuánto tiempo hacía?

¿Cuánto tiempo hacía que **trabajaban** allí cuando tú los viste?

Hacía cinco meses que **trabajaban** allí cuando los vi.

How long had they been working there when you saw them?

They had been working there for five months when I saw them.

2. The sentences above express an action or situation that had begun in the past and was still going on at some point in the past—usually indicated by an occurrence expressed in the preterite (**. . . cuando los vi**). To construct sentences like these, use the following formulas:

To form a question: **cuánto tiempo hacía que** + *imperfect tense*
To form a statement: **hacía** + *time* + **que** + *imperfect tense*

Practice B: Complete the Spanish sentences.

1. How long had they been living in Chicago when he met them?

   ¿_____ que vivían en Chicago cuando los conoció?

2. They had been living there for about four months.

   Hacía unos cuatro meses que _____ allí.

3. How long had Paul been sleeping when we arrived?

   ¿Cuánto tiempo hacía que Pablo _____ cuando llegamos?

4. Mary had been playing the piano for twenty minutes when the doorbell rang.

   _____ que María tocaba el piano cuando sonó el timbre de la puerta.

5. How long had you known these gentlemen when the robbery occurred?

   ¿_____ que Ud. conocía a estos señores cuando ocurrió el robo?

6. I had known them for six years.

   Hacía seis años que yo los _____.

EJERCICIOS

A. Answer the question or write the question that is answered by the given statement.

EXAMPLES: ¿Cuánto tiempo hace que compras discos?
Hace tres años que compro discos.

Hace dos días que estamos aquí.
¿Cuánto tiempo hace que Uds. están aquí?

1. ¿Cuánto tiempo hace que Ud. vive en su casa?

_____

2. Hace una hora que miro la televisión.

_____

3. ¿Cuánto tiempo hace que los Mets están en Nueva York?

_____

4. Hace dos años que asistimos a esta escuela.

_____

5. ¿Cuánto tiempo hace que Ud. estudia el español?

_____

6. Hace cuatro horas que Alberto duerme.

_____

B. Answer the question or write the question that is answered by the given statement.

EXAMPLES: ¿Cuánto tiempo hacía que jugabas en ese parque?
Hacía cuatro meses que yo jugaba en ese parque.

Hacía una semana que estaban allí.
¿Cuánto tiempo hacía que estaban allí?

1. ¿Cuánto tiempo hacía que sus amigos jugaban en la calle cuando su madre los llamó?

_____

_____

2. Hacía mucho tiempo que trabajábamos en esa tienda.

_____

_____

3. ¿Cuánto tiempo hacía que Uds. vivían en su casa cuando la vendieron?

_____

_____

4. Hacía una hora que yo escuchaba la radio cuando entró Teresa.

_____

_____

5. ¿Cuánto tiempo hacía que ellos estaban en la playa cuando empezó a llover?

_____

_____

6. Hacía seis minutos que ella conducía su coche cuando tuvo el accidente.

_____

_____

C. Express in Spanish:

1. How long have you (_tú_) had this car?

_____

2. How long had they had that television set?

_____

3. We had been dancing for fifteen minutes when they came.

_____

_____

4. I have been going to that theater for five years.

_____

5. How long had he been traveling when he met her?

_____

_____

6. How long has she been waiting here?

_____

7. We have been in this hotel for six days.

_____

8. We had been in that store for a half hour.

_____

9. How long have you (_Ud._) been his friend?

_____

10. How long had you (_tú_) been his friend when he died?

_____

_____

SUPPLEMENT: Using *LLEVAR* to Express the Passage of Time

¿Cuánto tiempo **lleva** Ud. aquí?	How long have you been here?
Yo **llevo** dos semanas aquí.	I have been here for two weeks.
¿Cuánto tiempo **llevan** las muchachas **jugando** al tenis?	How long have the girls been playing tennis?
Llevan tres horas **jugando** al tenis.	They have been playing tennis for three hours.

3. The verb **llevar** is often used instead of **estar** before a time interval. If the interval begins in the past and continues into the present, **llevar** is used in the present tense and means *has been* or *have been* (depending on whether its subject is in the singular or the plural): **llevamos dos días aquí,** *we have been here for two days.*

4. The verb **llevar** followed by a present participle is often used to express an action or situation that began in the past and continues into the present. Note the similar meanings:

¿Cuánto tiempo llevan ellos durmiendo?
= **¿Cuánto tiempo hace que ellos duermen?**

Ellos llevan seis horas durmiendo.
= **Hace seis horas que ellos duermen.**

EJERCICIOS

D. Replace the sentence with an equivalent sentence using the verb *llevar.*

EXAMPLES: ¿Cuánto tiempo hace que estás aquí?
¿Cuánto tiempo llevas aquí?

Hace tres horas que esperamos.
Llevamos tres horas esperando.

1. ¿Cuánto tiempo hace que Uds. están en Madrid?

_____

2. Hace tres meses que estamos en la ciudad.

_____

3. ¿Cuánto tiempo hace que Ud. trabaja aquí?

_____

4. Hace dos años que estudio el español.

_____

5. ¿Cuánto tiempo hace que tocas el piano?

_____

6. Hace seis años que hago este tipo de trabajo.

_____

E. Translate into Spanish, using the verb _llevar:_

1. How long have you (_tú_) been waiting?

_____

2. I have been waiting here for an hour.

_____

3. They have been in that hotel for three days.

_____

4. She has been traveling with us for two weeks.

_____

5. How long have you (_Uds._) been watching television?

_____

6. We have been watching television for three hours.

_____

Una estación de metro en la ciudad de México

33
Indefinite Pronouns
and Negatives

algo, something, anything

todo, everything

nada, nothing, (not) anything

alguien, someone, somebody, anyone,
anybody

nadie, no one, nobody, (not) anybody

siempre, always

jamás, ever

nunca
jamás } never, (not) ever

Tengo **algo.**
I have something.

¿Tienes **algo**?
Do you have anything?

Nada tengo. } *I have nothing.*
No tengo **nada.** } *I do not have anything.*

Alguien viene.
Someone is coming.

¿Viene **alguien**?
Is someone coming?

Nadie viene. } *No one is coming.*
No viene **nadie.** }

Veo a **alguien.**
I see somebody.

A **nadie** veo. } *I see no one.*
No veo a **nadie.** } *I do not see anybody.*

Todo está listo.
Everything is ready.

Nada está listo.
Nothing is ready.

Siempre hay exámenes los viernes.
There are always exams on Friday.

Nunca (Jamás) hay exámenes los jueves.
There are never exams on Thursday.

¿Has visto **jamás** tal película?
Have you ever seen such a movie?

{ No, **jamás (nunca)** he visto tal película. }
{ No, **no** he visto **jamás (nunca)** tal película. }
{ *No, I have never seen such a movie.* }

1. The personal **a** precedes **alguien** and **nadie** when they are direct objects: veo **a** alguien; **a** nadie veo (no veo **a** nadie).

2. Negative words may precede or follow the verb. If they follow the verb, it is preceded by **no:**

Nada tengo.	*But:*	**No** tengo **nada.**
A **nadie** veo.		**No** veo a **nadie.**
Nunca estudian.		**No** estudian **nunca.**

3. The words **jamás** and **nunca** are interchangeable in negative sentences, but only **jamás** can be used if the sentence is affirmative:

Es el edificio más alto que **jamás** he visto.   It is the tallest building that I have ever seen.

4. Although the words *anything* and *anybody* are included among the meanings of **algo** and **alguien,** avoid the error of using **algo** or **alguien** in translating negative sentences such as "I did not see anything (anybody)." The word *not* indicates that the negative words **nada** and **nadie** should be used instead.

EJERCICIOS

A. Change the sentence to the negative in two ways.

EXAMPLE:

Alguien tiene la respuesta.

    a. Nadie tiene la respuesta.
    b. No tiene nadie la respuesta.

1. Tú siempre dices mentiras.

    a. _____

    b. _____

2. Conozco a alguien en esa oficina.

    a. _____

    b. _____

3. Tengo algo para ti.

    a. _____

    b. _____

4. ¿Han oído Uds. jamás este disco? (Reply in the negative.)

    a. _____

    b. _____

5. Alguien nos acompaña al baile.

    a. _____

    b. _____

B. Answer negatively in two ways.

EXAMPLE: ¿Han hecho Uds. todo?
a. *No hemos hecho nada.*
b. *Nada hemos hecho.*

1. ¿Ha ido Ud. jamás a España?

   a. _____

   b. _____

2. ¿Ves todo en la televisión por la noche?

   a. _____

   b. _____

3. ¿Le ha dado a Ud. algo en su cumpleaños su profesor(-ra) de español?

   a. _____

   b. _____

4. ¿Siempre visita Ud. al Presidente de los Estados Unidos?

   a. _____

   b. _____

5. ¿Ama Ud. a alguien en su clase de inglés?

   a. _____

   b. _____

6. ¿Va Ud. con alguien al cine esta noche?

   a. _____

   b. _____

7. ¿Ha visitado su padre jamás a la directora (al director) de su escuela?

   a. _____

   b. _____

8. ¿Tiene Ud. algo interesante que decir a sus amigos hoy?

   a. _____

   b. _____

9. ¿Saben Uds. todo acerca de la cultura japonesa (Japanese)?

   a. _____

   b. _____

10. ¿Viene alguien con Ud. a la escuela por la mañana?

a. _____

b. _____

C. Express in Spanish. Translate the negative sentences in two ways.

1. Have you anything good? _____

2. No, I have nothing for you.   *a.* _____

      b. _____

3. Someone is knocking at the door. _____

4. Nobody watches television in our house.   *a.* _____

      b. _____

5. Do you (*Ud.*) ever go to the museum? _____

6. No, we never go.   *a.* _____

      b. _____

7. Does she know anyone there? _____

8. No, she does not know anybody.   *a.* _____

      b. _____

9. Say something to the class. _____

10. She isn't saying anything to the class.   *a.* _____

      b. _____

La Catedral de México en el Zócalo, la plaza principal de la ciudad de México

34
POR and *PARA*

Some Uses of *POR*

A. *for* (see page 279)

B. *by*

> El libro fue escrito **por** un famoso autor.
>
> The book was written by a famous author.

C. *through*

> Siempre andamos **por** el parque.
>
> We always walk through the park.

D. *along*

> Muchos coches iban **por** la carretera.
>
> Many cars were going along the highway.

E. *because of*

> Nos quedamos en casa **por** la lluvia.
>
> We stayed home because of the rain.

F. *in* or *at* = *during*

> Visitaban a sus amigos . . .
> . . . **por** la mañana.
> . . . **por** la tarde.
> . . . **por** la noche.
>
> They used to visit their friends . . .
> . . . in the morning.
> . . . in the afternoon.
> . . . in the evening, at night.

Some Uses of *PARA*

A. *for* (see page 279)

B. *by* (= "at the latest")

> Terminaré el trabajo **para** las ocho.
>
> I shall finish the work by eight o'clock.

> Dijeron que llegarían **para** el viernes.
>
> They said that they would arrive by Friday.

C. *to* = *in order to* (+ an infinitive)

Para hacer eso, necesitas mucho dinero.   To do that, you need a lot of money.

Estudiamos **para sacar** buenas notas.   We study to (in order to) get good marks.

Practice A: POR or PARA? Complete the sentence with the correct preposition.

1. _____ llegar temprano, hay que tomar el tren.

2. Muchos autobuses pasaban _____ la avenida.

3. La lección fue explicada _____ el profesor.

4. Uds. tienen que terminar la tarea _____ el jueves.

5. Yo siempre llego temprano _____ satisfacer a mis padres.

6. _____ la nieve las escuelas estaban cerradas.

7. ¿Qué vas a hacer el sábado _____ la noche?

Using *POR* and *PARA* to Express the Different Meanings of "For"

POR

A. *in exchange for*

Mi madre pagó diez mil dólares **por** el coche.   My mother paid ten thousand dollars for the car.

B. *for the sake of*

Mi padre hace todo **por** la familia.   My father does everything for the family.

C. *for the period of* (+ time interval)

Se quedaron allí **por** tres días.   They stayed there for three days.

D. *in search of, to get*

El dueño vino **por** el alquiler.   The landlord came for (= came to get) the rent.

Vamos **por** una hamburguesa.   Let's go for ("get") a hamburger.

La profesora mandó **por** el director.   The teacher sent for the principal.

PARA

A. *meant or intended for*

Este libro es **para** ti.   This book is for you.

Eso es bueno **para** su salud.   That is good for your health.

B. *bound for* (+ destination)

Mañana partimos **para** Puerto Rico.   Tomorrow we leave for Puerto Rico.

Practice B: POR or PARA? Complete the sentence with the correct preposition.

1. El verano próximo saldrán _____ España.

2. Anoche estudié _____ tres horas.

3. Estos discos son _____ Ud.

4. Las aspirinas son buenas _____ la fiebre y los dolores de cabeza.

5. Hay que pagar cien dólares _____ el abrigo.

6. Los buenos padres siempre hacen todo lo posible _____ sus hijos.

7. Este autobús sale _____ la ciudad en cinco minutos.

8. Iremos al restaurante _____ un sandwich y una bebida.

9. ¿Cuánto pagaron Uds. _____ ese televisor en colores?

10. Tengo algo bueno _____ mi tío.

EJERCICIOS

A. POR or PARA? Complete the sentence with the correct preposition.

1. _____ comer bien iremos a ese restaurante.

2. ¿_____ cuántos días estuvieron ellos en Buenos Aires?

3. Tienen que terminar el proyecto _____ el quince de enero.

4. Voy al banco _____ mi dinero.

5. ¿Quiere Ud. aceptar este cheque _____ cincuenta dólares?

6. _____ la temperatura baja tenemos que llevar abrigo y sombrero.

7. ¿A qué hora sales _____ la escuela esta mañana?

8. La música *rock* es mala _____ los oídos.

9. Mandamos la carta _____ avión.

10. ¿Qué hacen Uds. _____ ganar tanto dinero?

B. Answer with a complete sentence in Spanish:

1. ¿Por dónde le gusta a Ud. andar por la noche?

_____

2. ¿Por cuántos minutos dura su clase de español?

_____

3. ¿Para quién es el libro de español?

_____

4. ¿Para qué usamos el ascensor?

_____

5. ¿Adónde va Ud. por libros?

_____

6. ¿Cuánto dinero se paga generalmente por una buena bicicleta?

_____

7. ¿Vive Ud. para comer o come Ud. para vivir?

_____

8. ¿Qué modo de transporte tomamos para ir de Los Ángeles a Nueva York en cinco horas?

_____

9. ¿Qué hace Ud. por sus padres?

_____

10. ¿Conduce su padre el coche por la acera?

_____

C. Write the question that is answered by the given statement.

EXAMPLE: Voy a viajar por avión.
¿Cómo va Ud. a viajar?

1. Lo hago para sacar buenas notas.

_____

2. Mandé por el doctor cuando mi hermano se enfermó.

_____

3. Son para mí.

_____

4. Lo uso para cortar el pan.

_____

5. Andamos por esa calle.

_____

D. Express in Spanish:

1. These packages are for them.

_____

2. Last night I studied for four hours.

_____

3. Let's go there for a good meal.

_____

4. You need (One needs) a ticket to enter.

_____

5. When are you (_tú_) leaving for the country?

_____

6. Don't walk through the garden.

_____

7. How much did you (_Ud._) pay for the record player?

_____

8. We stayed home because of the bad weather.

_____

9. These eyeglasses are not good for the eyes.

_____

10. Finish   the   job   by   three   o'clock.

_____

La Calle Florida en Buenos Aires, la Argentina

PART SEVEN

REVIEWING
VOCABULARY
AND IDIOMS
IN CONTEXT

**PASSAGES AND DIALOGUES
ON SCHOOL LIFE, POPULAR PASTIMES, ETC.;
PRACTICE IN COMPOSITION**

35
Llegando a la escuela

Before reading the passages and dialogues of this chapter, study the following vocabulary and idioms.

VOCABULARY

adentro, inside

afuera, outside

ausente, absent

casi, almost

charlar, to chat

el **destino,** destination

la **esquina,** (street) corner

llevar, to take

la **sala (de clase),** classroom

IDIOMS

a eso de, about (with time of day)

al lado de, next to

a propósito, by the way

a tiempo, on time

en medio de, in the middle of

en punto, sharp, on the dot (with time of day)

frente a, opposite

por eso, therefore, for that reason

por completo, completely

asistir a, to attend

bajar de, to get off or out of (a vehicle)

despedirse de, to say good-bye to

encontrarse, to be situated

encontrarse con, to meet (with)

hay que + *inf.,* one must, it is necessary

pasar un rato, to spend a while

se me olvidó, I forgot

subir a, to get into (a vehicle)

tener prisa, to be in a hurry

tocar el timbre, to ring the bell

tratar de + *inf.,* to try to

A. Me llamo Francisco pero todo el mundo me llama Pancho. Mi escuela se encuentra en medio de la ciudad al lado de una iglesia y frente a un parque. Todas las mañanas trato de llegar a la escuela a tiempo, y por eso me despido de mi familia a eso de las siete y media. Espero el autobús que me lleva a la escuela. El autobús casi siempre llega a mi esquina a las ocho menos veinte. Subo al autobús y me encuentro con mis amigos que asisten a la misma escuela. Me gusta charlar con ellos acerca de nuestras clases y nuestros profesores. A las ocho en punto llego a mi destino y bajo del autobús.

Circle the letter of the correct answer.

1. La escuela está
   a. cerca de un parque
   b. detrás de una iglesia
   c. en el campo

2. Pancho sale de casa
   a. después de mediodía
   b. a las ocho y veinte
   c. antes de las ocho

3. ¿Quiénes están en el autobús?
   a. Pancho y unos compañeros suyos
   b. muy pocas personas
   c. los profesores y los estudiantes

4. ¿De qué hablan los chicos?
   a. del cine
   b. de cosas de la escuela
   c. del autobús

B. This paragraph is a continuation of the passage in **A,** but several words have been left out. Write the missing words, choosing them from among the words that appear below the blanks.

Hay que _____ veinte minutos para _____
          volar/caminar/dormir   llegar/salir/amar

a la escuela. No tengo _____ porque las clases no _____
                        helado/prisa/razón   empiezan/terminan/interesan

hasta las ocho y media. _____ de entrar en la escuela paso un
                         Cerca/Lejos/Antes

_____ afuera charlando. Por fin toca el _____ que
día/rato/desayuno   timbre/piano/chico

anuncia que tengo _____ entrar. Otro día escolar va a
                   de/a/que

_____. ¿Qué me espera _____?
comenzar/leer/mirar   ayer/adentro/semana

C. *Diálogo:* Pepe y Lola están charlando en el autobús.

PEPE: Estoy alegre cuando un profesor está ausente.

LOLA: ¿Por qué, chico?

PEPE: Porque no tenemos que hacer nada.

LOLA: Es verdad. Y podemos hacer mucho ruido y echar aviones de papel de un lado de la sala al otro.

PEPE: A propósito, ¿has escrito tu composición para la clase de inglés?

LOLA: ¡Ay, Dios mío! Se me olvidó por completo.

PEPE: ¿Qué vas a hacer?

LOLA: Aceptaré el cero muy valientemente.

Circle the letter of the correct answer.

1. ¿Cuándo está contento el chico?
   a. cuando se queda en casa
   b. cuando tiene muchas cosas que hacer
   c. cuando un profesor no está presente

2. ¿Qué hacen los alumnos durante la ausencia del profesor?
   a. Hacen cosas ridículas.
   b. Leen y escriben composiciones.
   c. Comen y beben.

3. ¿Qué ha olvidado la chica?
   a. su sándwich
   b. hacer una tarea para una de sus clases
   c. algo en el autobús

4. ¿Qué va a recibir Lola?
   a. un cero
   b. una composición
   c. un avión de papel

D. Complete the following dialogue, using expressions such as:

el **club,** club

debiera (+ *inf.*), ought to

el **director**
la **directora** } principal

el **equipo,** team

estar de acuerdo, to agree

pasar, to spend (time)

el **semestre,** (school) term

severo, -a, strict

PEPE: No puedo aguantar esta escuela. Los profesores son muy severos.
LOLA: (Tell him you agree, and the principal is even stricter.)

1. _____

PEPE: Todos mis profesores asignan muchas horas de trabajo.
LOLA: (Tell him you spend three hours every night doing homework [*haciendo mis tareas*].)

2. _____

PEPE: No hay suficientes actividades después de las clases.
LOLA: (Tell him the school ought to have more clubs and teams.)

3. _____

PEPE: Sólo hay un equipo de básquetbol.
LOLA: (Tell him the school ought to have a baseball and football team too.)

4. _____

E. *Tema*

1. On the lines below, write a composition in Spanish about getting to school every morning. Include the following ideas: (*a*) You are always in a hurry in the morning and try to arrive at school on time. (*b*) You say good-bye to your parents after having breakfast. (*c*) You wait for the bus on the corner opposite your house. (*d*) You chat with your friends on the bus and talk about yesterday's activities. (*e*) After getting off the bus, you spend a short time (a while) outside the school.

Llegando a la escuela

_____

_____

_____

_____

_____

_____

_____

2. Vary the above composition by telling how you got to school yesterday. Start with the Spanish equivalent of a statement such as "Yesterday morning I was in a hurry because I wanted to get to school on time."

_____

_____

_____

_____

_____

_____

_____

Una vista de Machu Picchu, la ciudad perdida de los incas en el Perú

36
Escuela y televisión

Before reading the passages and dialogues of this chapter, study the following vocabulary and idioms.

VOCABULARY

anterior, previous

el año escolar, school year

bastante, quite, rather

el canal, TV channel

el canto, singing

el centro comercial, shopping mall

el cuento de amores, love story

diario, -a, daily

el dibujo animado, movie cartoon

educativo, -a, educational

la **oficina,** office

guardar, to keep

imaginarse, to imagine

la **lengua extranjera,** foreign language

la **nevera** ⎫
el **refrigerador** ⎭ refrigerator

ofrecer, to offer

el **rato,** while, short time

el **refresco,** refreshment

la **representación,** performance

IDIOMS

acompañado(-a) de, accompanied by

aun cuando, even when

a veces, at times

de ningún modo, in no way

de vez en cuando, from time to time

entrar en, to enter, come (go) into

hacer preguntas, to ask questions

interesarse en, to be interested in

llevarse bien (con), to get along well (with)

por lo común ⎫
por lo general ⎭ generally

¡Qué lástima! What a pity!

Que le(s) vaya bien, may things go well for you (*said when saying good-bye*)

todos los días, every day

quedar, to be left, to remain

reunirse con, to get together with

servir de, to serve as

tener lugar, to take place

A. Asisto a una escuela en el centro de la ciudad. A eso de las ocho y veinte entro en la escuela acompañado de mis amigos. Como me quedan diez minutos antes de empezar las clases, paso a la oficina del señor Aguador, el jefe del departamento de lenguas extranjeras. Esta oficina sirve de mi segunda casa durante las horas de escuela. Aquí me reúno con unos amigos y con el señor Aguador. Al señor Aguador le gusta hablar con nosotros y hacernos preguntas sobre nuestras familias, actividades diarias y los progresos que hacemos en la escuela. De vez en cuando nos ofrece refrescos que guarda en su nevera. Él siempre nos dice "Que les vaya bien" cuando salimos para pasar a nuestras clases. Todos los días pasamos el período del almuerzo en su oficina. Por lo general nos divertimos aun cuando hay trabajo que hacer.

Circle the letter of the correct answer.

1. ¿Quiénes llegan a la escuela?
   a. el narrador y sus profesores
   b. sólo el narrador
   c. el narrador y sus amigos

2. ¿Adónde van estos muchachos antes de ir a sus clases?
   a. a una de las oficinas de la escuela
   b. a la cafetería
   c. al gimnasio

3. ¿Qué hace el Sr. Aguador cuando los estudiantes lo visitan?
   a. Les sirve el almuerzo.
   b. Les pregunta sobre las vidas de ellos.
   c. Les da mucho trabajo.

4. ¿Dónde almuerzan el narrador y sus amigos?
   a. en la oficina del Sr. Aguador
   b. en la cafetería
   c. en sus casas

B. Complete the paragraph by writing the missing words. Choose them from the following list:

bien, año, religiones, semana, casi, escuela, asignaturas, estudiantes, profesores, conciertos, lugar, deportes

Estoy en el segundo _____ de mis estudios escolares. Mis

_____ son: el inglés, las matemáticas, la ciencia, la historia y el español (por

supuesto). Nuestra _____ es una *high school* a que asisten tres mil

_____ de diversas nacionalidades y _____. Por lo común

nos llevamos bastante _____. A veces hay disputas, pero se resuelven muy

rápidamente. Varias actividades tienen _____ durante el año escolar. Unos

ejemplos son: representaciones musicales, _____ de orquesta y de banda,

competiciones de canto y de _____. Yo trato de tomar parte en

_____ todas las actividades.

C. *Diálogo:* En la oficina del señor Aguador

PABLO: Buenos días, señor Aguador. ¿Cómo está Ud. esta mañana?

SR. AGUADOR: Bien, gracias, Pablo. ¿Cómo lo pasaste anoche?

PABLO: Lo pasé bien, pero tenía mucho trabajo que hacer.

SR. AGUADOR: ¿Qué tenías que hacer?

PABLO: Tuve que pasar casi toda la noche estudiando para un examen en mi clase de matemáticas.

SR. AGUADOR: ¡Qué lástima! (*Riéndose*) Yo sé cuánto te gusta estudiar.

PABLO: De ningún modo. Prefiero mirar la televisión o ir al centro comercial con mis amigos.

SR. AGUADOR: Pero ¿qué se puede aprender mirando la televisión todo el tiempo?

PABLO: En la televisión hay programas educativos y cuentos interesantes.

SR. AGUADOR: ¡Ya me imagino! ¿Cuáles son?

Circle the letter of the correct answer.

1. ¿Quién le saluda al profesor?
   a. otro profesor
   b. un alumno suyo
   c. un actor de televisión

2. ¿Cómo está el Sr. Aguador?
   a. Se siente cansado.
   b. Está triste.
   c. Está bien.

3. ¿Qué hizo Pablo la noche anterior?
   a. Se preparó para un examen.
   b. Miró la televisión.
   c. Pasó un rato con sus amigos.

D. *Diálogo entre Pablo y el Sr. Aguador* (continued). Complete the following dialogue, using expressions such as:

cambiar de canal, to change (TV) channels

demasiado, too (much)

el **noticiario,** the newscast

servir para, to be good for

valer la pena, to be worthwhile

el **valor educativo,** the educational value

PABLO: A veces veo los dibujos animados.

SR. AGUADOR: (Tell him that they're not worth anything.)

1. _____

PABLO: Al contrario, vale la pena mirarlos porque son muy divertidos. Pero también veo otros tipos de programas. Por ejemplo, me gustan los cuentos de amores.

SR. AGUADOR: (Ask him what they're good for.)

2. _____

PABLO: Son muy románticos. Me gusta esta clase de cuento.

SR. AGUADOR: (Ask him if he watches other types of programs.)

3. _____

PABLO: Claro. Si el cuento me aburre, puedo cambiar de canal y ver el noticiario.

SR. AGUADOR: (Tell him that's a better idea, since newscasts have some educational value.)

4. _____

E. *Tema*

1. Write a short composition about your school on the lines below. Include the following information: (*a*) at what time and with whom you enter the school building; (*b*) where you get together with your friends before classes and during lunch; (*c*) how you get along with your friends and teachers; (*d*) which activities you take part in; (*e*) which classes you like best and why.

_____

_____

_____

_____

_____

_____

_____

2. Give your opinion about television-watching. Note the following expressions:

> to *watch* TV = **mirar** la televisión
> to *watch* a program = **ver** un programa

Include answers to the following questions: (*a*) How much time do you prefer to spend watching TV each day? (*b*) What types of programs do you watch? What types are you interested in? (*c*) Do you think TV should be used during classes to improve instruction (*mejorar la enseñanza*)? (*d*) What value does TV have? (*e*) What programs should children watch or avoid (*evitar*)?

_____

_____

_____

_____

_____

_____

_____

37
Los pasatiempos

Before reading the passages and dialogues of this chapter, study the following vocabulary and idioms.

VOCABULARY

el **anuncio comercial,** advertisement, "commercial" (TV, radio)

el **cuento policíaco,** detective story

cuidar, to take care of

emocionante, exciting

la **ensalada de atún,** tuna-fish salad

el **equipo,** team

el **fin de semana,** weekend

la **guía,** guide

el **juego,*** game

el **partido,*** game (= match)

la **tarea** (el **trabajo**) **escolar,** schoolwork

el **televisor,** TV set

IDIOMS

A ver, . . .
Vamos a ver, . . . } Let's see, . . .

al día siguiente, (on) the next day

encantar, to delight; **me encantan esas canciones,** I love those songs

hacer el papel (de), to play the role (of)

hacía mal tiempo, the weather was bad

llamar por teléfono, to call up

del siguiente modo
de la siguiente manera } in the following way

ya no, no longer, not . . . any more

pasar un buen rato, to have a good time

tener hambre, to be hungry

tener miedo de, to be afraid of

tener razón, to be right

---

*Note the difference in meaning between **juego** and **partido:**

—¿Qué **juegos** te gustan?
—Me gustan el tenis, el béisbol y el ajedrez.

"What games do you like?"
"I like tennis, baseball, and chess."

Nuestro equipo de béisbol jugó tres **partidos** la semana pasada.

Our baseball team played three games last week.

A. Me llamo Isabel pero mis amigas me llaman Belita. Soy una estudiante diligente los días de escuela, pero durante los fines de semana me gusta divertirme. En nuestra ciudad hay mucho que hacer. Los sábados y domingos hago mis tareas por la mañana. Así el resto del día queda para las diversiones. Pasé el sábado pasado del siguiente modo:

Me levanté a las nueve. Hice mis tareas hasta las once. Llamé por teléfono a mi amiga Lola para preguntarle qué quería hacer. Como hacía mal tiempo, decidimos ir al cine para ver una película sobre la vida de una mujer policía (policewoman). Después del cine, fuimos a tomar un refresco. Por la noche tuve que quedarme en casa para cuidar a mi hermano menor. Él tiene diez años, pero tiene miedo de quedarse en casa solo. Mis padres dicen que soy una hermana mayor muy buena.

Circle the letter of the correct answer.

1. ¿Qué le gusta a Belita hacer los sábados y domingos?
   a. pasar buenos ratos con sus amigas
   b. quedarse en casa
   c. ayudar a sus padres

2. Durante el fin de semana, ¿cuándo hace su trabajo escolar?
   a. sólo los sábados
   b. por la mañana
   c. por la noche

3. ¿Quiénes fueron al cine?
   a. Belita y su amiga
   b. Belita y su tía
   c. sólo Lola

4. El hermano de Belita
   a. tiene menos años que su hermana
   b. va al cine con su hermana
   c. prefiere quedarse en casa solo

B. Complete the paragraph by writing the missing words. Choose them from the following list:

miré, escuela, partido, contento, ganas, miró, acostarme, pasado, deportes, invitó, siguiente, béisbol

El domingo _____ mi tío Paco me _____ a ir a un partido de beísbol. Como me gustan los _____, tenía muchas _____ de acompañarlo. Fue un _____ emocionante. Mi equipo favorito ganó el partido. Por la noche _____ la televisión por sólo una hora. Tuve que _____ temprano porque al día _____ tenía que ir a la _____. ¡Qué lástima! Ya no estoy _____.

C. *Diálogo:* Mirando la televisión

GLORIA: Quiero mirar la televisión por sólo una hora. ¿Qué programas hay para ver?

PACA: Vamos a consultar la guía de programas. A ver, casi son las ocho. En el Canal 2 hay una película, pero dura dos horas. En el Canal 4 hay un cuento policíaco de una hora.

GLORIA: Me encantan los cuentos policíacos. Vamos a verlo.

PACA: Está bien. Pero antes, vamos a ver lo que hay en la nevera. Me gusta comer mientras miro la televisión.

GLORIA: Hay rosbif, pollo y ensalada de atún. Vamos a tomar un poco de todo.

PACA: ¡Magnífico! Así será más divertido ver el programa.

GLORIA: Ahora empieza el programa. ¡Atención!

PACA: Como siempre, empieza con un anuncio comercial. Sin estos anuncios los programas serían más divertidos.

GLORIA: Es verdad, pero son necesarios porque pagan los programas. Hay que tolerarlos. No duran mucho tiempo.

PACA: ¡Cállate! Por fin empieza el cuento.

Circle the letter of the correct answer.

1. Se puede saber qué programas hay
   a. consultando la guía
   b. leyendo un cuento
   c. cambiando de canal

2. Las dos muchachas van a comer
   a. antes de mirar la televisión
   b. mientras ven el programa
   c. después de acostarse

3. La comida está
   a. en la mesa
   b. sobre el televisor
   c. en el refrigerador

4. Los anuncios comerciales
   a. ocupan casi todo el programa
   b. son de poca duración
   c. no se necesitan

D. Complete the following dialogue:

PACA: ¿Te gustan los cuentos policíacos?
GLORIA: (Tell her you like them very much.)

1. _____

PACA: ¿Qué piensas de este programa?

GLORIA: (Tell her you think it is very exciting.)

2. _____

PACA: Sí, es muy emocionante, y los actores son muy buenos.

GLORIA: (Say that they play their roles very well.)

3. _____

PACA: Yo creo que sólo la actriz hace bien su papel. El actor es bueno, pero no tan bueno como la actriz.

GLORIA: (Tell her you are hungry.)

4. _____

PACA: Chica, tú siempre tienes hambre cuando miras la televisión.

GLORIA: (Tell her that she is right, but that you like to eat during a program.)

5. _____

E. *Tema*

1. On the lines below, write a composition about a television program or a movie that you saw recently. Include the following information: (*a*) when you saw the film or program; (*b*) whether you liked it or not; (*c*) what type of film or program it was; (*d*) who went (was) with you; (*e*) what you did while you were watching: eat, chat, do homework, etc.

_____

_____

_____

_____

_____

_____

_____

_____

2. Write a composition describing how you spend your time baby-sitting. (Write about yourself *or* someone you know—a friend, a brother or sister.) Note the following expressions:

> to baby-sit = **vigilar a los niños**
> to behave well ("be good") = **portarse bien**

Include the following information: (*a*) why you baby-sit; (*b*) how old the child is (the children are); (*c*) whether you do your homework, invite friends over, talk on the phone, or do something else to pass the time while the children are sleeping; (*d*) how much money you earn generally; (*e*) whether the children behave well; what you do if they do *not* behave (*leerles un cuento, ofrecerles dinero, cantar para divertirlos, amenazar con pegarlos* [threaten to hit them], etc.).

_____

_____

_____

_____

_____

_____

_____

_____

_____

_____

Celebrando el día de San Fermín en Pamplona, España. Los toros, corriendo por las calles hacia la plaza de toros, van acompañados de muchos jóvenes atrevidos. (Véase la página 330.)

38
El Esquí

Before reading the passages and dialogues of this chapter, study the following vocabulary and idioms.

VOCABULARY

la **alfombra,** rug, carpet

la **carretera,** road, highway

cercano, -a, nearby

criticar, to criticize

el **chófer,** driver

demasiado, too much

esquiar, to ski

la **manera** ⎫
el **modo** ⎬ way, manner

el **patinaje sobre hielo,** ice skating

patinar, to skate

la **pista de patinaje,** skating rink

la **pista de salto (de esquí),** ski run

próximo, -a, next

el **salto de esquí,** ski jump

IDIOMS

dentro de, inside of, within

de prisa, fast

aprovecharse de, to take advantage of

estar listo(-a), to be ready

gozar de,* to enjoy

pensar en, to think of

para el desayuno, for breakfast

por ahora, for now

ponerse en camino, to start out

tener cuidado, to be careful

tener muchas (tantas) ganas de + *inf.*, to be eager to

---

*Do not use this expression if the thing enjoyed is a form or source of entertainment (a play, film, book, concert, etc.); use **gustar** instead:

Me **gustó** la novela.   I enjoyed the novel.

    But:

Yo **gozaba de** la vida de campo.   I enjoyed life in the country.

A. A veces tenemos un largo fin de semana que dura tres o cuatro días. Hay que aprovecharse de estas ocasiones para gozar de la vida sin pensar en la escuela. El próximo fin de semana será el cumpleaños de Jorge Wáshington. Como estamos en invierno, hay que pensar en deportes como el patinaje sobre hielo y el esquí. Hay una pista de patinaje no muy lejos de nuestra casa. Para ir a esquiar, en cambio, tenemos que viajar dos o tres horas en coche. La pista de salto más cercana queda a unos ciento sesenta kilómetros (100 miles) de la ciudad. Pues, como tenemos tres días de libertad, ¿por qué no ir a esquiar?

Circle the letter of the correct answer.

1. Al narrador le gusta
    a. divertirse
    b. pensar en la escuela
    c. quedarse en casa

2. El narrador quiere ir
    a. a Wáshington
    b. a esquiar
    c. a patinar sobre hielo

3. ¿Dónde está situada la pista de salto?
    a. a cierta distancia de la ciudad
    b. cerca de Wáshington
    c. dentro de la ciudad

B. Complete the paragraph by writing the missing words, choosing them from among the words that appear below the blanks.

Según mis padres, el salto de esquí es muy _____, pero esto no me
                                            peligroso/pintura/correr

impide (*stops*). Hay que divertirse de vez en _____. Mi padre ha prometido
                                                  día/cuando/tarde

llevarnos en su _____. A él le gusta esquiar _____. Aquí
                  alfombra/mesa/coche   también/ayer/dinero

están nuestros planes:

El día de nuestra excursión _____ levantaremos a las cinco en punto de la
                             me/te/nos

mañana y saldremos de casa a las seis porque queremos _____ a la pista a
                                                       llegar/comer/salir

eso de las ocho. _____ tan temprano porque el esquí es un
                  Partimos/Cenamos/Cantamos

_____ muy popular y queremos evitar la muchedumbre (*crowd*). Creo
cine/deporte/diversión

que pasaremos un buen _____ si no hay accidentes. Por eso hay que tener
                       mañana/rato/fin

mucho _____. ¡Hasta el fin de semana!
       cuidado/dinero/pronto

C. *Diálogo:* Padre e hijo se preparan para un día de esquí.

PADRE: Levántate, chico. Tenemos que salir de casa muy temprano.

HIJO: Sí, papá, ya me desperté hace poco. Estaré listo en quince minutos.

PADRE: Pero antes de salir, tenemos que tomar el desayuno. ¿Qué vas a tomar: huevos, jugo, café?

HIJO: Quiero sólo un vaso de jugo de naranja. Estoy muy (too) nervioso para comer.

PADRE: Está bien. Podremos tomar algo al llegar a la pista.

HIJO: Estoy listo, papá. Vámonos. Tengo tantas ganas de ir a esquiar.

PADRE: Y yo también. Pero no hay que tener prisa. Quiero evitar un accidente en el camino.

HIJO: Si me dejas conducir el coche, no tendremos ningún accidente.

PADRE: Ya veremos. Primero vamos a ponernos en camino. Por ahora conduciré yo.

HIJO: ¡Qué lástima! Qué manera de empezar un fin de semana largo.

Circle the letter of the correct answer.

1. Tienen que levantarse temprano para
   a. no llegar tarde a la pista
   b. tomar el desayuno
   c. encontrarse con sus amigos

2. ¿Qué va a tomar el hijo para el desayuno?
   a. café y huevos
   b. nada
   c. jugo de naranja

3. Puede ocurrir un accidente si uno
   a. come demasiado antes de salir
   b. va de prisa
   c. conduce con cuidado

4. ¿Qué quiere hacer el hijo?
   a. conducir el automóvil
   b. tener un accidente
   c. comer mientras viaja

D. Complete the following dialogue:

HIJO: Papá, ya has conducido por una hora. ¿No estás cansado? ¿Puedo conducir ahora?

PADRE: (Tell him you know he wants to drive but you're not tired.)

1. _____

_____

HIJO: ¿Cuándo me vas a dar la oportunidad de conducir?

PADRE: (Tell him you'll let him drive soon.)

2. _____

HIJO: Papá, estás conduciendo muy de prisa. Cuidado con los otros coches en el camino.

PADRE: (Tell him you are a good driver and that he should not criticize you.)

3. _____

_____

HIJO: No te critico, papá. Sé que eres un buen chófer. Mira: la carretera está llena de coches esta mañana.

PADRE: (Tell him they're all going skiing too.)

4. _____

HIJO: Estoy tan impaciente. ¿Cuándo llegamos?

PADRE: (Tell him that you will arrive within a quarter of an hour [*un cuarto de hora*].)

5. _____

_____

E. *Tema*

1. On the lines below, write a composition about a ski trip you intend to take. Include the following ideas: (*a*) You are eager to go skiing this weekend. (*b*) There is a ski run not too far from your city or town. (*c*) You generally take advantage of long weekends to enjoy life. (*d*) You will start out very early in the morning. (*e*) For breakfast you will have ("take") only one or two things because you're too (*muy*) nervous to eat.

_____

_____

_____

_____

_____

_____

2. Write about your drive to the ski run. Include the following ideas: (*a*) Your father or mother drove too fast. (*b*) You wanted to drive, but your father (or mother) was afraid. (*c*) The roads were filled with cars that morning. (*d*) During the ride (*el paseo*) you thought of your arrival at the ski run. (*e*) You promised your father (or mother) that you would be careful on the ski jumps.

_____

_____

_____

_____

_____

_____

39
Una tarde musical

Before reading the passages and dialogues of this chapter, study the following vocabulary and idioms.

VOCABULARY

el **altavoz,** loudspeaker

el **amplificador de sonidos,** amplifier

el **aparato estereofónico,** stereo set

el **clarinete,** clarinet

grabar (en cinta), to tape

el **magnetófono** ⎫
la **grabadora** ⎭ tape recorder

el **panel de mandos,** control panel

el **plato giratorio,** turntable

poner, to turn on (the radio, etc.)

el **radio de frecuencia modulada,** FM radio

el **tambor,** drum

tampoco, neither, (not) either

la **trompeta,** trumpet

IDIOMS

más tarde, later

consistir en, to consist of

empezar a + *inf.*, to begin to

hacer (ir de) compras, to go shopping

A. A veces mis amigos y yo pasamos la tarde escuchando discos o haciendo nuestra propia música. Como tocamos diferentes instrumentos musicales, resulta algo emocionante. Una tarde de la semana pasada, como no teníamos mucho trabajo escolar que hacer, decidimos ir a casa de Roberto para grabar un concierto. Roberto tiene un aparato estereofónico muy complicado que consiste en muchos componentes: plato giratorio, amplificador de sonidos, dos altavoces, panel de mandos, magnetófono, radio de frecuencia modulada. Yo toco el tambor, Roberto toca el clarinete y Margarita toca la trompeta.

Circle the letter of the correct answer.

1. ¿Dónde tuvo lugar el concierto?
    a. en casa de un amigo del narrador
    b. en casa del narrador
    c. en la escuela

2. ¿En qué consiste el aparato estereofónico?
   a. solamente en una parte
   b. en varias partes
   c. en algunos instrumentos musicales

3. ¿Cuántas personas tomaron parte en el concierto?
   a. una chica y dos chicos
   b. dos chicos
   c. una madre y dos niños

B. Complete the paragraph by writing the missing words. Choose them from among the following list:

concierto, duró, mejor, era, rato, hora, centro, ciudad, terminó, estaba, nadie, compras

Es _____ tener estos conciertos cuando _____ está en casa. Aquella tarde mi madre _____ en el centro haciendo _____. ¡Pobres vecinos! Pero nosotros pasamos un _____ magnífico. El concierto _____ dos horas y media: de las tres y media a las seis, la _____ en que mi madre volvió del _____. A ella le gusta la música, pero no podría tolerar la nuestra. Y así _____ nuestra tarde musical. ¡Hasta el próximo _____!

C. *Diálogo:* Roberto y Margarita planean una tarde musical.

ROBERTO: Esta tarde nos divertiremos mucho. Afortunadamente mi madre no está en casa. A ella no le gusta nuestra música.

MARGARITA: A mis padres no les gusta tampoco. Creen que es horrible.

ROBERTO: Yo tengo unas cintas magníficas del grupo llamado "Las Estrellas del Rock."

MARGARITA: Sé que tocan bien. Tengo dos discos de ellos. Vamos a escuchar una de las cintas.

ROBERTO: Más tarde podemos poner las cintas. Ahora vamos a practicar. ¿Has traído tu trompeta?

MARGARITA: Sí, hombre. Aquí está. ¿No la ves? Pero tú puedes empezar a tocar.

ROBERTO: Y yo pondré una cinta para grabar nuestra música.

MARGARITA: Buena idea. Y luego escucharemos nuestro concierto.

Circle the letter of the correct answer.

1. ¿Por qué está contento Roberto?

   a. Puede tocar su música sin molestar a nadie.

   b. A su madre le gusta su música.

   c. Los padres de Margarita vienen al concierto.

2. ¿Quién tiene discos de las "Estrellas del Rock"?

    a. la madre de Roberto

    b. Roberto

    c. Margarita

3. ¿Qué piensa Margarita de "Las Estrellas del Rock"?

    a. No saben tocar.

    b. Son buenos músicos.

    c. No tocan tan bien como ella.

4. ¿Qué harán los dos después del concierto?

    a. Oirán su propia música en una cinta.

    b. Invitarán a "Las Estrellas del Rock" a oírlos.

    c. Saldrán de casa.

D. Complete the following dialogue, using expressions such as:

lo siento, I'm sorry

estar listo(-a) para + *inf.*, to be ready to

juntos, -as, together

no sentirse bien, not to feel well

el perro caliente, hot dog

la mostaza, mustard

el batido
la batida } milkshake

las palomitas de maíz, popcorn

las papas (patatas) fritas, French fried potatoes

MARGARITA: Por fin has llegado. ¿Qué te pasó?
FELIPE: (Tell her you had to buy something for your mother at the mall [*centro comercial*].)
1. _____

MARGARITA: Roberto ya ha puesto la cinta. ¿Has traído tu tambor?
FELIPE: (Tell her you have it and you are ready to play.)
2. _____

MARGARITA: Bueno, puedes empezar ahora, y luego te seguiremos.
FELIPE: (Agree, and tell her that you should all play together.)
3. _____

MARGARITA: Chico, no tocas bien hoy. ¿Qué te pasa?
FELIPE: (Tell her that you don't feel well. While you were at the mall, you ate three hot dogs
    with mustard, a milkshake and popcorn with French fried potatoes.)
4. _____

_____

_____

E. *Tema*

1. On the lines below, write a composition about a musical afternoon you spent with your friends. Include the following ideas: (*a*) You like to tape music. (*b*) You or your friends have very good stereophonic equipment (*componentes*). (*c*) Your mother likes music but can't stand ("tolerate") your rock concerts (*conciertos de música rock*). (*d*) One afternoon ("of the") last week, your mother went shopping. (*e*) While she was out (*estaba fuera*), you and your friends spent three hours playing and taping and driving the neighbors crazy (*volviendo locos a los vecinos*).

---

2. Write about a rock or jazz concert that you attended. Include answers to the following questions: (*a*) When and where did the concert take place? (*b*) Which group performed (*tocó*)? (*c*) At what time did they begin to play? (*d*) Did you like the group? Why? Or why not? (*e*) What did you eat and drink during the concert?

40
Preparativos para un viaje a Puerto Rico

Before reading the passages and dialogues of this chapter, study the following vocabulary and idioms.

VOCABULARY

además, besides

arreglar, to arrange, fix

la **confianza,** confidence

el **equipo de escafandra,** diving equipment

extranjero, -a, foreign

inolvidable, unforgettable

ligero, -a, light (in weight)

la **maleta,** suitcase

el **paisaje,** landscape, countryside

partir, to leave, depart

recorrer, to tour, go through

la **reserva,** reservation

seguro, -a, sure (used with **estar**)

el **sitio**
el **lugar** } place

la **suerte,** luck

el **traje de baño,** bathing suit, swimsuit

tratar, to treat

las **vacaciones de Navidad,** Christmas vacation

valer, to be worth

ya, already

IDIOMS

fuera de, outside of

hacer la maleta, to pack the suitcase

no hacer caso a, to ignore, not to pay attention to (a person)

pensar + *inf.*, to intend to

la mayor parte de, most of

quisiera
me gustaría } I would like

sacar fotos, to take pictures

tener celos (de), to be jealous (of)

A. Durante mis vacaciones de Navidad mis padres piensan hacer un viaje a Puerto Rico. Van a llevar a toda la familia. Como éste es mi primer viaje fuera de los Estados Unidos, tengo muchas ganas de ir. El profesor de español dice que será una experiencia muy buena y educativa.

Ahora tendré la oportunidad de practicar el español que he aprendido en la escuela. Partimos por avión el veinticuatro de diciembre. Mis amigos tienen celos. Me llaman "Rosa la Dichosa" (Lucky Rose). Todos dicen que les gustaría ir conmigo.

Circle the letter of the correct answer.

1. La familia va a Puerto Rico
   a. en diciembre
   b. durante la primavera
   c. por un fin de semana

2. Hasta ahora, ¿cuántos viajes a otros países ha hecho Rosa?
   a. dos
   b. tres
   c. ninguno

3. El profesor de español dice que
   a. no se debe visitar a Puerto Rico
   b. él ha visitado a Puerto Rico muchas veces
   c. Rosa podrá aprender algo en su viaje

4. ¿Quiénes irán a Puerto Rico?
   a. todos los miembros de la familia
   b. sólo el padre
   c. los padres de Rosa

5. Rosa
   a. va a estudiar el español en Puerto Rico
   b. habla español ya
   c. invita a sus amigos a ir con ella

B. Complete the paragraph by writing the missing words, choosing them from among the words that appear below the blanks.

Voy a hacer mi _____ la noche anterior al viaje. Como siempre hace
                  maleta/coche/avión

_____ en Puerto Rico, necesito llevar _____ ligera
    frío/calor/tiempo   guante/zapato/ropa

de verano. Y no debo _____ mi traje de baño y el equipo de escafandra.
                    olvidar/comer/volar

También voy a llevar mi cámara para sacar muchas _____. Dicen que
                                  veces/fotos/bicicletas

en Puerto Rico hay mucho que ver y que _____ de San Juan hay un
                           a eso/fuera/dentro

paisaje muy bonito. Podremos visitar algunos _____ de interés, además
                          lugares/casas/libros

de pasar tiempo en la _____ tomando el sol y _____
          escuela/playa/sitio   escribiendo/trayendo/nadando

en el mar. Yo creo que este _____ será inolvidable para mí.
                  viaje/océano/excursión

C. *Diálogo:* Rosa charla con su profesor de español.

PROFESOR: Rosa, ¡qué suerte tienes! Un viaje a un país hispano vale mucho.

ROSA: Ud. ha dicho siempre que es importante viajar por países extranjeros.

PROFESOR: Ahora vas a utilizar el español hablando con los habitantes del país.

ROSA: ¿Cree Ud. que podré conversar con ellos?

PROFESOR: Eres una estudiante muy aplicada. No tendrás ninguna dificultad con la lengua. Además, los puertorriqueños son muy amables y te ayudarán.

ROSA: Gracias, señor Aguador. Ud. me ha dado mucha confianza.

PROFESOR: ¿Cuándo parten Uds.?

ROSA: El día 24 de diciembre. Mi papá ha hecho ya las reservas en los hoteles.

PROFESOR: ¿Y dónde van a quedarse?

ROSA: La mayor parte del tiempo en San Juan. Pero por unos días vamos a recorrer la isla.

Circle the letter of the correct answer.

1. ¿Qué piensa el profesor de los planes de Rosa?
   a. Le gustan.
   b. Cree que es una mala idea.
   c. Quiere ir con ella.

2. ¿Qué va a hacer Rosa en Puerto Rico?
   a. Visitará a una amiga suya.
   b. Irá a la playa todos los días.
   c. Conversará con los puertorriqueños.

3. Los puertorriqueños
   a. tratarán bien a Rosa
   b. no le harán caso a Rosa
   c. Llevaran a Rosa a sus casas

4. ¿Quién ha arreglado el viaje?
   a. el señor Aguador
   b. el padre de Rosa
   c. una amiga puertorriqueña de Rosa

5. ¿Qué verá Rosa en Puerto Rico?
   a. solamente la ciudad de San Juan
   b. unas playas bonitas
   c. varias partes de la isla

D. Complete the following dialogue:

PANCHO: Me dicen que vas a Puerto Rico. Quisiera ir contigo. ¿Quiénes van?

DIEGO: (Tell him the whole family is going.)

1. _____

PANCHO: ¿Por cuántos días van a estar allí?

DIEGO: (Tell him you will be there for ten days, the whole Christmas vacation.)

2. _____

PANCHO: ¿Y qué van a hacer allí en la Isla del Encanto?

DIEGO: (Tell him you will see San Juan, go swimming, and use your diving outfit.)

3. _____

PANCHO: ¿Piensan visitar otros sitios?

DIEGO: (Tell him you intend to go around the island to see the beautiful landscape.)

4. _____

PANCHO: ¿Vas a hablar español con los puertorriqueños?

DIEGO: (Tell him your teacher is sure you will be able to converse in Spanish with the people there.)

5. _____

_____

E. *Tema*

1. On the lines below, write about a trip you intend to take to a Spanish-speaking country. Include answers to the following questions: (*a*) Who is arranging the trip? (*b*) When are you going? With whom? Where? (*c*) What will you take along with you? (*d*) What do you intend to do there most of the time? (*e*) Will you be able to converse with the inhabitants?

_____

_____

_____

_____

_____

_____

2. Rewrite the above composition in the past tense, telling about a trip that you took.

_____

_____

_____

_____

_____

_____

41
Un día en la playa

Before reading the passages and dialogues of this chapter, study the following vocabulary and idioms.

VOCABULARY

la **arena,** sand

la **carrera,** race, racing

competir, to compete

conducir } to drive
manejar }

conseguir, to get

divertido, -a, enjoyable, entertaining

el **gorro de baño,** bathing cap

juntos, -as, together

mojarse, to get wet

la **nube,** cloud

probar, to taste, try (out)

según, according to

unos cuantos } some, a few
unas cuantas }

IDIOMS

basta de, enough of

con cuidado, carefully

acabar de + *inf.*, to have just

preocuparse por, to worry about

tener calor, to be warm

cuanto antes, as soon as possible

¡Vaya! Come now!

tener deseos de + *inf.*, to be eager to

tomar un baño de sol, to sunbathe

A. Cuando hace calor, pienso en la playa. Como hoy es sábado y tengo pocas tareas que hacer, me gustaría ir allá esta mañana—pero la playa está a unos doce kilómetros de aquí. Me ocurre una idea: mi amiga Catalina ya tiene su licencia de conducir y muchas veces usa el coche de su papá. ¿Por qué no llamarla por teléfono? También voy a llamar a mi amiga Dorotea; ella me pregunta casi cada semana: «Oye, Diego, ¿por qué no vamos a la playa este sábado?» Y recuerdo ahora que debo invitar a Vicente también. Él acaba de comprar su equipo de escafandra y quiere probarlo cuanto antes. Los cuatro nos llevamos muy bien juntos. Pasaremos un día muy divertido—¡si no llueve! Según la radio, hará buen tiempo con mucho sol y pocas nubes.

Circle the letter of the correct answer.

1. Es un buen día para la playa porque
    a. está muy cerca de la casa de Diego
    b. hace calor
    c. Diego está ocupado

2. Diego llama a Catalina porque
    a. ella tiene un coche
    b. a ella le gusta nadar
    c. ella toma baños de sol

3. ¿Cómo sabe Diego que hará buen tiempo?
    a. Lo oyó en la radio.
    b. Su padre se lo dijo.
    c. Lo leyó en el periódico.

4. ¿Cuántas personas acompañarán a Diego a la playa?
    a. cuatro   *b.* tres   *c.* dos

B. Complete the paragraph by writing the missing words. Choose them from the following list:

pelo, conseguir, cabeza, playa, comer, tiempo, cuidado, comprar, arena, agua, equipo, sol, nadar

Ya estamos en la playa. Catalina pudo _____ el coche de su padre

después de prometerle que manejaría con mucho _____. Vicente ya ha ido

al _____ para probar su _____ de escafandra. A Dorotea

le gusta el _____ y quiere broncearse acostada en la _____.

Catalina y yo somos grandes nadadores y pasaremos la mayor parte del _____

en el mar. Catalina lleva siempre un gorro de baño en el agua para no mojarse el

_____. Así son las chicas. Esta vez no hemos traído nada de

_____ porque queremos probar las hamburguesas del "Rey de las

Hamburguesas" que ha abierto una sucursal (*branch*) en la _____.

C. *Diálogo:* Diego y Catalina se divierten en la playa.

DIEGO: Vamos al agua, chica. Tengo mucho calor.

CATALINA: Tengo muchos deseos de nadar. Pero primero tengo que ponerme el gorro de baño.

DIEGO: ¡Siempre con ese gorro de baño! ¿Por qué tienes miedo de mojarte el pelo?

CATALINA: Porque no podré arreglarlo más tarde. Y a ti, ¿qué te importa?

DIEGO: Siempre lo mismo con las chicas. Los muchachos no se preocupan por esas cosas.

CATALINA: ¡Vaya! Basta de eso. Vamos a competir en una carrera. A ver quién llega primero al agua.

DIEGO: ¡Cuidado! No corras tan de prisa. Te vas a caer.

CATALINA: Y tú, ¿tienes miedo de caerte en la arena? ¡Corre!

DIEGO: Yo gané la carrera. ¿Qué te pasa, chica? ¿Por qué no vas al agua?

CATALINA: El agua está muy fría. Además no quiero perder el gorro de baño y desarreglarme el pelo.

Circle the letter of the correct answer.

1. ¿Por qué quiere Diego ir al agua?
   a. Tiene calor.
   b. Quiere nadar.
   c. Le gusta el agua.

2. ¿Qué necesita llevar Catalina?
   a. un abrigo
   b. un gorro de baño
   c. un vestido

3. ¿Qué quiere hacer Catalina?
   a. tomar un baño de sol
   b. correr con Diego
   c. quedarse en el agua

4. ¿Quién corrió más de prisa?
   a. Diego
   b. Catalina
   c. ninguno de los dos

5. ¿Qué le importa más a Catalina?
   a. la arena
   b. su pelo
   c. la carrera

D. Complete the following dialogue:

VICENTE: ¿Quieres ver mi equipo de escafandra? Acabo de comprarlo.

DOROTEA: (Tell him you prefer to sunbathe, that you will see it later.)

1. _____

VICENTE: Pero, chica, ¿no te interesan esas cosas?

DOROTEA: (Tell him it is interesting, but you like the sun better [*más*].)

2. _____

VICENTE: Está bien. Te dejo al sol. Hasta luego.

DOROTEA: (Tell him you will see him later, after sunbathing.)

3. _____

VICENTE: Te espero en el agua, guapa.

DOROTEA: (Tell him you're hungry and you're going to get a hamburger.)

4. _____

VICENTE: Cómprame una hamburguesa también. Yo comeré después de salir del agua.

DOROTEA: (Ask him if he likes cold hamburgers.)

5. _____

E. *Tema*

1. On the lines below, write about a day you spent at the beach. Include the following ideas: (*a*) You were eager to go to the beach because it was very warm. (*b*) You wanted to get there as soon as possible, to avoid the crowd (*evitar la muchedumbre*). (*c*) You wanted to use the family car, but your mother had to use it to go to the dentist or the doctor. (*d*) You called a friend and the two of you went to the beach in his or her car. (*e*) At the beach, you both took sunbaths before going into the water.

_____

_____

_____

_____

_____

_____

_____

2. Write about your day at the beach. Include the following ideas: (*a*) You and your friend raced to the water together. (*b*) Your friend won because you fell in the hot sand. (*c*) You wore a bathing cap in order not to muss up your hair (*or* your friend wore a bathing cap in order not to muss up *her* hair). (*d*) After a half hour you were both hungry and went to get some hamburgers. (*e*) It was a very enjoyable day and you would like to go again soon.

    (to muss up one's hair = *desarreglarse el cabello*)

_____

_____

_____

_____

_____

_____

_____

La Plaza de Mayo, Buenos Aires, la Argentina

42
Una fiesta

Before reading the passages and dialogues of this chapter, study the following vocabulary and idioms.

VOCABULARY

adivinar, to guess

el bizcocho, cake

borracho, -a, drunk

la cerveza, beer

la costumbre, custom

la empanada de carne, meat pie

la gaseosa, (carbonated) soda

platicar, to chat

el sótano, basement

el vino, wine

IDIOMS

algo de comer, something to eat

a medianoche, at midnight

a pie, on foot

de nada, you're welcome

de ninguna manera
de ningún modo } in no way

hacer un viaje, to take a trip

ponerse, to become

el año pasado, last year

él mismo, he himself

el primero
la primera } en + *inf.*, the first (one) to

todo el mundo, everybody

quedar, to be (situated); **¿Dónde queda su casa?** Where is your house?

A. Me gustan las fiestas. Este fin de semana habrá una fiesta en casa de María. Ella vive en una casa muy grande que tiene un sótano amplio (spacious) para fiestas. Ella ha invitado a treinta personas. Cada persona tiene que traer algo de comer o de beber. Yo traeré una empanada de carne que mi mamá va a preparar. Ella aprendió a preparar las empanadas cuando hizo un viaje a la Argentina el año pasado. Creo que son deliciosas. Todo el mundo va a llevar *blue jeans*, el uniforme de los jóvenes de hoy día. Nadie se viste de etiqueta (dresses up) en las fiestas.

Circle the letter of the correct answer.

1. ¿Dónde tendrá lugar la fiesta?
   a. en casa del narrador
   b. en la escuela
   c. en casa de una amiga del narrador

2. ¿Cuántas personas irán a la fiesta?
   a. más de veinte
   b. muy pocas
   c. menos de quince

3. ¿Quién va a traer una empanada?
   a. la madre del narrador
   b. el narrador
   c. María

4. ¿Por qué llevan todos *blue jeans*?
   a. Es la costumbre.
   b. Los padres insisten.
   c. Los jóvenes son pobres.

B. Complete the paragraph by writing the missing words, choosing them from among the words that appear below the blanks.

Mi amiga Diana va a _____ una botella de sangría preparada por su
                        traer/comer/romper

padre. La sangría es la única _____ alcohólica que nuestros padres nos
                                comida/bebida/casa

permiten _____ en las fiestas. El padre de Diana la prepara con muy
          escribir/tomar/estudiar

poco _____ y mucho jugo de fruta y gaseosa. Así
      vino/cerveza/papel

_____ se pondrá borracho. ¿Qué hacemos en la fiesta? Pues,
   todos/mamá/nadie

_____, platicamos, tomamos refrescos y generalmente nos
   leemos/dormimos/bailamos

_____. Las fiestas deben _____ a medianoche.
  divertimos/levantamos/ponemos   empezar/preparar/terminar

A esa hora me _____ de mis amigos y vuelvo a casa
                quejo/acuerdo/despido

_____, como la casa de María queda muy cerca de la mía.
   por avión/a pie/de nada

C. *Diálogo*

DIEGO: Hola, María, parece que soy el primero en llegar a la fiesta.

MARÍA: De ninguna manera. Ya han llegado ocho personas. ¿Qué has traído?

DIEGO: Te traje una empanada preparada por mi mamá.

MARÍA: ¡Ay! Me encantan las empanadas. Muchas gracias.

DIEGO: ¿Qué han traído los demás?

MARÍA: Roberto trajo un bizcocho de chocolate y Ana trajo una botella grande de gaseosa. ¿Y sabes lo que trajo José?

DIEGO: No puedo adivinar. Dime.

MARÍA: Un rosbif que él mismo preparó.

DIEGO: Dios mío. No sabía que José sabía preparar rosbif. Tengo que probarlo.

MARÍA: Veremos si es tan delicioso como tu empanada. Ahora, vamos a bailar. Comeremos más tarde.

Circle the letter of the correct answer.

1. ¿Cuántas personas ya han venido a la fiesta?
   a. nueve   *b.* ocho   *c.* sólo una

2. ¿Quién dice que le gustan las empanadas?
   a. nadie   *b.* Diego   *c.* María

3. ¿Quién trajo el rosbif?
   a. María   *b.* José   *c.* la madre de Diego

4. ¿Qué le sorprende a Diego?
   a. Él es el primero en llegar.
   b. Roberto y Ana trajeron refrescos también.
   c. José sabe preparar rosbif.

5. ¿Cuándo van a comer?
   a. antes de bailar
   b. después de bailar
   c. al comienzo de la fiesta

D. Complete the following dialogue, using expressions such as:

tener mucho gusto en + *inf.*, to be very glad to

estar aburrido(-a), to be bored

simpático, -a, nice, likeable

estar de acuerdo, to agree

probar, to taste, try

sobre todo, especially

no hacer caso a, to ignore (someone)

DIEGO: Hola, Rosa, ¿quieres bailar conmigo?
ROSA: (Tell him you would be very glad to dance with him.)

1. _____

DIEGO: ¿Te gusta la fiesta?
ROSA: (Tell him you don't like it because you are bored.)

2. _____

DIEGO: ¿Aburrida? Pero ¿por qué?
ROSA: (Tell him some of the guests [*algunos invitados*] are not nice.)

3. _____

DIEGO: ¿Por qué dices eso?
ROSA: (Tell him they ignore you. They only talk to [*con*] their school friends.)

4. _____

DIEGO: Hay tales personas en todas las fiestas. Pero yo estoy aquí, y yo soy muy simpático, ¿verdad?

ROSA: (Agree with him, and tell him that he dances well, too.)

5. _____

DIEGO: Gracias. Mi hermana menor me enseñó a bailar. A ella le encanta bailar.

ROSA: (Tell him that his younger sister is a good teacher. Now you would like to try some of the refreshments, especially the sangría.)

6. _____

_____

E. *Tema*

1. On the lines below, write about a party you attended. Include the following information: (*a*) where and when the party took place; (*b*) how you got there; (*c*) who the guests were—describe some of them; (*d*) what activities you took part in; (*e*) what you had to eat and drink.

_____

_____

_____

_____

_____

_____

_____

2. Write about a trip you will have to take to attend a party. Include answers to the following questions: (*a*) In what city or country will the party take place? (*b*) How will you get there? (*c*) What gift will you bring to the host (*el anfitrión*) or the hostess (*la anfitriona*)? (*d*) How many people will attend the party? (*e*) Where will you stay? (at the home of the host or hostess, in a hotel, etc.)

_____

_____

_____

_____

_____

_____

_____

43
Las lecciones de conducción

Before reading the passages and dialogues of this chapter, study the following vocabulary and idioms.

VOCABULARY

andar, to go; **el coche anda,** the car is going

así, (in) this way

conducir
manejar } to drive

el espejo retrovisor, rear-view mirror

el freno, brake

la lección de conducción (de manejo), driving lesson

libremente, freely

moverse, to move

pasearse, to ride

pegar, to hit, strike

el permiso
la licencia } **de conducir,** driver's license

recordar, to remind

soltar, to loosen, set free

la ventanilla, window (in a vehicle)

IDIOMS

hoy día, nowadays

lo más pronto posible, as soon as possible

lo mejor, the best

abrocharse el cinturón de seguridad, to fasten one's seat belt

acercarse a, to approach

alegrarse de + *inf.*, to be glad to

hacer arrancar el motor, to start the engine

negarse a + *inf.*, to refuse to

ponerse en marcha, to start out, "get going"

salir bien en
aprobar (ue) } **un examen,** to pass a test

salir mal en
no aprobar } **un examen,** to fail a test

A. Yo me acerco a la edad de conducir un coche. Como todos los jóvenes de hoy día, tengo muchas ganas de aprender a manejar. Es muy divertido y también es importante saber conducir. El señor Ruiz, uno de los profesores de nuestra escuela, da lecciones de conducción después de las clases. Él lleva a cuatro estudiantes en su coche. Cada uno tiene su turno de media hora. Todos tratamos de hacer lo mejor que podemos porque para nosotros es muy importante obtener la licencia de conducir lo más pronto posible. Mientras nos paseamos, hablamos de nuestras experiencias en la escuela, pero no podemos hablar muy libremente porque el señor Ruiz está escuchando.

Circle the letter of the correct answer.

1. ¿Qué desean hacer los jóvenes?
   a. dar lecciones de conducción a sus profesores
   b. aprender a manejar un coche
   c. divertirse todos los días

2. Es muy importante para los estudiantes
   a. conseguir su licencia
   b. llevar a sus amigos en coche
   c. salir mal en los exámenes

3. ¿Qué hacen los estudiantes en el coche?
   a. Se quedan silenciosos.
   b. Hablan acerca del señor Ruiz.
   c. Discuten sus actividades en la escuela.

4. ¿Qué hace el señor Ruiz mientras los estudiantes conducen?
   a. Oye sus conversaciones.
   b. Lee un libro.
   c. Habla con ellos.

B. Complete the paragraph by writing the missing words, choosing them from among the words that appear below the blanks.

Los inspectores son muy severos con los _____ y muchas veces uno
profesores/jóvenes/padres

sale _____ en el examen de conducción. Por eso hay que
mal/coche/paseo

_____ mucho. Mi padre me deja manejar su coche los domingos
llevar/comer/practicar

por una hora. Pero él me critica demasiado. Todos los _____
amigos/padres/años

son así, ¿verdad? Mamá se niega a _____ en coche conmigo porque
pasearse/beber/poder

tiene mucho _____. Así son todas las madres, ¿verdad? El Sr. Ruiz
paciencia/dinero/miedo

tiene mucha _____, y cuando cometo un error, me
escuela/paciencia/carácter

_____ con mucha calma, explicándome lo que debo hacer. Estoy
pega/corrige/grita

_____ de que saldré bien en mi _____.
seguro/bien/cansado   conducir/examen/profesor

C. *Diálogo*

SR. RUIZ: Luisa, ¿estás lista para la lección hoy?

LUISA: Claro. Siempre estoy lista. Me encanta manejar un coche.

SR. RUIZ: Primero tienes que abrocharte el cinturón de seguridad.

LUISA: Yo nunca olvido este detalle, señor. No es necesario recordarme.

SR. RUIZ: Me alegro mucho de oír esto. Y ahora, ¿qué haces?

LUISA: Muy fácil. Hay que hacer arrancar el motor. Luego hay que mirar en el espejo retrovisor y luego por la ventanilla para ver si vienen otros coches.

SR. RUIZ: ¡Perfecto! Parece que sabes exactamente lo que se debe hacer. Entonces, vamos a ponernos en marcha.

LUISA: ¿Qué pasa? El coche no se mueve.

SR. RUIZ: ¿Has soltado el freno de emergencia?

LUISA: ¡Ay, Dios mío! Ahora sé por qué el coche no anda.

Circle the letter of the correct answer.

1. ¿Quién es el Sr. Ruiz?
   a. el profesor de manejo
   b. el padre de Luisa
   c. un profesor de español

2. ¿Cuándo es necesario abrocharse el cinturón de seguridad?
   a. después de hacer arrancar el motor
   b. antes de subir al coche
   c. antes de ponerse en marcha

3. ¿Por qué se debe mirar por la ventanilla?
   a. para abrocharse el cinturón de seguridad
   b. para ver si se acercan otros automóviles
   c. para ver si viene un policía

4. ¿Por qué no se mueve el coche?
   a. Luisa no ha soltado el freno de emergencia.
   b. No hay gasolina en el tanque.
   c. El profesor no le permite a Luisa manejar.

D. Complete the following dialogue, using expressions such as:

ahora mismo, right now

aprobar el examen, to pass the exam

así, (in) this way, so, thus

ciego, -a, blind

la **confianza,** confidence

parar, to stop

pierde cuidado, don't worry

PADRE: Vamos a ver lo que has aprendido. Llévame a la estación de gasolina. Tenemos que llenar el tanque.

HIJA: (Tell him you have learned a lot and that you will take him there right now.)

1. _____

_____

PADRE: ¡Cuidado! Hay una señal de *Stop* a unos pocos metros. ¿No la ves?

HIJA: (Tell him of course you see the sign and that you are going to stop.)

2. _____

PADRE: ¡Ay, Dios mío! Hay luz roja. ¿No vas a parar?
HIJA: (Tell him not to worry; you are not blind.)

3. _____

PADRE: No sé si vas a salir bien en el examen de manejo. Tú manejas con poco cuidado.
HIJA: (Tell him that he should have more confidence in you, that you are a good driver.)

4. _____

PADRE: Tengo que decir la verdad: estoy muy nervioso cuando conduces.
HIJA: (Tell him that all fathers are like that [así].)

5. _____

E. *Tema*

1. On the lines below, write about your desire to learn to drive. Include the following ideas: (*a*) You would like to learn; tell why. (*b*) Your mother or father refuses to teach you; tell why. (*c*) A driving school (*auto-escuela*) is best for you; tell why. (*d*) You intend to practice a lot; tell when. (*e*) You want to start your lessons as soon as possible.

_____

_____

_____

_____

_____

_____

_____

2. Write about a driving lesson. Include the following information: (*a*) who is teaching you and where; (*b*) how good your teacher is (describe him or her); (*c*) what was said in a conversation with your teacher; (*d*) an error you made during the lesson; (*e*) you hope to pass the test the first time.

_____

_____

_____

_____

_____

_____

_____

44
El centro comercial

Before reading the passages and dialogues of this chapter, study the following vocabulary and idioms.

VOCABULARY

atraer, to attract

el **barco,** boat

el **centro comercial,** shopping mall, business district

deber, should, have to, to be supposed to; **debo hablar,** I should speak

la **heladería,** ice-cream shop

llevar, to take; to wear

meter, to put in(to), insert

la **moneda,** coin

la **ranura,** (coin) slot

el **sonido,** sound

tanto, -a, so much

tras, after, behind

IDIOMS

al + *inf.,* upon . . . -ing

de acuerdo, agreed, OK

de veras, really

en vez de, instead of

lo mismo, the same

mientras tanto, meanwhile

por fin, finally

por medio de, by means of

o sea, or rather

por lo menos, at least

A. La escuela no ocupa toda mi vida. Soy un chico activo. Al salir de la escuela, después de mi última clase, pienso en lo que voy a hacer el resto del día. No hago siempre lo mismo. Por ejemplo, hoy tengo que volver directamente a casa porque mi mamá quiere llevarme a comprar ropa. Al llegar a casa, saludo a mi mamá, quien me dice que el coche está averiado (broken down) y que papá tuvo que llevarlo a la estación de servicio por medio de un camión-grúa (tow-truck). Por eso tenemos que tomar el autobús en vez del coche.

El centro comercial contiene tiendas de todos tipos: restaurantes, heladerías, tiendas de ropa, de música, de deportes, etc. Me gustan más las galerías de juegos electrónicos. Por una moneda de veinticinco centavos uno puede entrar en otro mundo por algunos minutos. A mí me interesan más los juegos de tiro (shooting games). Puedo pasar mucho tiempo metiendo moneda tras moneda en la ranura para destruir barcos, aviones y otros objetos móviles (moving). Las luces y los sonidos electrónicos son muy emocionantes (exciting). Los juegos de billar romano (pin-ball) también me atraen, y trato de ganar un gran número de puntos. Pero hoy recuerdo que no he venido aquí para pasar tiempo con los juegos electrónicos. Hay que comprar ropa. Mamá insiste.

Circle the letter of the correct answer.

1. Madre e hijo van al centro comercial
   a. en coche   *b.* en autobús   *c.* a pie

2. ¿Dónde está el coche?
   a. en el garaje de la casa
   b. en el centro
   c. en la estación de servicio

3. En el centro comercial no se puede
   a. ir a la escuela
   b. comer
   c. comprar cosas

4. ¿Qué prefiere el chico?
   a. las tiendas de ropa
   b. las monedas de 25 centavos
   c. los juegos de tiro

5. Los dos van al centro comercial para
   a. comprar ropa
   b. jugar con los juegos electrónicos
   c. pasar tiempo

B. *Diálogo*

MADRE: Ahora, hijo, estamos en el *mall*. Te doy un cuarto de hora para los juegos electrónicos.

HIJO: Pero, mamá, me gustan tanto los juegos electrónicos. Quiero quedarme por lo menos media hora.

MADRE: Pues, vamos a llegar a un acuerdo (reach an agreement). Veinte minutos, pero no más. ¿Entiendes?

HIJO: De acuerdo. Vamos a encontrarnos delante de la tienda llamada "Ropa de Moda" en veinte minutos.

MADRE: Mientras tanto, yo iré a buscar un regalo para la tía Silvia, que va a celebrar su cumpleaños el domingo.

HIJO: Hasta entonces, mamá.

Circle the letter of the correct answer.

1. La mamá y su hijo entran en el centro comercial para
   a. comprar unos juegos electrónicos
   b. pasar quince minutos paseando
   c. obtener ropa para el hijo

2. El chico quiere divertirse por
   a. treinta minutos
   b. un cuarto de hora
   c. veinte minutos

3. ¿Quién va a recibir un regalo?
   a. la madre
   b. la hermana de la madre
   c. el chico

4. ¿Qué harán los dos después de veinte minutos?
   a. Comerán en un restaurante.
   b. Comprarán ropa.
   c. Irán a casa.

C. Complete the following dialogue:

MADRE: Hijo, llegaste tarde. ¿Qué hacías?
HIJO: (Tell her you were in the electronic-games gallery.)

1. _____

MADRE: Sé que te gustan esos juegos, pero tenemos que comprarte una camisa, un par de pantalones y zapatos. Vamos a entrar en la tienda, por fin.
HIJO: (Ask her what she will buy first.)

2. _____

MADRE: Primero quiero mirar las camisas. ¿Cuál prefieres?
HIJO: (Tell her you prefer the red one [*la roja*] with horizontal stripes, because it's pretty.)

3. _____

_____

MADRE: De ningún modo. Las camisas con rayas horizontales son muy feas. Yo prefiero esta blanca y verde.
HIJO: (Tell her you insist on the red one.)

4. _____

MADRE: Muy bien, si insistes, aunque de veras no me gusta.
HIJO: (Thank her but tell her you should wear what [*lo que*] you like.)

5. _____

D. *Tema*

1. On the lines below, write about a visit to a shopping mall. Include answers to the following questions: (*a*) Why do you go to a shopping mall? (*b*) Where is the shopping mall that is nearest to your home? (*c*) How large is the mall? (number of stores, restaurants, etc.) (*d*) What do you like to do most when you are there? (*e*) How often do you go to the mall? (*dos veces al día, una vez por semana*, etc.)

_____

_____

_____

_____

_____

_____

_____

2. Write about a shopping trip that you will take. Include the following information: (*a*) why you are going, and with whom; (*b*) how long you will stay there; (*c*) how you will get there; (*d*) how you feel about a particular store or restaurant—describe it in detail; (*e*) how much money you think you will spend and where you will get it. (to spend = *gastar*)

_____

_____

_____

_____

_____

_____

_____

Un mercado indio en Pujili, el Ecuador

PART EIGHT

EL MUNDO
DE HABLA ESPAÑOLA

45
El mundo hispánico

La Diferencia Entre «Hispano» y «Español»

Al usar la palabra «hispano(-a)» o «hispánico(-a)», nos referimos a todas las personas que hablan español o a cualquier cosa típica del mundo de habla española. La palabra «español(-la)», en cambio, se refiere solamente a las personas y la cultura de España. Un *hispano* puede ser de México, Cuba, la Argentina o España, pero sólo un habitante de España puede ser *español*. Un plato hispano como enchiladas con guacamole no es un ejemplo de «comida española» sino de comida mexicana.

1. Un español es de _____. Todos los que hablan español son _____.

El mundo hispano (o hispánico) se compone de España, las 19 naciones de habla española del Hemisferio Occidental y las comunidades hispanas de los Estados Unidos. El español es la lengua materna (native) de unos 20.000.000 de norteamericanos. La población hispana del mundo es de unos 250.000.000.

2. _____ naciones del mundo son hispánicas.

Hispanoamérica (la América Española)

Los países de Hispanoamérica se pueden dividir en los siguientes grupos:

A. **México**

B. **Centroamérica (La América Central).** Las repúblicas hispánicas de la América Central son:

1. *Guatemala*   3. *Nicaragua*   5. *Costa Rica*
2. *Honduras*   4. *El Salvador*   6. *Panamá*

(No se incluye a *Belice* en esta lista porque su lengua oficial es el inglés, pero muchos de sus habitantes hablan español también.)

C. **Las Antillas (las islas del Caribe).** Los países hispanos de este grupo son:

1. *Puerto Rico*, un Estado Libre Asociado a los Estados Unidos
2. *Cuba*

3. *La República Dominicana*, que comparte (shares) con Haití la isla llamada *Hispaniola* o *La Española*. Como la lengua oficial de Haití es el francés, Haití no es parte del mundo hispánico.

3. Haití no es un país hispano porque allí no se habla _____.

D. **Sudamérica (La América del Sur).** Los países hispánicos de Sudamérica son:

1. *Venezuela*	4. *el Perú*	7. *la Argentina*
2. *Colombia*	5. *Chile*	8. *el Uruguay*
3. *el Ecuador*	6. *Bolivia*	9. *el Paraguay*

Estos países se difieren el uno del otro en unos aspectos importantes, pero todos tienen una lengua en común y muchas semejanzas (similarities) culturales que reflejan la misma herencia (heritage) española.

4. En _____ naciones de Sudamérica se habla _____.

Unos Aspectos de la Civilización Hispánica

1. La Lengua Española

La lengua española tiene sus variaciones. Cada país hispano tiene sus diferencias con respecto al idioma. Por ejemplo, hay diferencias en la pronunciación. En España, la mayoría de los españoles pronuncian la letra *z* y la *c* en *ce* y *ci* (*acera*, *cinco*) como la *th* en la palabra inglesa *think*. La letra *j* tiene un sonido mucho más fuerte en España que la *j* de Hispanoamérica. Los argentinos (y otros hispanoamericanos) pronuncian la *ll* y la *y* como la *s* en la palabra inglesa «plea*s*ure». En Hispanoamérica y la España meridional (southern), muchas personas no pronuncian ni la *s* final ni la *s* que precede a una consonante. Tampoco pronuncian la *d* de la terminación *-ado* o *-ido*. Por ejemplo, *los mismos estados* se pronuncia «lo' mi'mo e'tao». A pesar de estas variaciones en la pronunciación, los hispanos de los diferentes países generalmente se entienden (understand one another) sin dificultad.

5. Hay diferencias en la _____ del español en los _____ donde se habla.

También hay diferencias en el vocabulario. Una *patata* en España es una *papa* en la América Española. Una naranja es una naranja para todos los hispanos menos los puertorriqueños, quienes la llaman una *china*. El autobús u ómnibus se llama una *guagua* en Cuba, Puerto Rico y las Islas Canarias. La misma palabra, *guagua*, quiere decir *bebé* (baby) en Chile. En México, la palabra *camión* (truck) también se usa como sinónimo de *autobús*.

Como ya saben ustedes, por la mayor parte de España el plural de *tú* es *vosotros(-as)*, mientras que los hispanoamericanos usan *ustedes* como plural de *tú* así como (as well as) *usted*.

6. Los _____ no usan la palabra *vosotros*.

2. Nombres y Apellidos

Muchos hispanos llevan los nombres de santos: *Pedro*, *José*, *Juan*, *María*, *Teresa*, etc. Generalmente celebran el día de su santo en vez de su cumpleaños. En general, los hispanos tienen más de un apellido. Por ejemplo, en el nombre *Ramón López Rodríguez*, López es el apellido del padre de Ramón, y Rodríguez es el apellido de soltera (maiden name) de su madre. Otro ejemplo: María Rodríguez Molina se casa con Pedro Vargas Vélez. Ahora ella se llama María Rodríguez de Vargas porque es la esposa *de* Vargas. La podemos llamar «señora de Vargas» o simplemente «señora Vargas». Carmen, la hija de Pedro y María, se llama Carmen Vargas Rodríguez—el apellido del padre seguido del (followed by the) apellido de la madre. La podemos llamar «señorita Vargas».

7. El apellido del padre de Felipe Santos González es _____.

8. Juan García Meléndez se casa con Ana Benítez Rivera. Ahora Ana se llama Ana _____

   de _____.

3. Los Deportes

Lo que los hispanos llaman **el fútbol** es nuestro «soccer». Este deporte es muy popular en todo el mundo hispano. No debemos confundirlo con el juego norteamericano de «football».

9. Football se juega en los _____; el *fútbol* se juega allí también, pero lo llamamos

   _____.

Por más de dos siglos **la corrida de toros** ha sido el deporte más popular de España y de algunos países hispanoamericanos. Hoy día, sin embargo, el fútbol ha llegado a ser más popular que la corrida de toros. Durante la temporada (season) de las corridas, la corrida tiene lugar los domingos a eso de las cinco de la tarde. En algunas ocasiones especiales, las corridas pueden tener lugar otros días de la semana.

10. Se puede ver una corrida de toros los _____.

11. La _____ ya no es tan popular en los países hispanos.

El jai alai, un deporte parecido al «handball», tuvo su origen en el País Vasco de España (véase la página 344). Se juega en una cancha (court) llamada un *frontón*. Es un juego rapidísimo y exige (requires) mucha destreza (skill).

12. El jai alai se jugaba originalmente en _____.

4. La Siesta

Por muchos siglos los pueblos (peoples) de habla española han observado en la tarde un largo período de descanso llamado *la siesta*. Esta costumbre tiene un motivo práctico: en España y otros países hispanos es muy difícil trabajar durante las primeras horas de la tarde porque hace mucho calor. Por eso, muchas tiendas y oficinas se cierran desde la una o la una y media hasta las cuatro o las cuatro y media de la tarde. Durante estas horas muchos vuelven a casa para tomar el almuerzo, que es generalmente una comida fuerte (heavy meal). Por lo común, descansan o duermen después de comer. En los últimos años, la costumbre de *tomar* (o *echar*) *una siesta* ha disminuido en muchas ciudades hispanas. Hoy día muchas tiendas se quedan abiertas durante las horas de la siesta.

13. En los pueblos hispanos se toma una _____ durante la _____

porque hace _____.

5. LAS COMIDAS

En los países de habla española las comidas se pueden describir así:

El desayuno, que se toma por la mañana, consiste en una taza de café o chocolate con un panecillo o bollo (bun). El café hispano es mucho más fuerte que el café norteamericano, y a menudo se toma con una gran cantidad de leche hervida (boiled) con azúcar.

14. Los hispanos toman el café con _____.

El almuerzo. En algunos países el almuerzo es un segundo desayuno y se toma a eso de las nueve y media o las diez. En otros países corresponde más a un «lunch» norteamericano, y se toma entre la una y media y las tres, es decir, inmediatamente antes de la siesta. En algunos lugares el almuerzo se llama **la comida** y generalmente consiste en varios platos.

15. En algunos sitios _____ es sinónimo de *almuerzo*.

La merienda (snack) se toma al final de la siesta y consiste en varias cosas como café, chocolate, panecillos y bollos. Muchas veces se toma un **aperitivo,** que puede ser cualquier (any) bebida alcohólica.

16. Al terminar la siesta, los hispanos toman _____.

La cena, que se toma muy tarde—entre las diez y las once de la noche—es generalmente una comida ligera.

6. LAS FIESTAS PATRONALES

En el mundo hispánico, cada país, ciudad y pueblo tiene al menos un santo patrón, quien ha sido adoptado como su protector. Por ejemplo, una santa patrona del Perú es Santa Rosa de Lima; el santo patrón de Madrid es San Isidro; el santo patrón de Puerto Rico es San Juan Bautista. Las fiestas patronales anuales son celebraciones que tienen lugar en honor del santo patrón. Estas festividades, que pueden durar una semana, incluyen fuegos artificiales (fireworks), desfiles (parades), y la venta de cosas de comer y beber en unas casetas provisionales (temporary stalls) construidas para la ocasión. Tiovivos (merry-go-rounds) y varios juegos añaden al ambiente festivo.

17. Las fiestas patronales pueden consistir en _____, _____

y _____.

Un aspecto notable de la fiesta patronal de Pamplona, una ciudad del nordeste de España, es la embestida (charge) de los toros bravos (wild bulls) por las calles de la ciudad. La celebración de San Fermín, santo patrón de Pamplona, empieza el 7 de julio y dura ocho días. Todos los días a las siete de la mañana explota un cohete (a rocket explodes) que anuncia que las puertas del corral están abiertas. Entonces los toros se escapan a la calle. Los toros corren por las calles hasta la plaza de toros. Muchas personas atrevidas (daring) corren con los toros, tratando de evitar sus cuernos (horns). Algunas de estas personas quedan heridas (get hurt). Después de este suceso (event) hay varias actividades, incluyendo una corrida de toros, que duran todo el día. El festival de Pamplona es una de la fiestas más emocionantes (exciting) que ocurren por todo el mundo hispano.

18. La celebración de _____ tiene lugar en Pamplona el

_____ de _____ y dura _____.

7. Las Escuelas

Los niños de los países hispanos generalmente empiezan su enseñanza (education) en una **escuela primaria** o **escuela elemental,** donde se quedan por seis años. Luego pasan a una escuela secundaria llamada un **instituto,** un **liceo** o un **colegio**—el nombre de la escuela secundaria depende del país. Los niños asisten a esta escuela por cinco o seis años. Al graduarse, reciben un diploma llamado **el bachillerato,** y luego van a la **universidad.** No se debe confundir un *colegio* con el «college» de los Estados Unidos. El colegio es un tipo de «private high school». «College» en español es *universidad.* En los países hispanos, el día escolar es por lo general más largo que el nuestro, y los estudiantes hispanos estudian más asignaturas por semestre que los estudiantes norteamericanos. Los muchachos y las muchachas suelen ir (generally go) a escuelas separadas.

19. Los institutos y colegios son _____.

20. El día escolar hispano dura más _____ que el día escolar de los Estados Unidos.

21. Los muchachos y las muchachas no van a la misma _____.

8. Los Días de Fiesta

La **Navidad** (Christmas), la **Pascua de Resurrección** (Easter) y el **Día de la Raza** (Columbus Day), también llamado el **Día de la Hispanidad,** se celebran en todos los países de habla española. El Día de la Raza es el día en que todos los pueblos (peoples) hispanos celebran el descubrimiento de América por Cristóbal Colón.

22. _____ descubrió a América.

Hasta hoy día los niños hispanos solían recibir (were accustomed to receiving) regalos el seis de enero en vez del día de Navidad. El 6 de enero, llamado el **Día de los Reyes Magos,** se celebra el día en que los Reyes Magos (the Three Wise Men) trajeron regalos al niño Jesús. Sin embargo, en algunos sitios de la América española se ha adoptado la costumbre de repartir (distribute) los regalos en la Navidad, como en los Estados Unidos.

23. En algunas partes de Hispanoamérica los niños reciben _____ el _____ de

_____. En otras partes los reciben el _____ de _____,

como nosotros.

Cada país hispano tiene su propio día de fiesta para conmemorar su descubrimiento o su independencia de España. Por ejemplo, Puerto Rico celebra su descubrimiento el 19 de noviembre. El Día de la Independencia de México es el 16 de septiembre.

24. El 19 de noviembre es un día de fiesta en _____.

9. El Mercado

El mercado en España y en los países hispanoamericanos es un lugar vivo y pintoresco. Muchos pueblos y aldeas tienen mercados al aire libre (outdoors) que se montan (are assembled) una vez por semana. Cada pueblo tiene su propio día de mercado. En los numerosos puestos (booths) y quioscos (stands), se vende toda clase de mercancías (merchandise): alimentos (food) y bebidas, ropa, recuerdos (souvenirs), juguetes, etc. El cliente muchas veces no acepta el primer precio que se pide y suele regatear (generally bargains) con el vendedor para rebajar (lower) el precio.

25. Una variedad de cosas se vende en _____.

Todos los pueblos tienen por lo menos un mercado situado dentro de un edificio. Este mercado generalmente queda abierto todos los días excepto los domingos. Aquí también se vende todo, incluso comestibles (groceries). El ama de casa (housewife) pasa de puesto en puesto, comparando los precios. Como muchas casas de los pueblos pequeños carecen de (lack) refrigeración adecuada, la típica ama de casa va al mercado todas las mañanas para comprar comida fresca.

26. Los mercados interiores se cierran los _____.

27. La mujer hispana generalmente va al mercado cada _____ para comprar sólo los alimentos que necesita para el mismo _____.

EJERCICIOS

A. *Cierto o falso.* Write *cierto* if the statement is true. If it is false, replace the words in capital letters with words that would make the statement true. (Write the correct words in the blanks.)

1. Después de terminar sus estudios en LA UNIVERSIDAD, los estudiantes hispanos reciben su bachillerato. _____

2. El 16 de SEPTIEMBRE es un día de fiesta en México. _____

3. En los mercados de los países hispanos, los VENDEDORES buscan precios bajos. _____

4. EL INSTITUTO es la primera escuela a que asisten los niños hispanos.
   _____

5. Se celebra el día de SAN PEDRO en Puerto Rico.
   _____

6. EL DÍA DE LA HISPANIDAD se celebra el 25 de diciembre.
   _____

7. "Orange juice" generalmente se llama jugo de NARANJA en Puerto Rico.
   _____

8. En Haití se habla FRANCÉS.
   _____

9. El desayuno se toma por LA NOCHE.
   _____

10. Las tiendas se cierran durante las horas de LA SIESTA.
    _____

11. EL FRONTÓN es un deporte popular que se parece al _handball_.
    _____

12. Los españoles toman LA CENA por la noche.
    _____

13. LA CORRIDA DE TOROS es un deporte muy popular en los Estados Unidos.
    _____

14. El Salvador es una nación DEL CARIBE.
    _____

15. En Pamplona, una ciudad de MÉXICO, hay una gran celebración en julio.
    _____

B. To the left of each expression in column I, write the letter of the related expression that appears in column II.

I	II
_____ 1. aperitivo	_a._ almuerzo
_____ 2. Honduras	_b._ Pamplona
_____ 3. Hispaniola	_c._ autobús
_____ 4. fútbol	_d._ soccer
_____ 5. guagua	_e._ Sudamérica
_____ 6. López	_f._ **País Vasco**
_____ 7. los Reyes Magos	_g._ café
_____ 8. San Fermín	_h._ Centroamérica
_____ 9. jai alai	_i._ merienda
_____ 10. leche hervida	_j._ apellido
	_k._ isla del Caribe
	_l._ Puerto Rico
	_m._ el 6 de enero

46
Influencias hispánicas en los Estados Unidos

Al mirar un mapa de los Estados Unidos, podemos ver muchas señales de la influencia de España en nuestro país. Por todo el Sudoeste hay lugares que tienen nombres españoles: por ejemplo, los estados de Texas, Colorado y Nuevo México; las ciudades de Los Angeles, San Francisco, Sacramento, Santa Fe y El Paso; el Parque Nacional de Mesa Verde; el Río Grande; el Valle de San Joaquín.

1. Muchos lugares del Sudoeste de los Estados Unidos tienen _____ españoles.

Otros indicios (signs) de la influencia hispana se encuentran en nuestra lengua. En las películas del «Wild West» se usan muchas expresiones de origen hispano: «lasso» (*lazo*), «lariat» (*la reata*), «vamoos» (*vamos*), «hoosegow» (*juzgado*), «sierra», «mesa», «rodeo», «sombrero».

España y México en los Estados Unidos: Una Breve Historia

España y México han hecho un papel (role) muy importante en la historia norteamericana. Después que Cristóbal Colón descubrió el Nuevo Mundo en 1492, vinieron muchos exploradores y conquistadores. En abril de 1513 Juan **Ponce de León** llegó a la embocadura (mouth) de un río que se encuentra cerca del sitio actual (present) de Jacksonville, Florida, y tomó posesión de toda la península, pensando que era una isla. La llamó *la Florida* a causa de sus muchas flores bonitas («florida» quiere decir *flowery*), y también porque la descubrió durante la temporada de la Pascua Florida (Easter).

2. _____ descubrió la Florida.

En 1519 Hernán **Cortés,** con unos 550 soldados, llegó al Golfo de México cerca de la actual ciudad de Veracruz. Después de dos años y medio de guerras intermitentes, Cortés subyugó (subdued) a los indios aztecas, mató a su rey, Moctezuma, y capturó su capital, Tenochtitlán (el sitio de la actual ciudad de México). Después de esta victoria, los españoles conquistaron poco a poco a todo México. El territorio de esta conquista incluía la mayor parte del Sudoeste norteamericano, que permaneció una parte íntegra de México hasta la Guerra Mexicana (1846–48).

3. Cortés conquistó a los _____. Moctezuma fue el _____ de los
_____.

En el año 1528, Álvar Núñez **Cabeza de Vaca** comandó una fuerza expedicionaria que se puso en camino en la Bahía de Tampa, Florida, y navegó por la costa de la península. Al llegar los españoles a la embocadura del río Misisipí, una tormenta violenta llevó el barco hasta la Isla de Galveston, cerca de la costa de Texas.

4. Cabeza de Vaca y sus hombres empezaron su viaje en _____.

Después de cruzar a tierra firme (mainland), Cabeza de Vaca y otros tres sobrevivientes (survivors) caminaron centenares (hundreds) de kilómetros a través de Texas, hasta que llegaron a San Miguel de Culiacán, un sitio en lo que hoy es el estado de Sinaloa, México. Durante esta expedición por México, Cabeza de Vaca fue capturado por los indios Sioux, y vivió un tiempo entre ellos, sirviendo de su hechicero (witch doctor).

5. _____ fue una vez el hechicero de los indios Sioux.

En 1539, Hernando **de Soto,** gobernador de Cuba, viajó a la Florida y las Carolinas. Después, volvió (he turned) hacia el oeste y descubrió el río Misisipí. En México, Francisco Vázquez de **Coronado,** conquistador, dirigió una expedición hacia el norte en busca de las fabulosas (fabled) ciudades de Cíbola. Muchos creían que estas siete "ciudades de oro" se encontraban en la región que hoy se llama Nuevo México. Coronado nunca logró encontrar estas ciudades legendarias, pero en cambio (instead) su expedición descubrió el Gran Cañón.

6. El río Misisipí fue descubierto por _____.

7. _____ descubrió el Gran Cañón.

Hay que mencionar a otros dos conquistadores importantes, aunque ellos no hicieron un papel en la historia de los Estados Unidos: Vasco Núñez de **Balboa,** que descubrió el Océano Pacífico a orillas de Panamá, y Francisco **Pizarro,** conquistador del Perú (véase la página 375).

Cuando California formaba parte del imperio español, se fundaron misiones allí con el propósito (purpose) de convertir a los indios al cristianismo. Esta tarea fue asignada a los misioneros franciscanos, cuyo (whose) jefe era el Padre Junípero **Serra.** Entre 1769 y 1823, los misioneros españoles construyeron 21 misiones a lo largo del *Camino Real* (the King's Highway), el cual (which) se extendió de San Diego a San Francisco. En 1824 México ganó su independencia de España—un suceso que abrió un capítulo nuevo en la historia del Sudoeste de los Estados Unidos.

8. Los _____ trataron de convertir a los indios al cristianismo.

9. El Camino Real va de _____ a _____.

Comunidades Hispanas en los Estados Unidos

---

1. EL SUDOESTE

La mayor parte de los residentes hispanos de California, Texas y otros estados del Sudoeste son descendientes de los colonizadores españoles que habían vivido en esas regiones cuando todavía eran partes de México. A estos residentes hay que añadir los miles de mexicanos que han estado cruzando nuestra frontera meridional (southern) desde el principio del siglo 20. Muchos de ellos se establecieron permanentemente en California y otros estados. La mayoría de estos mexicanos han sido *braceros*, es decir, labradores (farm workers) migratorios.

10. Los _____ forman parte de la población de California.

Los norteamericanos de origen mexicano se llaman popularmente *chicanos*, una palabra derivada de *mexicano*. Los chicanos están orgullosos (proud) de su origen mexicano y dan énfasis a valores hispánicos como la lealtad (loyalty) dentro de la familia, la honra personal y el machismo (manliness). En las ciudades del Sudoeste, el barrio chicano más grande o más viejo se llama «la colonia» o simplemente «el Barrio».

11. Los chicanos son norteamericanos de _____.

Los norteamericanos de origen mexicano también se enorgullecen (are proud) de una herencia (heritage) lingüística que ellos comparten con todas las demás comunidades hispanas: la lengua española. En 1968, un decreto (act) del Congreso proporcionó fondos (provided funds) para apoyar (support) y estimular programas de educación bilingüe en las escuelas públicas donde asisten grandes números de niños de habla española. Tales (such) programas han sido introducidos en muchos distritos escolares (school) a través del país. Tienen el propósito de ayudar al alumno a desarrollar las destrezas (skills) necesarias en el uso del inglés y del español.

12. Todos los grupos hispanos de los Estados Unidos tienen en común

_____.

13. Los programas de _____ se proponen ayudar a los niños hispanos.

2. La Florida

Después de la Revolución Cubana de 1959, muchos cubanos que no deseaban vivir bajo un gobierno comunista buscaron refugio en los Estados Unidos. Unos 500.000 de ellos se establecieron en la región de Miami, Florida. La mayor parte de estos refugiados eran graduados de una escuela secundaria o de la universidad, quienes habían tenido negocios o habían sido personas profesionales (médicos, abogados, etc.) antes de salir de Cuba. Aunque tenían que empezar la vida de nuevo (again) al llegar a la Florida, muchos de ellos lograron establecer nuevas empresas (businesses) o recomenzaron sus carreras (careers) anteriores. Hoy día la *colonia* cubana en Miami es una de las comunidades hispanas más prósperas de los Estados Unidos.

14. Muchos cubanos que vinieron a los Estados Unidos viven ahora en _____.

3. La Ciudad de Nueva York

Los neoyorquinos (New Yorkers) de habla española vienen de todas partes del mundo hispánico, pero la mayoría de ellos son de la isla de Puerto Rico. En Nueva York hay cosa de (about) 1,5 millones de personas de origen puertorriqueño.

15. La mayor parte de los hispanos de Nueva York son de _____.

Los puertorriqueños comenzaron a venir al continente cuando los Estados Unidos ganaron posesión de la isla de Puerto Rico en 1898, a fines de la Guerra Hispanoamericana. Gran número de ellos han podido entrar en el país porque, como ciudadanos (citizens) de los Estados Unidos, no están sujetos (subject) a las cuotas de inmigración.

16. Los puertorriqueños son _____ de los Estados Unidos.

La entrada del mayor número de puertorriqueños ocurrió entre 1945 y 1951. La mayoría de ellos se establecieron en Nueva York porque tenían amigos y parientes en esa ciudad, la cual (which) también ofrecía una gran variedad de oportunidades de empleo a los trabajadores inexpertos (unskilled) y semiexpertos (semiskilled).

17. Había muchas oportunidades de empleo para los _____ en

_____.

Muchos puertorriqueños que llegaron a Nueva York en las décadas de 1940 y 1950 han llegado a ser americanos asimilados, y ahora viven en todas partes de la ciudad. Algunos de sus hijos hablan muy poco español. Muchos borinqueños,* sin embargo, continúan hablando español entre sí (among themselves) y viven en sus propias comunidades: secciones de Brooklyn, el sur del Bronx y un distrito de Manhattan que ellos llaman *el Barrio*.

18. Muchos puertorriqueños residen en «el _____», un vecindario de Manhattan.

En la década de 1950, un grupo de jóvenes borinqueños creó el *Foro Puertorriqueño* para fomentar (promote) los intereses de los puertorriqueños en la ciudad de Nueva York. En 1961 el Foro fundó una organización llamada *Aspira*—una palabra que significa «esforzarse» (strive) o «aspirar». Aspira tiene el propósito de fomentar la enseñanza superior (higher education) para los puertorriqueños. Los anima (encourages) a tener fe (faith) en su habilidad de obtener (achieve) un porvenir mejor para sí mismos (themselves) por medio de la educación.

19. *Aspira* propone _____ para los _____.

Aspira ha hecho un papel importante en el desarrollo de los programas escolares bilingües en la ciudad de Nueva York. Estos programas son para los estudiantes hispanos que tienen poco conocimiento del inglés. Para ayudarlos a vencer este obstáculo, se enseñan algunas clases en español. Las clases bilingües también proporcionan (provide) una instrucción intensiva en la lengua inglesa. Aspira actualmente (at the present time) tiene sucursales (branches) en varios estados, y ofrece sus servicios no solamente a los puertorriqueños sino también a todos los norteamericanos de habla española.

20. Aspira ayuda a los _____ a aprender mejor el _____.

4. Otros Grupos Hispánicos

Como hemos visto, la mayoría de los hispanos que viven en los Estados Unidos son de origen mexicano, cubano o puertorriqueño. Pero hay también un gran número de inmigrantes que

---

*Los puertorriqueños se llaman también *borinqueños* o *boricuas*, los nombres indios de los antiguos habitantes de la isla.

vinieron de España, la República Dominicana y los países de Centroamérica y Sudamérica. Como todos los demás inmigrantes de cualquier nacionalidad, estas personas han venido a nuestro país por las mismas razones básicas: para escaparse de una pobreza irremediable (hopeless) o de la opresión política, para hacerse una vida mejor y para obtener un porvenir mejor para sus hijos en la Tierra de la Oportunidad.

21. Los inmigrantes hispanos vienen a los Estados Unidos para _____

_____ .

Famosos Hispanos en los Estados Unidos

A pesar de grandes obstáculos, muchas personas de origen hispano han podido encontrar carreras en los Estados Unidos sin perder su identidad cultural. De Puerto Rico viene **José Ferrer,** el famoso actor de cine que ha ganado un «Oscar». Otro puertorriqueño, **Roberto Clemente**, fue campeón nacional de béisbol; perdió la vida en 1972 en un accidente de avión mientras iba a ayudar a las víctimas de un terremoto (earthquake) en Nicaragua. Un puerto-rriqueño célebre que ha ganado muchos premios por su servicio sobresaliente (outstanding) es **Horacio Rivero,** Almirante de la Marina (Navy) de los Estados Unidos.

22. José Ferrer es un _____ que nació en _____ .

El distinguido mexicano Dr. **Ernesto Galarza,** quien de joven había sido trabajador migratorio, llegó a ser un experto en asuntos de inmigrantes (immigrant affairs). **Richard («Pancho») Gonzales,** el famoso jugador de tenis, es también de origen mexicano. Él ganó los finales en los campeonatos nacionales de 1948 y 1949. El chicano **César Chávez** sindicalizó (organized) a los braceros de California y, como jefe del United Farm Workers, ha hecho mucho para mejorar la vida del obrero migratorio mexicano. De Cuba vino el célebre compositor y pianista **Ernesto Lecuona,** que murió en 1963. Muchas de sus canciones tienen temas africanos que reflejan la cultura africana en Cuba. Ejemplos de su talento musical son las canciones «Malagueña» y «Siboney», que han sido muy populares por el mundo hispano y en los Estados Unidos. Otro cubano famoso es el actor **Desi Arnaz.**

23. El Dr. Ernesto Galarza y Pancho Gonzales son de origen _____ .

24. Desi Arnaz y Ernesto Lecuona son de _____ .

EJERCICIOS

A. *Cierto o falso.* If the statement is true, write *cierto*. If it is false, replace the words in capital letters with words that would make the statement true. (Write the correct words in the blank.)

1. Los braceros son labradores migratorios de ESPAÑA. _____

2. Coronado ENCONTRÓ las «siete ciudades de Cíbola». _____

3. La ciudad de VERACRUZ está en el Golfo de México. _____

4. JUNÍPERO SERRA fue el jefe de los misioneros franciscanos.   _____

5. Los puertorriqueños vinieron a NUEVA YORK en busca de trabajo.   _____

6. Roberto Clemente nació en NICARAGUA.   _____

7. El gran jugador de tenis de origen CUBANO es Pancho Gonzales.   _____

8. ASPIRA trata de mejorar la educación de los puertorriqueños y otros grupos hispanos.   _____

9. En el NORDESTE de los Estados Unidos hay mucha influencia hispana.   _____

10. CRISTÓBAL COLÓN descubrió la Florida en 1513.   _____

11. Sacramento es un nombre ESPAÑOL.   _____

12. Tenochtitlán fue la capital de los indios de GUATEMALA.   _____

13. Hay una colonia cubana en MIAMI.   _____

14. Las personas de origen mexicano se llaman BARRIOS.   _____

15. Cabeza de Vaca hizo una expedición por COLORADO.   _____

B. To the left of each expression in column I, write the letter of the related expression that appears in column II.

I	II
_____ **1.** Pizarro	*a.* de San Francisco a San Diego
_____ **2.** Horacio Rivero	*b.* San Miguel de Culiacán
_____ **3.** el Gran Cañón	*c.* Nuevo Mundo
_____ **4.** Colorado	*d.* el Perú
_____ **5.** Cristóbal Colón	*e.* el río Misisipí
_____ **6.** hoosegow	*f.* puertorriqueños
_____ **7.** borinqueños	*g.* almirante de origen puertorriqueño
_____ **8.** Guerra Hispanoamericana	*h.* Pancho Gonzales
_____ **9.** Camino Real	*i.* 1898
_____ **10.** Hernando de Soto	*j.* Coronado
	k. 1846
	l. juzgado
	m. Balboa
	n. estado del Sudoeste

47
España:
geografía y lugares de interés

España ocupa las cinco sextas partes (five sixths) de la Península Ibérica en el sudoeste de Europa. (Portugal ocupa el resto de la península.) Políticamente el país se extiende más allá de (beyond) la península hasta sus provincias y posesiones de ultramar (overseas): las **Islas Baleares** en el Mar Mediterráneo, las **Islas Canarias** en el Océano Atlántico cerca de la costa occidental de África, y los puertos de **Ceuta** y **Melilla** en Marruecos (Morocco).

1. La Península Ibérica está en el _____ de Europa.

2. España comparte la Península Ibérica con _____.

Al norte de España están el Mar Cantábrico y la Cordillera Pirenaica (los Pirineos), la cual separa a España de Francia; al oeste están Portugal y el Oceáno Atlántico; y al sur están el Estrecho de Gibraltar y el Mar Mediterráneo, que separan a España de África.

3. Entre España y África están el _____ y el_____.

Hay partes de España que son tan montañosas como Suiza (Switzerland). Las cordilleras principales son los Pirineos y los Cantábricos en el norte; la Sierra de Guadarrama, al norte de Madrid (en el centro de España); y las dos sierras del sur, la Nevada y la Morena.

4. España es casi tan _____ como Suiza.

Anque España está situada en la Zona Templada (Temperate Zone), hay variaciones en su clima. En el norte, hay lluvias frecuentes, inviernos poco severos (mild) y veranos frescos. Al sur de la Cordillera Cantábrica llueve muy poco, los veranos son my calurosos y los cielos son intensamente azules.

5. En España se nota una variedad de _____.

Hasta los años sesenta, España era principalmente una nación agrícola, aunque la mayor parte de su terreno era muy (too) seco para ser cultivado. Sin embargo, durante las tres últimas décadas, el país ha llegado a ser una de las naciones más industrializadas de Europa. España produce carbón (coal), maquinaria, automóviles y textiles, entre otras cosas. El turismo es otra industria importante: más de 30.000.000 de turistas visitan a España todos los años. (La población de España es de 38.000.000.)

6. Hoy día España es un país _____.

Las Regiones de España

Por su diviersidad geográfica y cultural, España ofrece muchos contrastes. El país se compone de quince regiones, y cada región tiene sus distintas costumbres y tradiciones—y en algunos casos, hasta su propia lengua.

GALICIA

Esta región está situada en el noroeste de España, directamente al norte de Portugal. El clima de Galicia es fresco y húmedo. Los gallegos (Galicians) hablan su propria lengua, el *gallego*, entre sí (among themselves). Esta lengua se parece mucho al portugués.

7. Portugal está cerca de la región de _____..

La Coruña, una ciudad del noroeste de Galicia, es un puerto importante. Es una ciudad encantadora (charming) por sus habitantes alegres y amantes de la diversión (fun-loving) y famosa por su buena comida—especialmente los mariscos (seafood) que vienen de las aguas cercanas. A unos de 56 km* (35 miles) al sur de la Coruña está Santiago de Compostela, donde se cree que el Apóstol Santiago (St. James) está enterrado (buried). Peregrinos (pilgrims) de todas partes del mundo vienen a visitar el Santuario (Shrine) de Santiago de Compostela para venerar a Santiago, el santo patrón de España.

8. A la gente de _____ le gusta divertirse y comer bien.

9. El santo patrón de España es _____.

ASTURIAS

Asturias está directamente al este de Galicia. La aldea asturiana de **Covadonga** fue el sitio de un suceso importante en la historia de España. En este sitio—en el año 718 después de Cristo (A.D.)—un rey cristiano llamado Pelayo derrotó (defeated) los ejércitos moros que habían invadido a España. Esta fue la primera victoria cristiana en la *Guerra de Reconquista*, que duro 700 años. La ciudad marítima de Gijón tiene una bellísima playa.

10. Los _____ que invadieron a España en el siglo octavo.

CANTABRIA

Cantabria está al este de Asturias. Allí se hallan las Cuevas de Altamira, famosas por sus pinturas prehistóricas.

11. Las Cuevas de Altamira son famosas por sus _____.

EL PAÍS VASCO

El País Vasco está cerca de los Pirineos, en la parte norte central del país. Es montañoso, bien irrigado y hermoso. Sus habitantes, los vascos, son descendientes de un pueblo de orígen desconocido y hablan el vascuence. Este idioma es también de orígen desconocido y no se ha podido relacionar con ningún otro idioma europeo. Los vascos tienen un carácter independiente y un profundo sentimiento religioso. En esta región se halla la célebre playa de San Sebastián, conocida como el «Biarritz» o el «Lido».

12. Los _____ son descendientes de un pueblo desconocido.

13. El Lido es una famosa _____.

NAVARRA

Navarra es una región montañosa al este del País Vasco. Pamplona, su capital, es famosa por sus ferias anuales. En el mes de julio se celebra la popular Fiesta de San Fermín, que atrae a turistas de todo el mundo.

LA RIOJA

La región de La Rioja es famosa por sus vinos de buena calidad.

CASTILLA

Castilla está dividida en Castilla y León, al norte, y Castilla-La Mancha, al sur. Castilla y León es la cuna (cradle) de la lengua española, el castellano, y el lugar de nacimiento de la reina Isabel la Católica (1451–1504), que se casó con el rey Fernando de Aragón para unificar a España. Algunas ciudades importantes de Castilla y León son:

Segovia. En Segovia hay un famoso acueducto construido por los romanos hace aproximadamente 2000 años.

Ávila. Ávila es una ciudad amurallada (walled). Las murallas de Ávila fueron construidas en el siglo once después de Cristo.

Burgos. En Burgos está la tumba del *Cid*, el famoso héroe nacional de España.

14. Los _____ construyeron el acueducto de Segovia.

Las cuidad principal de Castilla-La Mancha es Toledo. Toledo es la capital religiosa de España. En esta ciudad vivía el famoso pintor El Greco. Toledo está situado a orillas del **Río Tajo**, el río más largo de España.

15. El Greco vivía en la ciudad de _____.

La gran llanura de la Mancha está en Castilla-La Mancha. Fue allí donde el héroe de la novela de Cervantes, *Don Quijote de la Mancha*, tuvo sus aventuras. La Mancha es famosa por sus molinos de viento (windmills).

16. Cervantes escribió _____.

EXTREMADURA

Extremadura, en el sudoeste de España, es una región seca, pobre, escasamente (sparsely) poblada. Su terreno consiste en pasto (pasture) para rebaños de ovejas (flocks of sheep) y cerdos (hogs). En esta parte de España nacieron muchos de los conquistadores y exploradores del Nuevo Mundo: Cortés, Pizarro, Balboa, etc.

17. Balboa y Cortés fueron de la región de _____.

ANDALUCÍA

Andalucía ocupa todo el sur de España. Es una región montañosa. Los *andaluces* son encantadores y de buena disposición (good-natured). El **río Guadalquivir**, uno de los pocos ríos navegables de España, fluye por las ciudades de Sevilla y Córdoba. Estas ciudades pintorescas muestran muchos aspectos de la influencia mora: los patios ocultos (hidden), las calles estrechas y tortuosas (winding), la arquitectura árabe. **Sevilla** tiene un ejemplo hermoso de esta arquitectura: la torre llamada **la Giralda**, que hoy forma parte de la Catedral de Sevilla. La torre fue construida por los moros en el siglo 12. **Córdoba** fue durante un tiempo la capital de los moros. Su famosa *Mezquita* (mosque) ha sido convertida en una catedral.

18. Dos ciudades que tienen ejemplos sobresalientes (outstanding) de la influencia árabe son _____

y _____.

19. La Giralda es una _____ de la _____.

20. La famosa Mezquita está en _____.

MURCIA

Murcia está al este de Andalucía. Murcia tiene un clima mediterráneo y es rica en minerales como el hierro y el cobre. Los productos principales de esta región son los dátiles, los limones y las naranjas.

Al sudeste de Córdoba se encuentra la ciudad de **Granada**—la última ciudad mora en rendirse (to surrender) a los ejércitos victoriosos de Fernando e Isabel. La famosa **Alhambra** en Granada fue un palacio moro. Durante su visita a este palacio, Washington Irving, el autor norteamericano del siglo 19, tuvo su inspiración para escribir *Tales of the Alhambra*, una colección de cuentos españoles.

21. _____ es un antiguo palacio moro.

CATALUÑA

Cataluña, en el nordeste de España, es la región más próspera del país. La ciudad de **Barcelona**, situada en la costa del Mediterráneo, es un puerto marítimo muy activo. Es el centro comercial y financiero de España. También es la ciudad más cosmopolita del país. Una de las partes más atractivas de Barcelona es un distrito llamado **las Ramblas**. Estas «ramblas» son avenidas anchas en que los carriles (lanes) del tráfico están separados por un paseo ancho para los peatones (pedestrians). Las avenidas se extienden desde la concurrida (crowded) **Plaza de Cataluña** hasta el puerto. Por todas las Ramblas hay numerosas librerías al aire libre, cafés y quioscos de flores.

22. El centro comerical de España es la ciudad de _____.

23. Los peatones pueden dar paseos por las _____.

En lo alto del **Monte Tibidabo**, que tiene vista (overlooks) a Barcelona, hay un santuario y un parque de atracciones (amusement park) muy popular. El Tibidabo ofrece una vista magnífica de la ciudad. Al otro extremo de Barcelona, en lo alto de una colina (hill), está el **Castillo de Montjuich**[1], que fue fortificado en 1640. Cerca del castillo se encuentra un parque de atracciones que se ilumina de noche. Cuando se encienden las luces, el parque se ve por toda la ciudad. A algunos kilómetros al noroeste de Barcelona, en la cumbre de una montaña, está el famoso **Monasterio de Montserrat**, que fue construido en el siglo noveno.

24. Hay parques de atracciones en _____ y cerca del _____.

25. A unos kilómetros de Barcelona está el Monasterio de _____.

Los catalanes hablan *catalán*, una lengua romance que se parece a una lengua hablada por muchos franceses al norte de los Pirineos.

Al sur de Andorra,[2] a una elevación muy alta en los Pirineos, está el pintoresco pueblo de **Seo**

---

[1]pronounced "mon-JWEEK," in which the "J" sounds like the *s* in "pleasure"

[2]Andorra es una república pequeña que se encuentra en los Pirineos entre España y Francia. Su lengua oficial es el catalán.

de Urgel. En este pueblo se puede ver una interesante catedral románica (Romanesque) que fue construida en el siglo once.

26. El catalán es el idioma de _____.

27. En los Pirineos en el norte de Cataluña, hay una catedral muy antigua en _____.

VALENCIA

Valencia es una región del este de España que tiene muchas tierras labradas y regadas (irrigated farm lands). Su ciudad principal, **Valencia**, es un puerto del Mediterráneo, y exporta vino, naranjas y arroz.

28. Las naranjas se cultivan en _____.

ARAGÓN

Aragón, una región del nordeste de España, es el lugar de nacimiento del rey Fernando (véase la página 341). Es una región muy montañosa. Su ciudad principal es **Zaragoza**, situada a orillas del **río Ebro**. Zaragoza fue fundada por los conquistadores romanos en el año 25 antes de Cristo (B.C.).

29. El rey Fernando nació en _____.

Madrid

Madrid, capital de España, está situado en el centro geográfico del país. Por eso es el eje (hub) de todas las líneas de ferrocarril y carreteras principales. Algunos sitios de interés:

1. **El museo del Prado**, que fue construido en el siglo 18, es el museo nacional de pintura y escultura. Contiene una de las colecciones más ricas del mundo. Se exhiben muchas pinturas españolas, italianas y flamencas (Flemish). Hay más de 50 obras maestras (masterpieces) de Diego Velázquez, pintor español del siglo 17. Hay una estatua de Velázquez delante de la entrada del museo.

30. La famosa galería de arte de Madrid se llama _____.

2. **El Palacio Real** (Royal Palace). En este edificio grandísimo, que fue construido en el siglo 18, vivían muchos reyes españoles. Contiene tesoros de arte y ricos tapices (tapestries). Es ahora un museo público.

31. Los reyes de España residían en el _____.

3. **La Puerta del Sol**. Esta plaza popular está más ocupada a la hora de la merienda (véase la página 329). Se dice que todas las carreteras de España empiezan en la Puerta del Sol. Lo más interesante de esta plaza es una escultura compuesta de dos objetos: un oso y un árbol llamado

el *madroño* (strawberry tree or arbutus). El oso y el árbol aparecen en el escudo de armas (coat of arms) de Madrid. Por las calles de la Puerta del Sol se ven muchos bares parecidos a los «snackbars» de los Estados Unidos. En Madrid y en otras ciudades españolas, estos bares sirven toda clase de refrescos ligeros. Un bocadillo (snack) muy popular es el *chocolate con churros*. El chocolate es una bebida muy espesa (thick) de chocolate caliente que se toma con churros (fritters). Los churros se fríen (are fried) en aceite muy caliente (very hot olive oil); se parecen a nuestros «donuts».

32. La escultura del oso-y-árbol está en una plaza llamada _____.

33. En la Puerta del Sol se puede obtener un refresco ligero en un _____.

34. Los churros son como los _____ norteamericanos.

4. **La Plaza de España.** En esta plaza grande y abierta hay un hermoso parque conocido por sus estatuas de Don Quijote y Sancho Panza, los dos personajes principales de la novela de Cervantes, *Don Quijote de la Mancha*. La estatua de Cervantes está entre las de sus personajes. Hay un garaje público debajo de esta plaza. La Plaza de España es el punto de partida (starting point) de la calle más concurrida (busiest) de Madrid: la **Avenida de José Antonio**, o sea (or) la **Gran Vía**.

35. En la Plaza de España hay estatuas de _____.

5. **La Plaza Mayor.** En casi todo pueblo español hay una plaza mayor (main square). En esta plaza se prohíben automóviles, y hay varios cafés al aire libre por las aceras (sidewalks). En Madrid, los edificios que encierran (surround) la Plaza Mayor son muy viejos pero están bien mantenidos.

36. Los _____ no pueden pasar por la Plaza Mayor.

6. **El Zoo** y **el Parque de Atracciones.** No se debe hacer un viaje a Madrid sin visitar el Parque Zoológico (el Zoo) y el Parque de Atracciones. Los dos están situados en una área cubierta de árboles llamada la *Casa de Campo*. El Zoo es moderno y está bien organizado: tiene pequeños terrenos (plots of land) y lagos para los animales, y flechas (arrows) que indican el circuito principal (main route). Así los que visitan el Zoo no pueden perder ninguna exhibición.

37. En la Casa de Campo están el _____ y el _____.

38. Para no perderse, los que visitan el Zoo se pasean por el _____.

En el Parque de Atracciones hay toda clase de paseos (rides), juegos y lugares donde comer. Una vía de cable elevada (elevated cableway), llamada *el teleférico*, viaja encima del Parque de Atracciones y también sale del parque para dar una vista aérea muy impresionante de la ciudad.

39. Se puede ver la ciudad desde el _____.

7. **El Escorial.** A unas 40 km (25 miles) de Madrid está el famoso Escorial, un monasterio, palacio y mausoleo construido por Felipe II en 1563. Por muchos años el Escorial fue la residencia del rey Felipe. Contiene *el Panteón de los Reyes*, donde están sepultados (buried) casi todos los reyes de España. Para visitar las tumbas hay que bajar una escalera muy larga. Los sarcófagos (stone coffins) están colocados el uno encima del otro (one on top of the other).

40. Casi todos los reyes de España están sepultados en el _____.

8. **El Valle de los Caídos.** A unos cuantos kilómetros del Escorial se encuentra el Valle de los Caídos (Valley of the Fallen), un monumento construido por Francisco Franco* para rendir homenaje (pay homage) a los soldados que murieron en la Guerra Civil (1936–39). Consiste en una basílica, una cripta y una cruz gigantesca que tiene 150 metros (500 feet) de alto. A la muerte de Franco, sus restos (remains) fueron trasladados (taken) allí.

41. Para honrar a los soldados que cayeron en la Guerra Civil española, se construyó el _____.

---

*Dictador de España desde 1939 hasta su muerte en 1975.

EJERCICIOS

A. In the blank to the left of each expression in column I, write the letter of the related expression that appears in column II.

I	II
_____ 1. Bilbao	*a.* otra lengua de España
_____ 2. Fernando e Isabel	*b.* río navegable
_____ 3. Santiago de Compostela	*c.* cueva
_____ 4. Guadalquivir	*d.* catedral románica
_____ 5. Montjuich	*e.* «Pittsburgh de España»
_____ 6. Las Ramblas	*f.* Gran Vía
_____ 7. Las Islas Canarias	*g.* Don Quijote
_____ 8. el gallego	*h.* montañas del sur
_____ 9. Gijón	*i.* peregrinos
_____ 10. Avenida de San Antonio	*j.* río Ebro
_____ 11. Zaragoza	*k.* Córdoba
_____ 12. Covadonga	*l.* castillo
_____ 13. La Mancha	*m.* Pelayo
_____ 14. Ávila	*n.* murallas
_____ 15. Altamira	*o.* unificación de España
	p. paseos anchos
	q. vista de Madrid
	r. playa
	s. Océano Atlántico

B. *Cierto o falso.* Write *cierto* if the statement is true. If it is false, replace the words in capital letters with words that would make the statement true. (Write the correct words in the blanks.)

1. Francia está al SUR de España. _____

2. La Coruña está en el SUDOESTE de España. _____

3. El castellano tuvo su origen en CASTILLA-LA MANCHA _____

4. En SEGOVIA hay un acueducto antiguo. _____

5. El Cid está enterrado (buried) en MADRID. _____

6. Muchos conquistadores españoles nacieron en GALICIA. _____

7. La Giralda es una CATEDRAL en la ciudad de Sevilla. _____

8. Washington Irving visitó LA ALHAMBRA de Granada. _____

9. La Plaza de Cataluña está en SAN SEBASTIÁN. _____

10. En EL TIBIDABO hay un santuario. _____

11. Los VASCOS viven en Francia y España.   _____

12. Delante del museo del Prado hay una estatua de VELÁZQUEZ.   _____

13. La Casa de Campo de BARCELONA contiene un zoo y un parque de atracciones.   _____

14. El Panteón de los Reyes está en EL ESCORIAL.   _____

15. Franco está enterrado en EL VALLE DE LOS CAÍDOS.   _____

El castillo de Chapultepec en la ciudad de México

48
España y la América Española: La gente y sus costumbres

A. España

En el capítulo 45 hemos mencionado algunas costumbres que todos los hispanos tienen en común. La mayoría de estas costumbres se originaron en España, la madre patria del mundo hispano.

El pueblo (people) español es una mezcla (mixture) de varias razas. Los españoles son descendientes de pueblos mediterráneos, africanos y germánicos que han invadido y ocupado la Península Ibérica desde el principio de la historia. La Península fue ocupada sucesivamente por los iberos, los celtas, los fenicios, los griegos, los cartagineses, los romanos, los godos y los árabes (moros).

1. Muchas razas invadieron la _____ —.

En España los hombres pasan mucho tiempo en los *cafés* y *casinos* charlando con sus amigos. Estos cafés y casinos no sólo son importantes como centros de la vida social; allí se hacen también transacciones comerciales y pactos políticos. Por lo general, los españoles se acuestan mucho más tarde que los norteamericanos: en cualquier ciudad española, es muy común ver a los niños pequeños pasearse con sus padres o jugar en los parques a las once de la noche.

2. A menudo se hacen negociaciones en los _____ .

3. Los norteamericanos generalmente se acuestan más _____ que los españoles.

La vida diaria (daily) en los pueblos puede ser bastante aburrida, pero el aburrimiento (boredom) se alivia (is relieved) por las numerosas fiestas—religiosas y no religiosas—que tienen lugar durante todo el año. (Véase la página 330.) Un suceso (event) popular es *la corrida de toros*, que tiene lugar los domingos. Aunque la corrida de toros no es tan popular como antes, todavía atrae a mucha gente. (Véase la página 328.)

4. Muchas _____ ocurren por el año entero.

5. La _____ todavía atrae a muchos espectadores.

Muchos pueblos son primitivos; algunos no tienen calles pavimentadas, y se consigue agua solamente de un pozo (well) o de una fuente (fountain) en el centro del pueblo. Las casas generalmente están recién blanqueadas (freshly whitewashed) por fuera (on the outside) y sumamente limpias por dentro (on the inside). Con mucha frecuencia se ve a una ama de casa de rodillas (on her knees) fregando (scrubbing) la acera a la entrada de su casa.

6. Muchos _____ españoles son primitivos.

Platos Españoles Típicos

Los platos típicos de España en realidad son platos regionales que han llegado a ser populares por todo el país. La **paella** es una mezcla (mixture) de mariscos (seafood), pollo, guisantes (peas), arroz con azafrán (saffron) y pimientos (red peppers). Se cree que este plato tuvo su origen en Valencia. En algunos restaurantes este plato se llama **paella valenciana.** La **empanada,** un plato gallego, es un pastel de carne de cerdo (pork) o de pescado con una corteza (crust) por fuera (on the outside). El **cordero asado** (roast lamb) y el **cochinillo asado** (roast pig) son populares en Castilla y León. Otro plato castellano es **menestra de ternera,** un estofado (stew) de ternera (veal) y verduras. Los **churros,** muy populares en los *bares* españoles, son como los «donuts» norteamericanos, pero en forma de palos (sticks) pequeños. (Véase la página 345.) Los churros a menudo se toman con chocolate a la hora de la merienda, es decir, a eso de las cinco de la tarde. (Véase la página 329.) El **flan** es un postre muy popular por toda España. Es semejante al «caramel custard».

7. Un plato que tiene arroz como base es _____ .

8. Los _____ con chocolate se toman a la hora de la merienda.

Bebidas Españolas Típicas

El **vino** se toma de ordinario (ordinarily) con las comidas españolas. El agua, aunque es potable (drinkable) por toda España, no es la bebida que normalmente se toma con las comidas. El **café** español es muy fuerte y a menudo se mezcla (is mixed) con igual cantidad de leche hervida. Esta mezcla se llama **café con leche.** El café que se toma sin mezcla se llama **café solo,** y se bebe en una taza muy pequeña. La **horchata** es una bebida hecha de almendras machacadas (crushed almonds) en agua y azúcar. El **chocolate** es como nuestro «hot chocolate» pero más espeso (thick). Se toma generalmente en el desayuno o durante la merienda.

9. Generalmente se bebe _____ con las comidas.

10. En el desayuno se toma _____ o _____ .

La Lotería y los Estancos

La lotería en España todavía es muy popular. Los billetes de lotería se pueden comprar de vendedores en la calle o en las tiendas de tabaco llamadas **estancos** o **tabacaleras.** Estos estancos están bajo el control del gobierno y son los únicos lugares donde se pueden comprar tabaco, cigarrillos y puros (cigars). También venden sellos.

11. Se venden cigarrillos en _____

La Tuna

Una tuna es un grupo de estudiantes universitarios que forman una banda de guitarristas y cantantes. Cada miembro del grupo se llama un **tuno,** y lleva una larga capa negra adornada de cintas (ribbons) de colores vivos. Se cree que el tuno ha recibido estas cintas de cada una de sus novias (sweethearts). Algunas tunas han grabado (recorded) su música en discos y cintas magnetofónicas (tapes). Hay tunas que han hecho representaciones (performances) en los Estados Unidos—muchas veces en las universidades. Si un miembro del grupo tiene novia, todo el grupo le da una serenata a la señorita bajo su ventana.

12. Los miembros de una _____ se llaman tunos y tocan la _____.

B. Costumbres Hispanoamericanas

PASEOS O RETRETAS

Esta costumbre tiene nombres diferentes y puede variar un poco de país en país. Es una clase de acto social (social function) que tiene lugar en una plaza pública los domingos por la tarde, generalmente durante un concierto de banda al aire libre. Mientras toca la banda, grupos de muchachas se pasean cogidas del brazo (arm in arm) alrededor del quiosco de música (bandstand), mientras que grupos de muchachos en un círculo exterior se pasean en dirección contraria. Cuando un grupo se encuentra con otro, durante una pausa en el concierto, los chicos flirtean con las chicas. Si un chico se siente atraído (attracted) por una chica, él la coquetea con los ojos (gives her the eye)—una costumbre llamada *dar cuerda* (to wind up).

13. La banda toca y las chicas _____.

14. Los chicos hacen lo mismo en _____.

Durante el próximo paseo, que comienza cuando la banda vuelve a tocar, el chico se pone al lado de la chica que le atrae, y juntos se pasearán alrededor de la plaza varias veces hasta que cesa (stops) la música. Entonces, se separan otra vez. Si a la chica le gusta el chico, ella puede aceptar su invitación a tomar un refresco con él en un café cercano. Pero el muchacho tendrá que invitar también a las amigas de la muchacha.

15. El muchacho invita a la _____ a _____

con él. Las _____ de la muchacha los acompañan.

LAS CITAS

En muchas partes de Hispanoamérica, sobre todo en las ciudades grandes, las costumbres con respecto a las citas son semejantes a las de los Estados Unidos. Sin embargo, en algunas partes prevalecen (prevail) las maneras hispanas tradicionales. En muchos lugares, el joven todavía tiene la costumbre de iniciar un *noviazgo* (courtship) dándole una serenata a la señorita bajo su ventana, cantando y tocando su guitarra. Con el tiempo (eventually) el muchacho le pide permiso a la muchacha para hacerle una visita, pero estas visitas, si le son concedidas (granted), pueden ocurrir sólo cuando otros miembros de la familia están presentes. Aún (even) después de estar comprometidos (engaged), los dos jóvenes irán acompañados de un miembro mayor de la familia cuando salen.

16. Cuando un joven empieza a cortejar a una señorita, le da una _____ con su

_____.

17. Antes de casarse con ella, el joven no puede _____ solo con su novia.

18. Una persona más vieja tiene que _____ a la pareja cuando salen juntos.

EJERCICIOS

A. *Cierto o falso.* Write *cierto* if the statement is true. If it is false, replace the words in capital letters with words that would make the statement true. (Write the correct words in the blanks.)

1. La tuna es UNA COMIDA.   _____

2. EL CAFÉ SOLO se toma con leche hervida.   _____

3. LA EMPANADA es un plato gallego.   _____

4. Los billetes de lotería generalmente se venden en LOS CAFÉS.   _____

5. La madre patria de los pueblos hispanos es ESPAÑA.   _____

6. Los churros muchas veces se toman con FLAN.   _____

7. Las corridas de toros tienen lugar LOS SÁBADOS.   _____

8. La Península FRANCESA ha sido invadida varias veces
   durante su larga historia.   _____

9. Generalmente se bebe VINO con las comidas.   _____

10. LA MERIENDA se toma generalmente a las cinco de la tarde.   _____

B. To the left of each expression in column I, write the letter of the related expression that appears in column II.

I	II
_____ 1. churros	*a.* chocolate
_____ 2. casinos	*b.* Castilla y León
_____ 3. pozo	*c.* empieza con una serenata
_____ 4. flan	*d.* pactos políticos
_____ 5. cochinillo asado	*e.* arroz con azafrán
_____ 6. retreta	*f.* agua para el pueblo
_____ 7. noviazgo	*g.* los cartagineses
_____ 8. tuno	*h.* postre
_____ 9. paella	*i.* horchata
_____ 10. estancos	*j.* paseo
	k. tabaco y sellos
	l. guitarra

Repaso de los capítulos 45-48

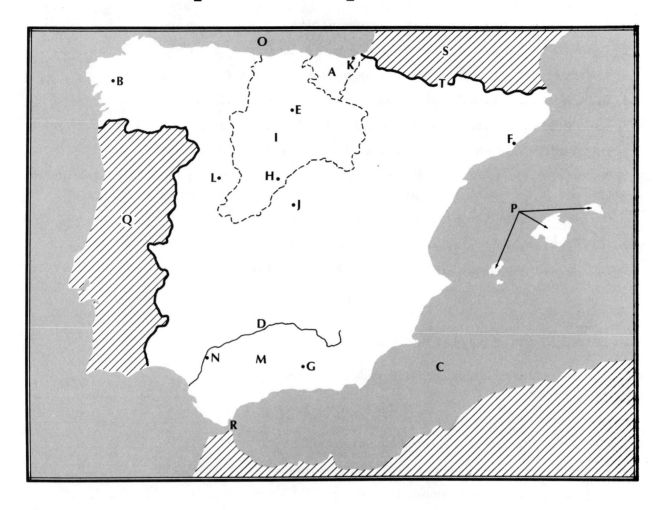

A. Next to each name, write the letter that indicates its location on the map above.

1. Granada _____
2. Portugal _____
3. San Sebastián _____
4. Sevilla _____
5. Mar Cantábrico _____
6. Francia _____
7. el río Guadalquivir _____
8. Salamanca _____
9. Segovia _____
10. Santiago de Compostela _____

11. Islas Baleares _____
12. los Pirineos _____
13. Castilla y León _____
14. Mar Mediterráneo _____
15. el País Vasco _____
16. el Estrecho de Gibraltar _____
17. Burgos _____
18. la Sierra Nevada _____
19. Madrid _____
20. Barcelona _____

B. Underline the expression that completes the sentence correctly.

1. Los romanos construyeron un acueducto en (Toledo, Madrid, Segovia).

2. La última ciudad mora en rendirse a los españoles fue (Granada, Córdoba, Sevilla).

3. Los (iberos, griegos, romanos) fueron los primeros habitantes de España.

4. El Escorial fue construido por (Fernando e Isabel, Felipe II, Carlos V).

5. La Florida fue descubierta por (Cabeza de Vaca, Ponce de León, Cristóbal Colón).

6. (El Padre Sierra, Coronado, Atahualpa) estableció misiones en California.

7. Muchos de los soldados que murieron en la Guerra Civil española están enterrados (buried) en (el Escorial, Santiago de Compostela, el Valle de los Caídos).

8. (Pizarro, De Soto, Cortés) descubrió el río Misisipí.

9. (El Greco, El Cid, Velázquez) es el más famoso héroe de España.

10. La región de (Andalucía, Galicia, Cataluña) está en la España meridional.

C. Write the name of the place or person.

1. la plaza de Madrid donde hay estatuas de Don Quijote y Sancho Panza   _____

2. Esta ciudad está cerca de la Cueva de Altamira.   _____

3. almirante norteamericano de origen puertorriqueño   _____

4. Casi todos los reyes españoles están enterrados aquí. _____

5. la ciudad que contiene la famosa *Mezquita*   _____

6. el santo patrón de España   _____

7. la ciudad llamada «el Pittsburgh de España»   _____

8. la ciudad donde hay un festival en honor de San Fermín _____

9. un famoso pintor español cuya estatua se encuentra a la entrada del museo del Prado   _____

10. la ciudad que es el centro financiero de España   _____

11. la ciudad amurallada de España   _____

12. la ciudad donde está la tumba del Cid   _____

13. la región donde se originó el juego de jai alai   _____

14. la ciudad que contiene la universidad más antigua de España   _____

15. región donde nació la reina Isabel   _____

16. Él buscaba las siete ciudades de oro de Cíbola.   _____

17. el autor de *Don Quijote de la Mancha*   _____

18. el estado que recibió su nombre de Ponce de León   _____

19. la región en que nacieron muchos conquistadores
españoles   _____

20. Él inició la Reconquista en España.   _____

D. Complete the sentences.

1. La Reconquista fue una lucha entre cristianos y _____.

2. Los pasteles que se parecen a los «donuts» norteamericanos se llaman _____.

3. El Día de la Raza también se llama _____.

4. Un _____ es un miembro de un grupo de estudiantes universitarios
que cantan y tocan la guitarra.

5. _____ es la lengua de todos los países hispánicos.

6. _____ es un plato que consiste en una mezcla de mariscos,
pollo y arroz.

7. _____ es una bebida española hecha de almendras, azúcar y agua.

8. _____ se formó en Nueva York para fomentar la enseñanza superior
para los puertorriqueños.

9. La _____ se toma al final de la siesta.

10. La papa se llama _____ en España.

11. Al terminar la escuela secundaria, el estudiante en la mayoría de los países hispanos
recibe su _____.

12. _____ es un postre español parecido a «caramel custard».

13. La fiesta patronal se celebra en honor de un _____.

14. Barajas es el aeropuerto de _____.

15. Lo que llamamos _____ en inglés es el deporte más popular del mundo
hispánico.

La Puerta del Sol, Madrid, España

49
México

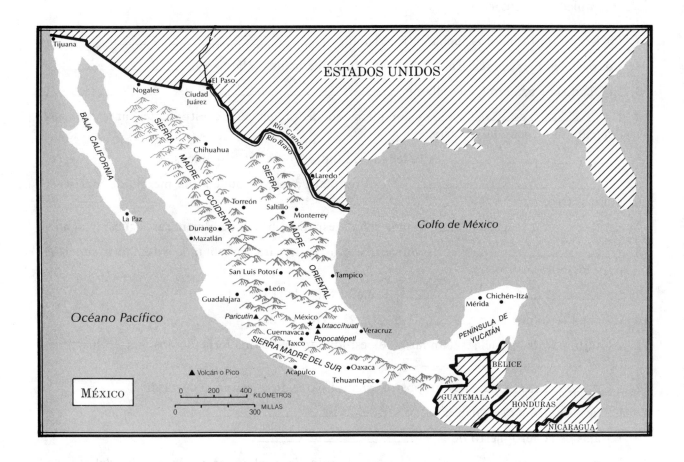

Hasta el fin de la Guerra Mexicana (1846–48) Nuevo México, Arizona, Texas, California, Nevada, Utah y parte de Colorado habían sido partes de México. Este país es nuestro vecino hispánico más cercano, y tiene fronteras con California, Arizona, Nuevo México y Texas. El **Río Grande** (que se llama el **Río Bravo** en México) es la frontera natural entre México y Texas.

1. México tiene _____ con cuatro estados norteamericanos.

México tiene la forma de un cuerno de carnero (ram's horn). A un extremo del «cuerno» está la **Península de Yucatán.** Más al sur están Guatemala y Belice (anteriormente Honduras Británica). Como el Trópico de Cáncer pasa por México, el país está situado en las Zonas Tórrida y Templada del Norte. Sin embargo, como gran parte del país es montañosa, el clima varía con la altitud.

2. México tiene variaciones en el _____.

México tiene muchos volcanes. Los más famosos, **Ixtaccíhuatl*** y **Popocatépetl,** ahora son inactivos. No están lejos de la capital, pero para verlos bien hay que viajar al pueblo de Amecameca. Desde este pueblo, se pueden ver en un día claro. Cuando son visibles, los dos volcanes parecen estar cerca el uno del otro. Los nombres de estos dos volcanes aparecen en una leyenda azteca muy conocida. Ixtaccíhuatl es una princesa que espera a su amante (lover) Popocatépetl, que va a volver de la guerra. Cuando éste vuelve, después de muchos años, descubre que su novia ha muerto durante su ausencia (absence). Afligido por el dolor (grief-stricken), le construye una tumba enorme y decide quedarse para siempre a su lado.

3. Hay una leyenda azteca acerca de los dos _____ llamados _____

   y _____.

En México hay un volcán activo, **Paricutín,** que no se conocía hasta 1943, cuando entró en erupción en el campo de un labrador (farmer). Dentro de dos años se había echado arriba (thrust upward) a una altura de 450 metros (1500 feet).

4. Paricutín entró en erupción en el año _____.

La mayoría de los mexicanos son de sangre mezclada (mixed), el resultado de matrimonio entre españoles e indias indígenas (native). Se le llama *mestizo* a uno que es parcialmente indio y parcialmente blanco.

5. El mestizo es de descendencia _____ y _____.

Este país tiene muchos lugares de interés. Por ejemplo:

La Ciudad de México

La ciudad de México, la capital del país, es una hermosa ciudad construida sobre una meseta (plateau) de 2250 metros (7500 feet) de alto. Anteriormente se llamaba *Tenochtitlán* por los indios aztecas. Tenochtitlán había sido la capital de los aztecas hasta que la ciudad fue capturada por los soldados de Cortés en 1521. Aunque la ciudad de México está situada en la Zona Tórrida, goza de un clima muy agradable a causa de su elevación. Es una ciudad moderna que contiene muchos ejemplos notables de una arquitectura muy avanzada.

6. El nombre antiguo de la ciudad de México era _____.

7. La ciudad de México tiene un _____ agradable.

La **Universidad de México** consiste en un magnífico grupo de edificios modernos que están decorados con motivos (motifs) indios. Sobre una colina en el **Bosque de Chapultepec,** el parque más grande de la ciudad, está el **castillo de Chapultepec.** Este castillo fue el domicilio

---

*pronounced "iss-tak-SEE-watl"

(residence) de los presidentes de México hasta 1940. Hoy es un museo de historia colonial. No lejos del castillo está el **Museo Nacional de Antropología,** que contiene exhibiciones de las civilizaciones precolombinas (es decir, las civilizaciones que existían en el Nuevo Mundo antes de su descubrimiento por Colón).

8. Hay edificios modernos en la _____.

9. El castillo de Chapultepec es hoy un _____.

10. _____ descubrió el Nuevo Mundo.

La plaza central de la ciudad de México se llama **el Zócalo.** Esta plaza está construida sobre la antigua plaza mayor de Tenochtitlán. En 1969 se abrió el *Sistema de Transporte Colectivo*, el metro (subway) de la ciudad de México. De 35 km (22 miles) de largo, es una obra extraordinaria de ingeniería. Para construir el metro, era necesario vencer (overcome) grandes dificultades, porque la ciudad está construida sobre un lago antiguo y también está situada en una zona de terremotos (earthquakes) activos. Los vagones (cars) de los trenes tienen ruedas de caucho (rubber wheels), y por eso los pasajeros gozan de un viaje cómodo y sin ruido.

11. El _____ de la ciudad de México es extraordinario.

12. El viaje en el _____ es _____ y _____.

Las Pirámides de Teotihuacán

Estas famosas pirámides, situadas a 48 km (30 miles) de la ciudad de México, fueron construidas por los indios pretoltecas entre los años 300 antes de Cristo y 600 después de Cristo. Hay tres estructuras interesantes en esta área:

1. La **Pirámide del Sol,** que mide 65 metros (216 feet) de alto. Hay que subir 248 escalones (steps) para llegar a la cumbre.

2. la **Pirámide de la Luna,** que es más pequeña que la Pirámide del Sol.

3. el **Templo de Quetzalcóatl,** el dios blanco de los toltecas.

13. La Pirámide del Sol es más _____ que la Pirámide de la Luna.

Xochimilco

Xochimilco es un suburbio de la ciudad de México. Es famoso por sus canales y *jardines flotantes*. Los indios aztecas de la época precolombina construyeron jardines sobre balsas (rafts) hechas de varitas entrelazadas (interwoven twigs), y luego las hacían flotar en los canales. Los jardines llegaron a ser islas arraigadas (rooted) al fondo (bottom) de los canales, y ya no flotan. Los turistas pueden pasar por los canales en *chalupas* (flat-bottomed boats) adornadas de flores, y pasan por varias islas cubiertas de flores y vegetales cultivados por los habitantes del pueblo.

14. Los _____ flotantes de _____ son muy famosos.

15. Los habitantes de Xochimilco cultivan _____ y _____ que

cubren las _____ .

Taxco

Al sudoeste de la ciudad de México está el pueblo colonial de Taxco, conocido por su plata. Las minas de plata datan del tiempo de Cortés, hace más de 400 años.

16. Taxco es el centro de la industria de _____ .

Acapulco

El famoso balneario (resort) de Acapulco, en la costa del Pacífico, se conoce como «la Riviera mexicana». Turistas de todas partes del mundo vienen aquí para gozar de las playas magníficas. Les gusta también mirar a los jóvenes valientes que se tiran (dive) desde rocas a una altura de 39 metros (130 feet) hacia las turbulentas aguas de abajo. Otra gran attracción es el jai alai, un deporte ya mencionado en el capítulo 45.

17. Hay playas bonitas en _____ .

La Península de Yucatán

Los que se interesan en la arqueología deben visitar este sitio encantador porque era el centro de la civilización maya. En el mercado de Mérida, capital de la península, se pueden comprar artículos hechos de *henequén* (sisal hemp), el producto principal de Yucatán. A unos 128 km (80 miles) al este de Mérida están las ruinas de Chichén-Itzá. Aquí se hallan (are found) pirámides y templos construidos por los mayas y los toltecas allá (way back) en el cuarto siglo después de Cristo.

18. Los indios mayas vivían en _____ .

19. En las ruinas de _____ hay _____ y _____

construidos por los indios _____ y _____ .

El Pueblo Mexicano y sus Costumbres

En las ciudades, los mexicanos se visten igual que (the same as) nosotros. El *campesino* mexicano, en cambio, lleva un *sombrero de ala ancha* (wide-brim hat) y un *sarape*—una manta (blanket) de muchos colores—sobre el hombro. La mujer lleva un *chal* (shawl) oscuro llamado un *rebozo*.

El baile nacional de México se llama el *jarabe tapatío* (Mexican Hat Dance). Para este baile los hombres visten como *charros* (Mexican cowboys) con pantalones de montar (riding pants), chaqueta corta, camisa de adornos (frilled) y sombrero de ala ancha. Las mujeres llevan un traje llamado *la china poblana*, que consiste en una blusa blanca, falda de colores vivos con lentejuelas (sequins) y huaraches (sandals). Cada hombre pone su sombrero en el suelo delante de su pareja (partner), y los dos bailan alrededor del sombrero a la música tocada por los mariachis—los músicos ambulantes (street musicians). El jarabe tapatío es muy popular en Guadalajara, la segunda ciudad de México.

20. El _____ es un baile en que los hombres y las mujeres bailan alrededor

de un _____ que está en el _____. Los _____

tocan la música para este _____.

La Cocina Mexicana (Mexican Cooking)

En vez de pan, los mexicanos generalmente comen **tortillas** con la comida. La tortilla es una hojuela (pancake) de maíz que se prepara en el horno (oven).* La mayor parte de los platos mexicanos son bastante picantes (rather spicy):

Las **enchiladas** son tortillas arrolladas (rolled) que están rellenas (stuffed) de carne picada (chopped beef) con salsa de ají (chili sauce).

Los **tamales** (singular **tamal**) son perfollas de maíz (cornhusks) rellenas de carne picada, pimientos y maíz machacado (crushed corn).

El **mole de guajolote,** popular plato mexicano, es pavo preparado en una salsa picante hecha de ají, chocolate y otros condimentos.

21. En general los _____ mexicanos son picantes.

22. El _____ de _____ se prepara con salsa de chocolate.

Bebidas

Dos bebidas alcohólicas populares se hacen de la fermentación del jugo de la planta **maguey:** pulque y tequila. El **pulque** es una especie (kind) de cerveza que contiene 6% alcohol. La **tequila** es como la ginebra (gin) y contiene de 40% a 50% alcohol.

---

*En España, la palabra *tortilla* significa una fritada de huevos batidos (omelet).

EJERCICIOS

A. *Cierto o falso.* Write *cierto* if the statement is true. If it is false, replace the words in capital letters with words that would make the statement true. (Write the correct words in the blanks.)

1. El nombre antiguo de la ciudad de México fue TEOTIHUACÁN. _____

2. MÉRIDA es la capital de la Península de Yucatán. _____

3. ACAPULCO está en la costa del Pacífico. _____

4. El Río Grande separa a México de CALIFORNIA. _____

5. Las enchiladas y los TAMALES se comen en México. _____

6. Los Jardines Flotantes están en TAXCO. _____

7. La Península de Yucatán contiene ruinas de la civilización MAYA. _____

8. El Museo Nacional de ARTE contiene exhibiciones de los indios precolombinos. _____

9. Mole de Guajolote es UNA BEBIDA. _____

10. El baile nacional de México es LA CHINA POBLANA. _____

B. To the left of each expression in column I, write the letter of the related expression that appears in column II.

I	II
_____ 1. Paricutín	*a.* ciudad del jarabe tapatío
_____ 2. Chichén-Itzá	*b.* músico
_____ 3. el Zócalo	*c.* se abrió el metro de la ciudad de México
_____ 4. pulque	*d.* Península de Yucatán
_____ 5. sarape	*e.* Popocatépetl
_____ 6. mariachi	*f.* volcán activo
_____ 7. Taxco	*g.* universidad
_____ 8. Ixtaccíhuatl	*h.* maguey
_____ 9. Acapulco	*i.* balneario
_____ 10. 1969	*j.* Pirámide del Sol
_____ 11. Guadalajara	*k.* plata
_____ 12. mestizo	*l.* Chapultepec
_____ 13. chalupas	*m.* plaza central
_____ 14. parque grande	*n.* Cortés
_____ 15. Quetzalcóatl	*o.* campesino
	p. Xochimilco
	q. dios blanco
	r. mezcla de indio y blanco
	s. henequén

50
Centroamérica
(la América Central)

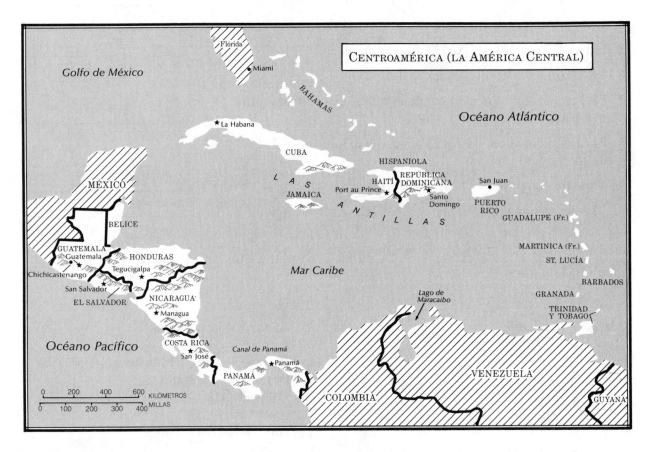

CENTROAMÉRICA (LA AMÉRICA CENTRAL)

Golfo de México

Flórida
• Miami

BAHAMAS

Océano Atlántico

★ La Habana

CUBA

HISPANIOLA

REPÚBLICA
DOMINICANA

San Juan •

L A S

HAITÍ
Port au Prince ★

★ Santo
Domingo

PUERTO
RICO

MÉXICO

JAMAICA

A N T I L L A S

GUADALUPE (Fr.)

MARTINICA (Fr.)

BELICE

ST. LUCÍA

GUATEMALA
★ Guatemala

HONDURAS

Mar Caribe

BARBADOS

Chichicastenango

★ Tegucigalpa

GRANADA

San Salvador ★

TRINIDAD
Y TOBAGO

EL SALVADOR

NICARAGUA

Lago de
Maracaibo

★ Managua

Océano Pacífico

COSTA RICA

Canal de Panamá

San José ★

• Panamá

VENEZUELA

PANAMÁ

0   200   400   600
KILÓMETROS
0   100   200   300   400
MILLAS

COLOMBIA

GUYANA

Las repúblicas centroamericanas forman un puente de tierra que junta las Américas del Norte y del Sur. Centroamérica consiste en *Belice* (anteriormente Honduras Británica) y seis países hispánicos: *Guatemala*, *El Salvador*, *Honduras*, *Nicaragua*, *Costa Rica* y *Panamá*. De estas siete repúblicas, todas menos Belice y El Salvador tienen dos litorales (coastlines): en el Océano Pacífico y el Mar Caribe. La región sufre de frecuentes terremotos y erupciones volcánicas. Algunas de estas erupciones han sido muy severas y han matado a millares de personas. Los países de Centroamérica exportan principalmente café y bananas. El importador principal de sus productos son los Estados Unidos.

1. _____ está entre Norteamérica y Sudamérica.

2. El español es la lengua nacional de todas las repúblicas centroamericanas menos _____.

362

3. Muchos habitantes de la América Central han muerto a causa de los _____.

4. Los Estados Unidos importan _____ y _____ de los países centroamericanos.

Guatemala es la más poblada de las repúblicas. Aproximadamente la mitad (half) de sus habitantes son descendientes de los indios mayas, quienes por muchos siglos antes de la conquista española regían (ruled) un imperio que incluía la Península de Yucatán, Guatemala, Honduras y parte de El Salvador.

5. El 50 por ciento de los *guatemaltecos* descienden de los _____.

La mayor parte de los indios de Guatemala todavía hablan sus idiomas mayas y no saben ni leer ni escribir el español. El producto más importante de Guatemala es el café. La capital es la **ciudad de Guatemala.**

6. Guatemala produce mucho _____.

El Salvador es la república más pequeña de la América Central. La mayoría de los habitantes son mestizos. Su producto principal es el café, pero también exporta henequén y azúcar. La capital es **San Salvador.**

7. El país más pequeño de Centroamérica es _____.

Honduras recibió su nombre de Cristóbal Colón, quien lo llamaba así a causa de las dificultades que él encontró mientras navegaba por la costa. (Honduras quiere decir «depths».) Casi todos los *hondureños* son mestizos. Su producto principal son las bananas. **Tegucigalpa** es la capital y la ciudad más grande.

8. La población de Honduras consiste principalmente en _____.

Nicaragua es el país más grande del grupo. Es el lugar de nacimiento de Rubén Darío, uno de los poetas más famosos del mundo hispánico. Más del 75 por ciento de los *nicaragüenses* son mestizos. Los habitantes han sufrido mucho a causa de la actividad volcánica del país. La mayoría vive cerca de la costa del Pacífico. Nicaragua exporta mucho algodón y tiene muchas fincas de ganado (cattle ranches). La capital es **Managua.**

9. _____, gran poeta hispano, nació en Nicaragua.

10. _____ es la capital de Nicaragua.

Costa Rica se llamó así por un conquistador en el siglo 16 a causa de la riqueza de la flora y la fauna de la región. Casi todos los *costarricenses* son blancos. El producto principal del país es el café. **San José** es la capital y la ciudad más grande.

11. Los habitantes de Costa Rica se llaman _____.

Panamá. En 1513 Balboa descubrió el Istmo de Panamá y el Océano Pacífico. Panamá fue parte de Colombia hasta 1903. Después que se separó de Colombia, su gobierno firmó un tratado (treaty) que permitía a los Estados Unidos construir el **Canal de Panamá** y asumir el control de la Zona del Canal. En 1978, los dos gobiernos se acordaron (agreed) que Panamá tomaría posesión del Canal en el año 2000.

12. El Canal de Panamá fue construido por _____.

La mayoría de los *panameños* son mestizos. El producto principal son las bananas. La **ciudad de Panamá,** su capital, está a orillas del Océano Pacífico. Otra ciudad importante es **Colón,** que está en la costa del Mar Caribe.

13. Dos ciudades importantes de Panamá son _____ y _____.

EJERCICIOS

A. Write the names of the Central American countries described below.

1. Casi todos los habitantes son mestizos.   _____

2. El producto principal son las bananas.   _____

3. Tiene volcanes activos.   _____

4. Hay dos costas de mar.   _____

5. Hay un canal que se extiende desde el Caribe hasta
   el Pacífico.   _____

B. To the left of each expression in column I, write the letter of the related expression that appears in column II.

I	II
_____ **1.** Tegucigalpa	*a.* tiene sólo un litoral
_____ **2.** Colón	*b.* Colombia
_____ **3.** San José	*c.* Balboa
_____ **4.** Océano Pacífico	*d.* Costa Rica
_____ **5.** El Salvador	*e.* poeta
	f. Nicaragua
_____ **6.** Nicaragua	*g.* Guatemala
_____ **7.** indios mayas	*h.* canal
_____ **8.** Belice	*i.* se habla inglés
_____ **9.** fincas de ganado	*j.* Honduras
_____ **10.** Rubén Darío	*k.* país más grande
	l. una ciudad de Panamá

51
Los Países del Caribe:
Cuba, la República Dominicana
y Puerto Rico

Por todo el Mar Caribe hay miles de islas llamadas **las Antillas** (the West Indies). (Véase el mapa en la página 362.) El español es la lengua oficial de sólo tres países antillanos: *Cuba*, *la República Dominicana* y *Puerto Rico*.

1. Se habla _____ en Puerto Rico, la República Dominicana y Cuba.

Cuba

Además de México, Cuba es nuestro vecino hispanoamericano más cercano. También es la isla más grande de las Antillas. Por su belleza y su riqueza natural, se ha llamado *la Perla de las Antillas.* Unos 75 por ciento de los cubanos son blancos, principalmente de origen español; los demás (the rest) son negros o *mulatos* (nacidos de negro y blanca o vice versa). Los productos más importantes de Cuba son el azúcar y el tabaco.

2. _____ es la isla más grande del Caribe.

3. Dos productos de Cuba son _____ y _____.

La capital de Cuba es **la Habana.** Antes de la Revolución de 1959, esta ciudad atraía a grandes números de turistas extranjeros, sobre todo los norteamericanos. Una de sus «vistas» interesantes es **el castillo y fortaleza del Morro,** que anteriormente fue una prisión.

4. Antes de 1959 muchos _____ norteamericanos visitaban la ciudad de _____.

5. _____ fue una prisión cubana.

Cuba ganó su independencia de España en 1898, al final de la Guerra Hispanoamericana. Un personaje importante en la historia de Cuba es José Martí, famoso poeta y patriota del siglo 19. José Martí hizo un papel importante en la lucha contra el mando (rule) español.

6. Cuando terminó la _____, Cuba ganó su _____.

7. _____ fue un famoso poeta cubano.

En 1960, el Primer Ministro Fidel Castro transformó a Cuba en la primera república comunista del Hemisferio Occidental. Los Estados Unidos no reconocen el gobierno de Castro, pero siguen manteniendo una base naval en **Guantánamo,** en la costa meridional de la isla. (La base está allí desde 1903.) Muchos cubanos se han escapado de la dictadura de Castro y ahora viven en los Estados Unidos, México, el Canadá, España y Puerto Rico.

8. En _____ hay una base _____ de los _____.

La República Dominicana

La República Dominicana comparte (shares) con Haití la isla llamada **La Española** o **Hispaniola.** La lengua oficial de Haití es el francés, y más del 90 por ciento de sus habitantes son negros. La República Dominicana está en la parte oriental (eastern) de Hispaniola y ocupa dos tercios (two thirds) de la isla. Sus productos principales son el azúcar, el café y el tabaco. Los dominicanos ganaron su independencia de España en 1865. Desde 1930 hasta 1961, la república fue regida (ruled) por el dictador Rafael Trujillo. Durante ese período, la capital, **Santo Domingo,** se llamaba Ciudad Trujillo. Muchos historiadores (historians) creen que Cristóbal Colón está enterrado en la antigua catedral de la ciudad. La **Universidad de Santo Tomás,** en Santo Domingo, es una de las universidades más antiguas del Nuevo Mundo. Los dominicanos son principalmente de descendencia española y africana. El nombre popular del país es *Quisqueya* («madre de todas las tierras»), el antiguo nombre indio de la isla de Hispaniola.

9. _____ está al oeste de la República Dominicana.

10. El dictador _____ rigió la _____ por _____ años.

11. En Santo Domingo hay una universidad muy vieja que se llama _____

_____ .

Puerto Rico

Puerto Rico es la más pequeña de las tres islas de la Antillas españolas. Tiene la forma de un rectángulo de 168 km (105 miles) de largo y 56 km (35 miles) de ancho. Al norte está el Océano Atlántico y al sur y al este está el Mar Caribe. El **Canal de la Mona** lo separa de la República Dominicana al oeste. En las tres cuartas partes (three fourths) de la isla hay colinas (hills) y montañas. Aunque la isla está situada en la Zona Tórrida, los vientos alisios (Trade Winds) del nordeste mantienen la temperatura a unos 32 grados centígrados (90° F) en el verano y 21 grados centígrados (70° F) en el invierno.

12. Puerto Rico está situado al _____ de Hispaniola.

13. Puerto Rico está en la Zona _____ .

La economía de Puerto Rico está muy industrializada y produce gran variedad de géneros fabricados (manufactured goods): textiles, materiales electrónicos, sustancias plásticas y químicas. Sus principales productos agrícolas son el azúcar, el tabaco, el café y las piñas (pineapples).

14. En Puerto Rico se cultivan el café, _____, _____, y _____.

Puerto Rico fue descubierto por Cristóbal Colón el 19 de noviembre de 1493. Entre los habitantes originales de la isla estaban los indios *taínos*, quienes llamaban su isla *Boriquén* («Tierra del noble señor»). Más tarde los colonizadores españoles cambiaron el nombre a *Borinquen*. En 1509 Ponce de León empezó a colonizar la isla, y se hizo el primer gobernador.

15. El nombre antiguo de Puerto Rico fue _____.

16. El primer gobernador de Puerto Rico fue _____.

Puerto Rico siguió siendo una colonia española hasta 1898, cuando fue cedido (ceded) a los Estados Unidos al final de la Guerra Hispanoamericana. Por un decreto (act) del Congreso en 1917, los puertorriqueños se hicieron (became) ciudadanos de los Estados Unidos. En 1952 Puerto Rico se hizo autónomo (self-governing) asumiendo el título de *Estado Libre Asociado* (Commonwealth) *de Puerto Rico*. Aunque está asociado a los Estados Unidos, Puerto Rico tiene su propia constitución y su gobernador es elegido por el pueblo (people).

17. Los puertorriqueños son _____ de los Estados Unidos.

18. Los puertorriqueños eligen (elect) a su _____.

En los años 40 (the 1940's) los Estados Unidos y Puerto Rico iniciaron un programa común llamado *Fomento* («Operation Bootstrap») para aliviar la extensa pobreza y desempleo (unemployment) de la isla. Muchos hombres de negocios norteamericanos fueron a Puerto Rico para establecer empresas (businesses) e industrias. El turismo fue fomentado (fostered) por la construcción de hoteles de lujo (luxury).

19. Se creó el programa «Fomento» para aliviar las condiciones de _____ y _____ en Puerto Rico.

La asociación larga y estrecha (close) con los Estados Unidos ha influido (influenced) mucho en el español que se habla en Puerto Rico. Muchas palabras inglesas han entrado en la lengua hablada de los puertorriqueños. Por ejemplo, en vez de *fábrica* (factory) dicen *factoría*.* En las aceras de sus ciudades, los puertorriqueños echan su basura (garbage) en un receptáculo llamado un *zafacón*. Esta palabra viene de la expresión inglesa «safe can».

20. El inglés norteamericano ha influido mucho en el _____ que se habla en Puerto Rico.

En Puerto Rico se usa la moneda (currency) de los Estados Unidos, pero un dólar se llama un *peso*, el quarter es una *peseta*, un penny es un *centavo* o familiarmente un *chavo*.

21. Los Estados Unidos y Puerto Rico usan la misma _____.

---

*Factoría es también una palabra española, pero quiere decir «trading post».

Después que los Estados Unidos tomaron posesión de la isla en 1898, trataron de convertir a Puerto Rico en un país bilingüe, pero sin éxito. Hasta 1930, las autoridades norteamericanas trataban de imponer (impose) el inglés como la lengua de instrucción en las escuelas públicas, pero los puertorriqueños se resistieron. En 1948, el español llegó a ser la lengua oficial de las escuelas, y todos los estudiantes tenían que estudiar el inglés como segunda lengua. Una institución muy notable es la **Universidad de Puerto Rico.** Su recinto (campus) principal está en Río Piedras, un suburbio de San Juan.

22. Después de 1948, la lengua oficial de las _____ ha sido el español.

23. Río Piedras es el sitio de la _____.

Los puertorriqueños son principalmente de descendencia española, con mezclas de orígenes indios y africanos.

El deporte nacional de Puerto Rico es el béisbol. Dos de sus famosos jugadores de béisbol son Roberto Clemente (véase la página 337) y Orlando Cepeda. El segundo deporte en popularidad es el básquetbol. El juego del dominó es muy popular entre los puertorriqueños. La pelea de gallos (cockfighting) es lícita (legal) y les gusta a muchos.

24. El deporte más popular de Puerto Rico es el _____.

A los borinqueños les gustan mucho la música y el baile. Dos instrumentos musicales típicos son el *cuatro*, una guitarra de doce cuerdas (strings), y el *güiro*, un tipo de tambor (drum) hecho de una calabaza (pumpkin gourd). Hasta su muerte en 1973, Pablo Casals, el famoso violoncelista de España, dirigía el Conservatorio Puertorriqueño de Música y la Orquesta Sinfónica.

25. El güiro es un tipo de _____.

26. Pablo Casals fue un gran _____ de _____.

PLATOS TÍPICOS PUERTORRIQUEÑOS

el **lechon asado** (roast suckling pig)

alcapurrias (fritters), que se hacen de bananas y se rellenan (are filled) de carne de vaca o de cangrejos (crabmeat)

el **plátano** (plantain), un tipo de banana que puede ser frito (fried), cocido (boiled) o asado al horno (baked)

27. Tres platos típicos de Puerto Rico son _____, _____

y _____.

PUERTORRIQUEÑOS FAMOSOS

Luis Muñoz Rivera, poeta, periodista y político, fue elegido comisionado residente en Wáshington, y ayudó a persuadir al Congreso a aprobar el proyecto de ley (to pass the bill) que concedía ciudadanía (citizenship) a los puertorriqueños. **Luis Muñoz Marín,** hijo de Luis Muñoz Rivera, fue el primer gobernador puertorriqueño en ser elegido por el pueblo. **Luis Palés Matos,** famoso poeta puertorriqueño que murió en 1959, era muy conocido en todo el mundo hispánico. Su poema *Pueblo negro* fue el primero en su serie de poemas que trataban de (dealt with) la herencia negra en Puerto Rico.

28. _____ obtuvo la ciudadanía para los puertorriqueños.

29. _____ fue el gran poeta borinqueño.

LUGARES DE INTERÉS

San Juan, la capital, está situado en la costa del Atlántico. La parte antigua de la ciudad tiene un aspecto español con sus calles estrechas y sus edificios viejos. Muchos de estos edificios fueron construidos durante los primeros años de la época colonial en el siglo 16. Muchas calles de esta sección de la ciudad están pavimentadas de adoquines (cobblestones)—las mismas piedras que servían de lastre (ballast) en las carabelas (ships) de Cristóbal Colón. En el centro de San Juan está la **Plaza Colón,** donde hay una estatua de Cristóbal Colón.

30. La parte vieja de San Juan se parece a una _____ española.

31. Hay una estatua de _____ en el centro de la capital.

La Fortaleza, la residencia del gobernador, está situada encima de las **Puertas** (gates) **de San Juan.** El **castillo del Morro,** a la entrada de la Bahía de San Juan, fue construido en 1539 y completado 250 años más tarde. Su propósito (purpose) era de rechazar (repel) los ataques de los piratas británicos, franceses y holandeses. **El Convento,** un hotel de lujo, fue originalmente un convento.

32. El gobernador de Puerto Rico vive en _____.

33. El castillo del Morro fue terminado en el año _____.

La parte moderna de San Juan, llamada **Santurce,** está unida al viejo San Juan por varios puentes. Santurce contiene un hermoso barrio modernísimo llamado *Condado* donde se han construido muchas casas de apartamentos.

34. Condado es una sección moderna de _____.

A una distancia corta de San Juan está la **playa de Luquillo,** una de las playas más hermosas del mundo, donde hay muchas palmeras (palm trees) y un mar siempre en calma y muy claro. No muy lejos de Luquillo se halla el bosque tropical de **El Yunque** (El Yunque Rain Forest), el único bosque tropical bajo la jurisdicción del «U.S. Forestry Service».

35. Luquillo es una _____.

36. El Yunque está cerca de _____.

Ponce, que lleva el nombre de Ponce de León, es un puerto importante en la costa meridional de la isla. Una de sus atracciones principales es la vieja estación de bomberos (firehouse) llamada el *Parque de Bombas.* Este edificio está pintado con rayas (stripes) rojas y negras.

Mayagüez es una ciudad situada en la costa occidental. Es el sitio del **Colegio de Agricultura y Artes Mecánicas,** que tiene una planta nuclear cuyo propósito es instruir a los físicos (physicists) de los Estados Unidos y la América latina.

37. Hay una planta nuclear en la ciudad de _____.

La **Bahía Fosforescente,** cerca de la región de **La Parguera** en la costa meridional, atrae a muchos turistas que van allí para ver sus aguas incandescentes (glowing) por la noche. Por desgracia, esta atracción turística puede desaparecer porque la luz extraña que brilla de noche se está disminuyendo (diminishing).

38. Se pueden ver las aguas incandescentes de la Bahía _____ por la noche.

EJERCICIOS

A. *Cierto o falso.* Write *cierto* if the statement is true. If it is false, replace the words in capital letters with words that would make the statement true. (Write the correct words in the blanks.)

1. HAITÍ ocupa la parte occidental de la isla de Hispaniola. _____

2. Hay una famosa estación de bomberos en MAYAGÜEZ, Puerto Rico. _____

3. Pablo Casals fue el director de la Orquesta Sinfónica de CUBA. _____

4. Hay una planta nuclear en LA PARGUERA, Puerto Rico. _____

5. El deporte nacional de Puerto Rico es el BÉISBOL. _____

6. Hay un «castillo del Morro» en LA HABANA Y SAN JUAN. _____

7. Puerto Rico tiene una hermosa playa en LUQUILLO. _____

8. PUERTO RICO se llama «la Perla de las Antillas». _____

9. Cuba es la isla más PEQUEÑA de las Antillas. _____

10. Puerto Rico fue descubierto por PONCE DE LEÓN. _____

11. Luis Palés Matos fue un poeta famoso de LA REPÚBLICA DOMINICANA. _____

12. Los indios taínos eran una de las tribus originales de PUERTO RICO. _____

13. El Condado es una parte moderna de SAN JUAN. _____

14. Los productos más importantes de Cuba son EL AZÚCAR y el tabaco. _____

15. La Universidad de Puerto Rico está en RÍO PIEDRAS. _____

B. To the left of each expression in column I, write the letter of the related expression that appears in column II.

I	II
_____ 1. La Parguera	*a.* Perla de las Antillas
_____ 2. Boriquén	*b.* Puerto Rico
_____ 3. la Habana	*c.* base naval
_____ 4. Quisqueya	*d.* plato típico borinqueño
_____ 5. Guantánamo	*e.* Ponce
_____ 6. El Yunque	*f.* hotel elegante
_____ 7. Fomento	*g.* capital de Cuba
_____ 8. Parque de Bombas	*h.* poeta cubano
_____ 9. chavo	*i.* entre Puerto Rico y la República Dominicana
_____ 10. Luis Muñoz Marín	*j.* dictador dominicano
_____ 11. Trujillo	*k.* gobernador de Puerto Rico
_____ 12. José Martí	*l.* jugador de béisbol
_____ 13. Estado Libre Asociado	*m.* Bahía Fosforescente
_____ 14. alcapurrias	*n.* rain forest
_____ 15. Canal de la Mona	*o.* centavo
	p. los taínos
	q. empresas norteamericanas introducidas en Puerto Rico
	r. nombre original de La Española

Una vista de Toledo, España

Sudamérica

52
Sudamérica:
Los países
de los Andes

Venezuela

Venezuela significa «pequeña Venecia» (Little Venice). Los exploradores españoles dieron este nombre a una aldea india construida sobre pilotes (piles) en las aguas bajas (shallow) del **lago de Maracaibo** porque la aldea les recordaba la ciudad de Venecia en Italia. Venezuela es el país donde nació Simón Bolívar (1783–1830). Los sudamericanos llamaron a Bolívar *el Libertador* porque él inició la lucha contra el mando español y logró liberar a cinco países de Sudamérica.

1. Los _____ dieron el nombre _____

   a una aldea india porque creían que se parecía a la ciudad italiana de _____.

2. El Libertador de Sudamérica fue _____.

La mayoría de los venezolanos son mestizos. Su industria más importante es el petróleo, que viene de los pozos (wells) a las orillas del lago de Maracaibo.

3. La gran industria de Venezuela es _____.

La capital de Venezuela es **Caracas,** que está a 19 km (12 miles) del Mar Caribe. Caracas es una metrópoli moderna que atrae a muchos turistas extranjeros. La ciudad está situada a unos 900 metros (3000 feet) sobre el nivel del mar, y por eso tiene un clima agradable. Caracas está unida a su puerto de mar, **La Guaira,** por medio de (by means of) una autopista (super-highway) que pasa por las montañas.

4. Muchos turistas van a _____.

5. _____ es el puerto de mar de Caracas.

Colombia

Este país fue nombrado Colombia en honor de Cristóbal Colón, cuyo nombre en italiano era Colombo. Es el único país de Sudamérica con costas en el Océano Pacífico y el Mar Caribe. La mayor parte de los colombianos son mestizos. La capital, **Bogotá,** es una ciudad interior que está a unos 2600 metros (8600 feet) sobre el nivel del mar.

 6. Colombia tiene dos _____.

 7. La capital de Colombia es _____.

El puerto de **Cartagena,** en el Mar Caribe, es una ciudad amurallada (walled). Las murallas fueron construidas por los españoles para proteger la ciudad contra los piratas franceses y británicos. El puerto de **Barranquilla,** también a orillas del Mar Caribe, es una ciudad más comercial que Cartagena.

 8. Dos puertos de mar de Colombia son _____ y _____.

Colombia produce más café que ningún otro país del mundo con la excepción del Brasil.

El Ecuador

El Ecuador se llama así porque el ecuador (equator) pasa por el país a 26 km (16 miles) al norte de Quito. El Ecuador es más propenso (prone) a las erupciones volcánicas que las demás naciones de Sudamérica. Aunque el Ecuador está completamente en la Zona Tórrida, su clima varía bastante a causa del terreno montañoso y las variaciones en la altitud. Su población consiste principalmente en indios y mestizos. **Quito,** la capital, está a unos 2800 metros (9400 feet) sobre el nivel del mar. Aunque es una ciudad moderna en muchos respectos, todavía conserva el áspecto (appearance) de una ciudad colonial.

 9. En el Ecuador hay muchas _____.

10. Hay gran variación en el _____ del Ecuador.

11. Casi todos los ecuatorianos son _____ y _____.

12. La capital del Ecuador es _____.

Guayaquil es la ciudad más grande del Ecuador. Situado en la costa del Pacífico, es el puerto principal del país.

El Ecuador tiene dos volcanes famosos: **Chimborazo,** que tiene casi 6300 metros (21,000 feet) de alto, y **Cotopaxi,** que tiene casi 6000 metros (20,000 feet) de alto. Cotopaxi no está lejos de Quito.

13. Cotopaxi y Chimborazo son _____.

El Perú

El Perú, tierra de los incas, se considera tan indio como español. A fines del siglo 15, el imperio de los incas se extendía del sur de Colombia al norte de Chile. La capital de los incas fue **Cuzco,** que está situado en los Andes a más de 3300 metros (11,000 feet) sobre el nivel del mar. Situadas en lo alto de un pico a unos 80 km (50 miles) de Cuzco están las ruinas de **Machu Picchu,** la ciudad perdida de los incas, que fue descubierta en 1911. Contiene las ruinas de una fortaleza y un templo incaico.

14. Los _____ vivían en el Perú.

15. En la antigua ciudad de _____ hay ruinas de los incas.

Lima, la capital del Perú, fue fundada por Pizarro después que venció a Atahualpa, rey de los incas. En Lima está situada la **Universidad de San Marcos,** fundada en 1551. El puerto de Lima es **Callao,** situado a once km (7 miles) al oeste.

16. Pizarro fundó la ciudad de _____ .

17. _____ fue el rey de los incas.

El Perú es un país agrícola. Dos de sus productos importantes son el algodón y el azúcar. Los indios cultivan *papas*, una palabra del *quechua*, la lengua de los incas.

18. Los incas hablaban _____ .

Bolivia

Bolivia no tiene costas. Es una nación con dos capitales: La Paz y Sucre. Como en el Perú y en el Ecuador, más del 50 por ciento de la población son indios. Muchos bolivianos todavía hablan quechua, la lengua de los incas. Casi todos los bolivianos viven en una ancha meseta llamada *el altiplano*. Situada sobre el altiplano, a una altura de 3600 metros (12,000 feet), está **La Paz,** la capital nacional más alta del mundo. La Paz se considera la verdadera capital, aunque **Sucre,** la capital oficial, tiene algunas oficinas del gobierno. Los recién llegados (newcomers) a La Paz al principio sufren de fuertes dolores de cabeza causados por la baja presión atmosférica, y tardan un rato (they take a while) en acostumbrarse a la altitud.

19. La Paz y Sucre son _____ de Bolivia.

20. _____ está a una elevación muy alta.

El **lago de Titicaca** forma parte de la frontera entre el Perú y Bolivia, pero la mayor parte del lago está en Bolivia. A 3750 metros (12,500 feet) sobre el nivel del mar, es el lago más alto del mundo. Algunas de las numerosas islas de Titicaca son famosas por sus tesoros arqueológicos. Los indios *aymará* que viven alrededor de la cuenca (basin) de Titicaca han podido conservar su lengua y sus costumbres antiguas.

21. Un lago muy alto de Bolivia se llama _____.

Las minas de Potosí son conocidas por sus ricos depósitos de plata y estaño (tin).

Chile

Chile es un país largo y estrecho que tiene más de 4800 km (3000 miles) de costa. Los indios lo llamaban «Chilli», que significa «rincón más extremo de la tierra». La mayoría de los chilenos son mestizos. El 70 por ciento de la población vive en la parte central del país. En el norte se encuentra el **desierto de Atacama,** que tiene fama de ser uno de los sitios más secos del mundo. Esta región tiene ricos depósitos de cobre (copper) y nitratos.

22. Chile tiene una _____ muy larga.

23. La mayoría de los chilenos viven en _____.

24. Hay cobre y nitratos en _____.

El extremo meridional de Chile es una tierra de vientos violentos y lluvias fuertes. **Punta Arenas,** un puerto franco* en el Estrecho de Magallanes, es la ciudad más meridional (southern-most) del mundo. Algunas de las tribus más primitivas del mundo se encuentran en el sur de Chile.

25. La ciudad situada más al sur del mundo es _____.

Santiago, la capital, fue fundada por Pedro de Valdivia durante sus guerras con los feroces indios araucanos del sur de Chile. Al noroeste de Santiago está el puerto de **Valparaíso.** A una corta distancia de Valparaíso está el hermoso balneario (resort) de **Viña del Mar.**

26. Pedro de Valdivia fundó la _____ de _____.

27. Los araucanos vivían en el _____ de Chile.

28. Hay una bella playa en _____.

En la frontera entre Chile y la Argentina, situada muy alta en los Andes, está la famosa estatua llamada *Cristo de los Andes.* Esta estatua fue erigida como símbolo de la paz entre los dos países.

29. El _____ simboliza la paz entre Chile y la Argentina.

---

*A *puerto franco*, or free port, is a seaport in which goods are received and shipped free of customs duty.

EJERCICIOS

A. Write the name of the South-American country associated with each of the following:

1. el país que lleva el nombre de Cristóbal Colón _____

2. la nación con la capital más alta del mundo _____

3. un país que no tiene costa de mar _____

4. el petróleo es la industria más importante _____

5. tiene dos costas de mar _____

6. la tierra de los incas _____

7. hay dos famosos volcanes _____

8. el lugar de nacimiento de Simón Bolívar _____

9. hay depósitos de nitratos y cobre _____

10. la tierra de los araucanos _____

B. *Cierto o falso.* If the statement is true, write *cierto*. If it is false, replace the words in capital letters with words that would make it true. (Write the correct words in the blanks.)

1. El lago de Titicaca está situado en Bolivia y EL ECUADOR. _____

2. Entre la Argentina y Chile está la estatua llamada CRISTO DE LOS ANDES. _____

3. LA GUAIRA es el puerto de mar de Caracas. _____

4. La ciudad más meridional del mundo es VIÑA DEL MAR. _____

5. La capital de Chile es VALPARAÍSO. _____

6. QUECHUA fue la lengua de los incas. _____

7. En el desierto de Atacama hay depósitos de PLATA Y ORO. _____

8. En Bolivia la plata y EL ESTAÑO vienen de las minas de Potosí. _____

9. QUITO es la capital del Ecuador. _____

10. El Altiplano está situado en CHILE. _____

11. El rey de los incas fue ATAHUALPA. _____

12. Las ruinas de Machu Picchu están cerca de LA PAZ. _____

13. Cartagena es un puerto de mar de VENEZUELA. _____

14. COLOMBIA produce mucho café. _____

15. Los indios araucanos vivían en EL ECUADOR. _____

53
Sudamérica:
La Argentina, el Paraguay
y el Uruguay

La Argentina

Con respecto a la superficie (area), la Argentina es la nación hispánica más grande del mundo. Comparte el sur del continente con Chile. La mayoría de los argentinos son de descendencia española e italiana. Los demás son principalmente los descendientes de inmigrantes vascos, suizos, alemanes y británicos. A diferencia de (unlike) los otros países de Sudamérica, la proporción de indios y mestizos en la población es insignificante.

1. _____ y _____ ocupan la parte meridional de Sudamérica.

La región más desarrollada del país es **la Pampa,** una vasta llanura que se extiende por centenares (hundreds) de kilómetros al oeste y al sur de Buenos Aires. Esta tierra fértil, con sus interminables campos de trigo y maíz y sus innumerables manadas de ganado (herds of cattle), es la fuente (source) principal de la riqueza de la nación. En esta región vive el *gaucho,* el «cowboy» de la Pampa. Antes del gran influjo de los labradores europeos a la Pampa a fines del siglo 19, el gaucho montaba su caballo en libertad por las llanuras en busca de aventuras. Le gustaba tocar su guitarra sentado enfrente de la hoguera (campfire), improvisando sus propias canciones. La llegada de los labradores inmigrantes y la modernización de la industria del ganado pusieron fin a su libertad. El gaucho de hoy generalmente trabaja de mozo de campo (hired hand) en una hacienda de ganado (cattle ranch).

2. Casi toda la riqueza de la Argentina viene de _____.

3. El gaucho ya no tiene tanta _____ como antes.

Aconcagua, la montaña más alta del Hemisferio Occidental, tiene casi 6900 metros (23,000 feet) de alto. Está situada en el norte del país en la frontera chilena.

Patagonia ocupa el tercio meridional (southern third) de la Argentina. Es una región de mesetas frescas y áridas, y de grandes fincas de ovejas (sheep ranches). En **Tierra del Fuego,** al sur del **Estrecho de Magallanes,** el clima es fresco y tempestuoso (stormy); en el sur extremo hace mucho frío. El suelo (soil) de Patagonia se compone principalmente de grava (gravel) natural. Charles Darwin, el eminente naturalista inglés del siglo 19, visitó a Patagonia durante su expedición a Sudamérica. En Patagonia Darwin acumuló muchos de sus datos (data) para su libro *Del origen de las especies* (Origin of Species).

4. La región llamada ————————————— está en el sur de la Argentina.

5. El famoso naturalista ————————————— pasó algún tiempo en Patagonia.

Buenos Aires, capital de la Argentina, se encuentra a orillas del Río de la Plata. Es el centro comercial y puerto principal del país. Buenos Aires se llama «el cerebro» de la Argentina por sus numerosas bibliotecas, museos e instituciones científicas. También rivaliza con la ciudad de México como el centro cultural de Hispanoamérica, sobre todo en los campos de la música, del teatro, de la literatura, de la publicación de libros y de la industria cinematográfica (movie). El elegante **Teatro Colón** es un magnífico teatro de ópera en que los más famosos cantantes del mundo han hecho representaciones (performances). Los habitantes de Buenos Aires se llaman *porteños* («habitantes del puerto»). La **Avenida Nueve de Julio** tiene fama de ser la calle más ancha del mundo. Debajo de esta calle hay un garaje con sitios para mil coches. Un impresionante obelisco se halla a un extremo de la avenida.

6. El «cerebro» de la Argentina es ————————————— .

7. Muchos famosos cantantes de ópera han cantado en ————————————— .

8. Hay un garaje muy grande debajo de la ————————————— .

El Paraguay

Como Bolivia, el Paraguay no tiene costa de mar. Es un país tropical con un clima templado (mild). Sus habitantes, casi todos mestizos, son descendientes de los indios *guaraníes*. La mayoría de ellos viven al este del río Paraguay, principalmente cerca de Asunción. Casi todos los paraguayos son bilingües; es decir, hablan español y guaraní.

9. Los paraguayos hablan dos ————————————— : el español y el ————————————— , una lengua india.

Asunción, la capital, está a orillas del río Paraguay. Es una ciudad tranquila y pintoresca, con hermosos jardines. Es mucho más pequeña que las demás capitales de Sudamérica.

10. Las otras capitales de los países sudamericanos son más ————————————— que Asunción.

Un producto importante del Paraguay es *yerba mate*, una hierba (herb) con la que se hace una bebida llamada *mate*. El mate es una clase de té que se bebe no sólo en el Paraguay sino también en otros países de Sudamérica. En los Estados Unidos se llama «Paraguayan tea».

El Uruguay

El Uruguay se llamaba *la Banda Oriental* («the Eastern Side») por los colonizadores originales porque el país está situado al lado oriental del río Uruguay. El Uruguay es la nación
hispánica más pequeña de Sudamérica. Hasta 1973, tenía el gobierno más democrático del
continente, y sus ciudadanos gozaban de un alto nivel de vida. Desde entonces, el país ha
sufrido de problemas políticos y una enorme subida (rise) en el costo de la vida.

11. Antes del año _____, el Uruguay había sido un país muy democrático.

Como los argentinos, la mayoría de los uruguayos son de origen europeo y casi todos son
descendientes de inmigrantes de España e Italia. No hay indios. Cosa de la mitad de la población vive en las cercanías (vicinity) de Montevideo.

12. La mayor parte de los uruguayos son de Italia y _____.

Montevideo, la capital, es el centro cultural y político del país. También es el centro del
distrito de los balnearios (resorts) por sus hermosas playas que se encuentran cerca de la
ciudad a lo largo del Océano Atlántico. El balneario más famoso del Uruguay es **Punta del
Este,** un sitio favorito para miles de turistas que vienen de otros países sudamericanos.

13. Cerca de Montevideo hay bonitas _____.

14. Punta del Este es un _____ popular.

Las fiestas nacionales del Uruguay difieren algo (somewhat) de las fiestas de otros países:
la Navidad se celebra como *el Día de la Familia,* y el 8 de diciembre es una fiesta llamada *el
Día de las Playas,* que indica el principio de la temporada (season) de las playas. (Hay que
recordar que el Uruguay está situado en la Zona Templada del Sur, y por eso sus estaciones
caen al revés [reverse] de las nuestras.)

15. Cuando es invierno en Nueva York, en Montevideo es _____.

Hoy día el Uruguay sufre de un problema serio de la inflación: entre los años 1975 y 1981,
por ejemplo, el costo de la vida subió más de 1200 por ciento. Una causa de esta inflación es el
extenso sistema de asistencia social (social welfare), que incluye subsidios familiares (family
allowances), seguro de desempleo (unemployment insurance), educación obligatoria y gratuita
(free), universidades gratuitas, viviendas subvencionadas (subsidized housing) y amplios subsidios de vejez (old-age benefits) y pensiones.

16. En el Uruguay la _____ es un problema grave.

EJERCICIOS

A. *Cierto o falso.* If the statement is true, write *cierto.* If it is false, replace the words in capital letters with words that would make the statement true. (Write the correct words in the blanks.)

1. Buenos Aires se llama «el cerebro» de LA ARGENTINA. _____

2. Patagonia está en el NORTE de la Argentina. _____

3. Los indios guaraníes viven en EL PARAGUAY. _____

4. La capital del Uruguay es MONTEVIDEO. _____

5. El Uruguay está en la zona TÓRRIDA. _____

6. Los vaqueros (cowboys) de la Argentina se llaman GAUCHOS. _____

7. Yerba mate es un producto del URUGUAY. _____

8. Los porteños son de LA PAMPA. _____

9. En su expedición a Sudamérica Charles Darwin visitó a PATAGONIA. _____

10. El país hispano más grande del mundo es EL PARAGUAY. _____

B. To the left of each expression in column I, write the letter of the related expression that appears in column II.

	I		II
_____	**1.** Asunción	*a.*	Tierra del Fuego
_____	**2.** Patagonia	*b.*	Día de la Familia
_____	**3.** Aconcagua	*c.*	pico alto
_____	**4.** Punta del Este	*d.*	8 de diciembre
_____	**5.** Banda Oriental	*e.*	balneario
_____	**6.** el Día de las Playas	*f.*	el Uruguay
_____	**7.** gaucho	*g.*	Río de la Plata
_____	**8.** Pampa	*h.*	vaquero
_____	**9.** Avenida Nueve de Julio	*i.*	obelisco
_____	**10.** Navidad uruguaya	*j.*	tierra fértil
		k.	capital del Paraguay
		l.	Buenos Aires

Repaso de los capítulos 49-53

A. Next to each name, write the letter that indicates its location on the map facing this page.

1. el Paraguay _____
2. Colombia _____
3. Yucatán _____
4. la Pampa _____
5. el lago de Titicaca _____
6. el Océano Atlántico _____
7. la América Central _____
8. Cuzco _____
9. La Paz _____
10. Aconcagua _____

11. el Golfo de México _____
12. el Uruguay _____
13. el Río Grande _____
14. el lago de Maracaibo _____
15. el desierto de Atacama _____
16. el Estrecho de Magallanes _____
17. islas del Caribe _____
18. el Canal de Panamá _____
19. Santiago _____
20. Buenos Aires _____

B. Underline the expression that completes the sentence correctly.

1. Puerto Rico fue descubierto el (19 de noviembre, 8 de diciembre, 16 de septiembre).
2. El nombre original (del Uruguay, de Venezuela, de México) fue la Banda Oriental.
3. El castillo de Chapultepec está situado en (Guantánamo, la ciudad de México, Buenos Aires).
4. Los indios guaraníes viven en (Bolivia, Costa Rica, el Paraguay).
5. Pizarro fundó la ciudad de (Buenos Aires, Quito, Lima).
6. A la entrada de la Bahía de San Juan en Puerto Rico está (el castillo del Morro, la Fortaleza, el Yunque).
7. El nombre antiguo de la ciudad de México fue (Sinaloa, Cuzco, Tenochtitlán).
8. En Chichén Itzá hay ruinas de los (mayas, incas, araucanos).
9. Borinquen fue el nombre antiguo de (Cuba, Puerto Rico, Venezuela).
10. (Simón Bolívar, Pedro de Valdivia, Luis Muñoz Marín) fue el «Libertador» de Sudamérica.

C. Identify:

1. el país cuyo nombre significa «el rincón más extremo de la tierra» _____
2. un país bilingüe en Sudamérica _____
3. la plaza central de la ciudad de México _____
4. bosque tropical de Puerto Rico _____
5. pico más alto de Sudamérica _____

6. región de México que contiene ruinas de los mayas y
   toltecas   _____

7. balneario mexicano en la costa del Pacífico   _____

8. la región de los gauchos   _____

9. región meridional de la Argentina   _____

10. el país que se llama «la tierra de los incas»   _____

11. tiene el título de «Estado Libre Asociado»   _____

12. el país hispano más pequeño de Sudamérica   _____

13. la ciudad de los «jardines flotantes»   _____

14. balneario cerca de Valparaíso, Chile   _____

15. «la Perla de las Antillas»   _____

D. Complete the sentences.

1. El güiro es un _____ de Puerto Rico.

2. Los _____ son los músicos ambulantes (traveling) de México.

3. Honduras recibió su nombre de _____.

4. Cuando es primavera en Montevideo, en Nueva York es _____.

5. La ciudad mexicana donde hay mucha plata es _____.

6. En Puerto Rico un «chavo» es un _____.

7. El Parque de Bombas es una atracción de la ciudad puertorriqueña de _____.

8. _____ fue un poeta y patriota cubano.

9. La capital del Ecuador es _____.

10. El deporte nacional de Puerto Rico es _____.

11. Los *porteños* son de la ciudad de _____.

12. _____ fue el rey de los incas.

13. Un plato mexicano de pavo en una salsa de chocolate se llama _____
    _____.

14. El mate es una _____ del Paraguay.

15. _____ fue el primer gobernador puertorriqueño en ser
    elegido por los puertorriqueños.

16. La Guaira es el puerto de mar de la ciudad de _____.

17. Los Estados Unidos tienen una base naval en _____, Cuba.

18. Paricutín es un _____ en México.

19. Mayagüez es una ciudad de _____.

20. Las Pirámides de _____ están cerca de la ciudad de México.

PART NINE

PASSAGES FOR READING COMPREHENSION

Read each passage and choose the correct answers to the questions that follow.

A. En Castilla hace mucho tiempo vivía un hombre noble pero muy pobre llamado Alonso Quijano. Con él vivían una criada que tenía cuarenta años y una prima que tenía veinte años. Don Alonso tenía unos cincuenta años. Era delgado y muy fuerte. Le gustaba ir de caza (hunting) de vez en cuando. Durante sus momentos libres le gustaba leer libros de caballería (chivalry). Leía día y noche acerca de los caballeros andantes (knights errant) y sus aventuras. Sus amigos y parientes trataban de disuadirle de leer estos libros porque lo veían cada día más absorto en la lectura. Le decían que las historias que leía no eran verdaderas. Sin embargo, don Alonso creía todo lo que leía. Todo le parecía la pura verdad. Por fin, con toda esta lectura el pobre hombre se volvió loco.

1. Alonso Quijano
    a. tenía poco dinero
    b. era joven
    c. tenía dos hijas
    d. era muy hermoso

2. ¿Quién era el más viejo de la casa?
    a. la criada
    b. la prima
    c. don Alonso
    d. No se sabe.

3. ¿Qué hacía Alonso Quijano cuando no tenía nada que hacer?
    a. Leía mucho.
    b. Salía con sus amigos.
    c. Miraba la televisión.
    d. Conversaba con sus parientes.

4. ¿Qué pensaban los amigos y parientes de los libros que leía don Alonso?
    a. Lo que contenían era falso.
    b. Eran muy interesantes.
    c. Él debía leer estos libros.
    d. Ellos también querían leer estos libros.

5. ¿Por qué se volvió loco don Alonso?
    a. Su familia le molestaba mucho.
    b. No tenía tiempo libre.
    c. Leía demasiado.
    d. Sus amigos le abandonaron.

B. Era el primer día de clases. Antes de empezar las clases, todos los alumnos tenían que pasar al salón de actos (auditorium) para oír un discurso del director. Después de entrar en el salón, los alumnos se sentaron en las sillas duras y esperaron la llegada del director. Los chicos estaban sentados a un lado del salón, y las chicas estaban sentadas al otro lado. De repente se oyó la voz de una maestra:

—¡El director!—exclamó.

Todos se levantaron y miraron hacia el señor que subía a la plataforma. Los alumnos se callaron unos segundos, curiosos por saber lo que el director iba a decir, pero algunos seguían charlando en voz baja. El director sacó unos papeles de su bolsillo y esperaba. Cuando todo quedó en silencio, empezó a hablar.

—Señores maestros y jóvenes alumnos—comenzó en voz débil y baja—, siéntense por favor.

1. ¿Qué tenían que hacer los alumnos antes de pasar a sus clases?
   a. escuchar un discurso
   b. estudiar sus lecciones
   c. hablar un rato
   d. tomar el desayuno

2. ¿Quién iba a hablar a los alumnos?
   a. una maestra
   b. uno de los alumnos
   c. el director
   d. una persona invitada

3. ¿Quiénes no podían sentarse juntos?
   a. los chicos y las chicas
   b. los maestros y las maestras
   c. los alumnos y los maestros
   d. los padres y sus hijos

4. ¿Qué hicieron los alumnos cuando entró el director?
   a. Salieron del salón de actos.
   b. Se pusieron en pie.
   c. Aplaudieron con entusiasmo.
   d. No le prestaron atención.

5. ¿Cómo escucharon los alumnos al director?
   a. con mucho ruido
   b. con poca atención
   c. de pie
   d. sin hablar

C. Una noche oscura, se acercó un ladrón a la casa de un hombre rico. Los pasos del ladrón despertaron al dueño de la casa, quien dijo a su esposa:

—Creo que afuera hay un ladrón que quiere robarnos. Pero no tengas miedo. Si entra en la casa, estaremos listos para él.

Y el hombre recogió un bate pesado que estaba debajo de la cama.

—Le daré un golpe con este palo.

Pensando que el dueño y su esposa estaban dormidos, el ladrón entró en la casa por una ventana abierta. El dueño le esperaba detrás de una cortina, y así que el ladrón entró, le dio un golpe en la cabeza. El hombre cayó al suelo, y el dueño le gritó a su esposa:

—¡Date prisa! (Hurry!) ¡Llama a la policía!

Pero la mujer, que estaba sentada en la cama, no se movió.

—¿Qué te pasa?

Su esposa, mirando con tristeza el cuerpo del ladrón, respondió: —Más vale llamar por una ambulancia.

1. El dueño de la casa
   a. tenía mucho dinero
   b. era un ladrón
   c. durmió toda la noche
   d. era muy viejo

2. ¿Dónde estaba el ladrón cuando el dueño se despertó?
   a. detrás de una cortina
   b. cerca de la cama
   c. fuera de la casa
   d. delante de la puerta

3. ¿Por qué decidió el ladrón entrar en la casa?
   a. Creía que podría hacerlo sin despertar a los dueños.
   b. Tenía un bate para defenderse.
   c. La noche estaba oscura.
   d. Las ventanas estaban cerradas.

4. El dueño estaba listo para
   a. abrir la ventana
   b. atacar al ladrón
   c. acostarse en la cama
   d. entrar en la casa

5. ¿Por qué no llamó su esposa a la policía?
   a. No podía moverse.
   b. No quería levantarse.
   c. No había teléfono.
   d. El ladrón estaba gravemente herido (injured).

D. Don Octavio Buscapenas sufría de una enfermedad bastante común: estaba aburrido de la vida. No podía interesarse en nada. Por eso fue a ver a una psicóloga (psychologist). Ella le dijo que debía buscar actividades interesantes y estimulantes. Al salir del consultorio de la psicóloga, don Octavio pensaba en los consejos que ella le había dado. Como primera actividad, decidió ir al teatro para ver una pieza que trataba de un crimen misterioso. Siempre le habían gustado los cuentos policíacos. Cuando salió del teatro, ya era casi medianoche. Como no tenía sueño, decidió volver a casa a pie en vez de esperar el autobús. A esas horas el autobús tardaba mucho en llegar. También quería estar solo un rato para pensar en la pieza que acababa de ver. Al pasar por una calle desierta, se fijó en un objeto que se hallaba en el suelo. Se acercó al objeto y vio una forma grande. Era el cuerpo de un hombre bien vestido. ¡Un cadáver! Don Octavio no reconoció la cara del muerto. Al principio quiso llamar a la policía desde una cabina telefónica que se encontraba muy cerca del sitio. Pero de repente se acordó de los consejos de la psicóloga: «buscar actividades interesantes y estimulantes». Don Octavio iba a hacer el papel de detective.

1. ¿Qué se sabe de don Octavio?
   a. Estaba aburrido.
   b. No le gustaban los psicólogos.
   c. Nunca seguía los consejos de nadie.
   d. Estaba enfermo.

2. ¿Por qué fue al teatro don Octavio?
   a. Quería ver una pieza emocionante.
   b. Le gustaba mucho el teatro.
   c. Allí se podía encontrar con amigos.
   d. No quería seguir los consejos de la psicóloga.

3. ¿Por qué no quiso don Octavio esperar el autobús?
   a. No le gustaban los transportes públicos.
   b. Los autobuses venían con poca frecuencia.
   c. Prefería tomar un taxi.
   d. Hacía buen tiempo.

4. ¿Qué vio don Octavio en la calle?
   a. un animal feroz
   b. un abrigo viejo
   c. el cuerpo de una persona sin vida
   d. una moneda de mucho valor

5. ¿Por qué no llamó don Octavio a la policía?
   a. Él mismo deseaba solucionar el crimen.
   b. Tenía miedo a la policía.
   c. La policía no venía tan tarde por la noche.
   d. No había teléfono cerca del lugar del crimen.

E. Felipe iba a casarse con Paulina. Ella era una mujer bonita e inteligente, pero tenía fama de ser muy dominadora y de mal genio (bad-tempered). Los amigos y parientes del joven le dijeron que no debía casarse con ella porque el matrimonio resultaría desastroso, pero Felipe no hizo caso de lo que le dijeron. Resolvió casarse con Paulina. Después de un mes el joven se encontró con algunos de sus amigos, quienes le preguntaron cómo iban las cosas. Felipe les contestó que todo iba bien, que su esposa era muy simpática y no tenían ningún problema doméstico. Los amigos quedaron muy asombrados al oír esto, y le preguntaron cómo resultó así. Felipe les respondió de este modo:

—Amigos míos, la cosa fue muy fácil. La noche en que nos casamos, al llegar a casa, nos sentamos en la sala para mirar la televisión. Yo quería ver una película en el Canal 4, y ella quería ver una representación musical en el Canal 2. Como no podíamos ponernos de acuerdo, yo me levanté y rompí el televisor con un bate de béisbol. Al ver esto, mi esposa se enfadó tanto que ella también levantó el bate y empezó a golpear mi aparato estereofónico hasta hacerlo pedazos. Ya no hay problema. No hay ni televisor ni aparato estereofónico y no tenemos motivo para disputar.

1. ¿Por qué decían los amigos de Felipe que él no debía casarse con Paulina?
   a. No les gustaba el carácter de la mujer.
   b. Felipe no tenía suficiente dinero.
   c. Un amigo del joven quería casarse con Paulina.
   d. Los padres de Paulina no aceptaban a Felipe.

2. ¿Quiénes se casaron?
   a. el padre de Paulina y la madre de Felipe
   b. Felipe y Paulina
   c. Paulina y un amigo de Felipe
   d. nadie

3. ¿Por qué estaban sorprendidos los amigos del joven?
   a. Los dos casados estaban muy tristes.
   b. Los padres no trataron de separarlos.
   c. El marido compró un televisor nuevo.
   d. Los dos no se habían divorciado.

4. ¿Qué hicieron los dos casados después de casarse?
   a. Hicieron un viaje.
   b. Invitaron a sus padres a su casa.
   c. Se sentaron para mirar la televisión.
   d. Fueron al cine para ver una película.

5. ¿Qué hicieron los dos jóvenes por fin?
   a. Vieron sus programas favoritos.
   b. Destruyeron dos aparatos.
   c. Vendieron el televisor.
   d. Compraron otro aparato estereofónico.

F. Una vez llegó a nuestro pueblo un hombre que tenía fama de interpretar sueños y de ser especialista en cosas del otro mundo. Nadie sabía de dónde había venido. Sus horas de consulta eran desde la una hasta las cuatro de la mañana, todos los días, incluso los sábados y domingos. A pesar de las horas extrañas, su oficina siempre estaba llena de gente. Una noche llegó a su oficina un campesino que había tenido un sueño muy extraño. Había soñado que llovía mucho, pero en vez de lluvia, caían unos palos (sticks) muy grandes. El intérprete le dijo al campesino que su sueño era muy fácil de interpretar. El sueño quería decir que el campesino iba a recibir una paliza (beating). El campesino salió de la oficina riéndose de esta tonta interpretación. Dos noches después, el campesino andaba hacia su casa por la noche. Antes de llegar a la puerta, un hombre que llevaba una máscara le dio una paliza muy grande. No se sabía quién había sido el asaltante ni de dónde había venido. Pero los más inteligentes del pueblo sospechaban que el criminal había sido el intérprete de sueños, quien quería cumplir con su profecía.

1. ¿De dónde era el especialista en sueños?
   a. de un pueblo lejano
   b. del mismo pueblo
   c. No se sabía.
   d. de una ciudad extranjera

2. ¿Cuándo recibía el intérprete a sus clientes?
   a. después de la medianoche
   b. por la tarde
   c. una vez por semana
   d. sólo los sábados y domingos

3. ¿Por qué vino el campesino a ver al intérprete?
   a. Le faltaba agua.
   b. Quería obtener la interpretación de un sueño.
   c. Tenía ganas de darle unos golpes.
   d. No podía tolerar la lluvia.

4. ¿Qué pensaba el campesino de la interpretación de su sueño?
   a. Pensaba que era correcta.
   b. Él mismo podía interpretarlo mejor.
   c. No la comprendió.
   d. No la creyó.

5. ¿A quién sospechaban algunos?
   a. a nadie
   b. a un hombre del pueblo
   c. al intérprete del sueño
   d. a uno de los amigos del campesino

G.

Ramón Jiménez, un chico de diez y seis años, estaba muy aburrido una noche, y decidió dar un paseo. Todos sus amigos estaban ocupados, y por eso tuvo que pasearse solo. Andando por una calle pasó por una casa de donde salía la melodía de una canción popular. Ramón se detuvo delante de la casa y descubrió que la melodía venía de una voz femenina. Ramón se imaginó que cantaba una muchacha de la misma edad que él. Se acercó a la ventana y empezó a escuchar el canto, esperando ver a la chica. De pronto oyó una voz masculina que le gritó:

—¿Qué hace Ud. aquí? ¿Qué pensaba Ud. hacer? ¡Voy a llamar a la policía!

En ese momento salió de la casa una hermosa muchacha de ojos azules y de pelo rubio, diciendo a su padre:

—Papá, ¿Qué haces? ¿Quién es ese muchacho?

El padre contestó que trataba de proteger a su hija de un criminal. El muchacho protestó que no era criminal, sino un admirador del buen canto. El padre se dio cuenta de que había sido demasiado severo con el chico. Le pidió perdón y le invitó a entrar en su casa para tomar un refresco. El chico aceptó la invitación, y así llegó a conocer a la muchacha que, años más tarde, iba a ser su esposa.

1. ¿Por qué dio un paseo Ramón?
   a. Quería visitar a un amigo.
   b. Pensaba gozar del aire fresco.
   c. No tenía otra cosa que hacer.
   d. Le gustaba salir por la noche.

2. ¿Por qué salió solo Ramón?
   a. Sus compañeros tenían otras cosas que hacer.
   b. No le gustaba ir con sus amigos.
   c. Sus amigos estaban con sus padres.
   d. Sus amigos no querían acompañarle.

3. ¿Qué oyó Ramón?
   a. un grupo que hacía ruido
   b. una banda que tocaba
   c. música de una ópera
   d. una voz que cantaba

4. ¿Por qué estaba enojado el padre?
   a. Su hija cantaba mal.
   b. Creía que Ramón iba a atacar a su hija.
   c. Ramón quería cantar también.
   d. Ramón quería casarse con su hija.

5. ¿Cuál fue el resultado de esta escena?
   a. Ramón y la chica se hicieron novios.
   b. El padre llamó a la policía.
   c. El muchacho volvió a casa.
   d. La muchacha no quería conocer a Ramón.

H. El Sr. Oviedo era profesor de español. Un día anunció a la clase que cada uno de sus alumnos iba a adquirir un amigo hispánico por correspondencia.

—Tengo un amigo, Raúl Ortega, que vive en Santiago, Chile. El Sr. Ortega enseña inglés en un colegio de esa ciudad. Uds. escribirán en español a sus alumnos, y en su clase ellos les escribirán a Uds. en inglés.

Este proyecto les gustó mucho a los alumnos del Sr. Oviedo. Ricardo preguntó al profesor cuándo iban a empezar. El profesor le contestó:

—Hoy mismo. Aquí tengo los nombres y las direcciones de todos los alumnos de mi amigo chileno. Jóvenes, cada uno de Uds. ya tiene un amigo chileno. Ahora Uds. van a poner en práctica el español que han aprendido en esta clase. ¿Hay preguntas?

—Sí —dijo Lupe—, ¿cómo se empieza la carta?

—Se empieza así: «Querido Juan» o «Querida María» —respondió el Sr. Oviedo.

—¿Y cómo se termina?

—Sólo hay que decir «sinceramente» o «su amiga».

—¿Sería una buena idea mandar mi foto con la primera carta? —preguntó Alberto.

—Con una cara como la tuya, lo dudo —dijo Miguel. Todo el mundo se rió.

—¡Basta! —gritó el profesor. —Los que acaban de reír deberían (ought to) mirarse en el espejo.

1. ¿Qué harán los estudiantes del Sr. Oviedo?
   a. Escribirán a unos estudiantes de Chile.
   b. Harán un viaje a Santiago.
   c. Visitarán al Sr. Ortega.
   d. Vivirán en Chile por un mes.

2. ¿Quién era el Sr. Ortega?
   a. un amigo de Ricardo
   b. un profesor de español
   c. un profesor de inglés
   d. un pariente del Sr. Oviedo

3. ¿Qué pensaban los estudiantes de la idea del Sr. Oviedo?
   a. Creían que era tonta.
   b. Pensaban que sería mejor viajar a Chile.
   c. No les gustaba.
   d. Les interesaba.

4. ¿Qué tenía el Sr. Oviedo?
   a. cartas de Chile
   b. toda la información necesaria
   c. sólo los nombres de algunos niños chilenos
   d. algunos amigos chilenos

5. ¿Qué deseaba saber una estudiante?
   a. cómo debía comenzar y terminar la carta
   b. cómo eran los chicos chilenos
   c. cómo se llamaba el profesor chileno
   d. por qué tenían que escribir cartas

I. Antonio Temelotodo era un hombre que tenía miedo de todo en la vida: las caídas, los coches, los autobuses, los trenes, y sobre todo las enfermedades. Él siempre pensaba que iba a ponerse enfermo. Por eso tomaba muchas precauciones. Una vez estaba tan enfermo que su médico le aconsejó tomar unas vacaciones en el campo. Antonio discutía con su esposa cuál sería el mejor lugar en que pasar sus vacaciones.

—Si vamos al norte —dijo él—, hará mucho frío, y muchas veces nieva. Si vamos al sur, hará mucho calor. Y además, he leído en el periódico que allí hay una gran epidemia de fiebre tifoidea.

Por fin decidieron ir a un pueblo pequeño en la parte oeste del país. Antonio estaba bastante seguro de que allí no habría ni enfermedades ni personas enfermas.

Cuando llegaron al hotel, se instalaron en un cuarto muy pequeño pero cómodo. En seguida Antonio notó un olor muy fuerte de desinfectante. Llamó al director del hotel para preguntarle quién se había quedado antes en esa habitación. El director contestó que el cuarto había estado desocupado desde hacía mucho tiempo. Sin embargo Antonio insistió en cambiar de habitación. En la próxima habitación había el mismo olor. Después de cambiar de cuarto cinco veces, Antonio decidió ir a otro hotel. Allí pasó lo mismo: siempre el mismo olor. Por fin decidió volver a casa en el próximo tren. Por desgracia, había el olor conocido en su compartimiento del tren. Antonio pensó que todo el mundo estaba enfermo a causa de una gran epidemia.

Al llegar a casa, Antonio empezó a deshacer su maleta, de donde se escapó un fuerte olor. Allí estaba la causa de todo. Fue el olor del medicamento que él había traído. La botella se había roto y el líquido, con su fuerte olor, se había difundido (spread) por toda la maleta.

—Aquí tienes tu epidemia de fiebre tifoidea—le dijo su esposa.

1. ¿Qué creía Antonio Temelotodo?
   a. Siempre estaría enfermo.
   b. Los médicos no podían curar nada.
   c. No era necesario tomar precauciones.
   d. La vida valía poco.

2. ¿Qué consejos le dio el médico a Antonio?
   a. Era necesario consultar a otro médico.
   b. No debía viajar en tren.
   c. Tenía que evitar los autobuses.
   d. Debía salir de la ciudad.

3. ¿Qué problema discutió Antonio con su esposa?
   a. No le gustaba el campo.
   b. No sabía dónde pasar sus vacaciones.
   c. No quería seguir los consejos del doctor.
   d. Había epidemias por todo el país.

4. ¿Qué encontró Antonio en todas las habitaciones de los hoteles?
   a. Había un olor muy fuerte.
   b. Las habitaciones eran muy pequeñas.
   c. Nadie había limpiado las habitaciones.
   d. Había insectos debajo de la cama.

5. ¿Cuál fue la causa de los problemas de Antonio?
   a. una epidemia verdadera
   b. algo que hizo el dueño del primer hotel
   c. algo que encontró en su maleta
   d. su mujer obstinada

J. Alejandro Martínez tenía una sola ambición: la de llegar a ser médico. Vivía en Barcelona, donde acababa de recibir su Bachillerato. Ahora iba a estudiar para médico en la Facultad de Medicina (Medical School) de Santiago de Compostela. Alejandro tenía diez y nueve años. Era alto, hermoso y un atleta excelente. Santiago de Compostela se encuentra en Galicia, al otro extremo de España. Aunque Alejandro no conocía a nadie en aquella ciudad, no iba a sentirse solo. Afortunadamente, allí vivía la familia de Francisco Sánchez, un antiguo amigo de su padre.

La noche antes de partir para Santiago, su padre le dijo:

—Alejandro, espero que visitarás a la familia de mi buen amigo Francisco. Te recibirán con mucha cordialidad y cariño. Francisco tiene tres hijos: Antonio, que tiene quince años; Federico, de diez y siete años; y Ana, la mayor, que tiene diez y nueve años. Ella es de la misma edad que tú. Es una familia muy feliz y te divertirás con ellos.

Cuando Alejandro llegó a Santiago, se instaló en una residencia (dormitory). Al principio, sólo se ocupaba con sus estudios. Una tarde, estaba cansado de estudiar y se sentía muy solo. De repente, recordó lo que su padre le había dicho. Llamó a la familia Sánchez. Habló con el padre, quien le invitó a cenar con ellos. Aquella noche pasó un rato muy divertido con la familia discutiendo sus estudios y su familia. Supo que Ana también quería estudiar para médica y que los dos tenían mucho en común: les gustaban los mismos deportes, se interesaban en la misma clase de música y no miraban nunca la televisión.

«Los próximos años van a ser muy agradables», pensaba Alejandro. «Creo que Ana y yo nos haremos muy buenos amigos.»

1. ¿Qué carrera deseaba seguir Alejandro?
   a. matemáticas
   b. medicina
   c. ciencias naturales
   d. enseñanza

2. ¿Dónde estaba la Facultad de Medicina?
   a. lejos de la ciudad de Alejandro
   b. en una ciudad cercana
   c. en su propia ciudad
   d. en otro país

3. ¿Quién era Francisco Sánchez?
   a. el abuelo de Alejandro
   b. el padre de un amigo de Alejandro
   c. un profesor de la Facultad de Medicina
   d. un amigo del Sr. Martínez

4. ¿Por qué llamó Alejandro a la familia Sánchez?
   a. Quería ver a Ana.
   b. Tenía unas preguntas que hacer al Sr. Sánchez.
   c. Se sentía solo.
   d. No le gustaba su habitación.

5. ¿Por qué pensó Alejandro que él y Ana serían buenos amigos?
   a. Tenían los mismos intereses.
   b. Ella era muy bonita.
   c. La familia de ella era muy rica.
   d. La familia vivía cerca de la Facultad de Medicina.

K. Muy lejos de la Tierra, en otro sistema solar, había un planeta muy semejante al nuestro. Los habitantes del planeta lo llamaban Xplz. Los xplzeros eran seres humanos como nosotros, pero más avanzados intelectualmente. Por ejemplo, algunos de sus científicos no tenían más que diez años.

En uno de los observatorios astronómicos del planeta trabajaba un joven científico llamado Ndnk. Tenía sólo diez y seis años. Un día, Ndnk miraba por su super-telescopio a cierta región de la galaxia. De repente observó, a muchos millares de millones de kilómetros de distancia, un pequeño planeta casi idéntico al suyo. Parecía tener los mismos mares, los mismos continentes, etc. Aquel planeta que acababa de descubrir era . . . ¡la Tierra!

El astrónomo dirigió su telescopio a una región del planeta donde era domingo por la tarde. Luego fijó el telescopio en un banco de un parque donde estaba sentada una señorita muy hermosa. En seguida el joven se enamoró de la dama y empezó a calcular cuánto tiempo necesitaría para viajar a la Tierra. Discutió su problema con otro astrónomo más viejo y más sabio que él. Su amigo le explicó que la mujer probablemente ya no existía, o, si existía todavía, debía de ser muy vieja.

—Ndnk, debes tener en cuenta la enorme distancia que hay entre su planeta y el nuestro.

El joven astrónomo se dio cuenta de que la luz que le llevaba la imagen de la señorita a través del espacio habría (would have) tardado muchos años en llegar a la lente de su telescopio. El pobre Ndnk se puso tan triste que no volvió a su telescopio, y trató de olvidar a la linda muchacha. ¡Qué solitaria es la vida de un astrónomo!

1. ¿Cómo son los habitantes de Xplz?
   a. Son más inteligentes que nosotros.
   b. Son más viejos que nosotros.
   c. No asisten a la escuela.
   d. Todos son científicos.

2. Sabemos que nosotros podríamos vivir en Xplz porque el planeta está
   a. cerca de la Tierra
   b. habitado por seres humanos
   c. en otro sistema solar
   d. sin mares y continentes

3. ¿Qué hacía el joven astrónomo?
   a. Estaba viajando a otro planeta.
   b. Ayudaba a otro astrónomo en el observatorio.
   c. Iba a la iglesia a oír misa.
   d. Estaba observando otro planeta.

4. ¿Por qué quería Ndnk ir a la Tierra?
   a. Quería visitar a un amigo.
   b. Tenía familia allí.
   c. Deseaba conocer a una muchacha que vivía allí.
   d. Pensaba vivir allí.

5. ¿Por qué estaba triste el joven?
   a. Se dio cuenta de que sería imposible satisfacer su deseo.
   b. La muchacha no le quería.
   c. Los telescopios no servían para nada.
   d. Su amigo no le decía la verdad.

L. Una noche dos amigos estaban charlando en un café. Como los dos habían tomado mucho vino, se sentían muy alegres. Los amigos se llamaban Quique y Paquito. En tono de burla (jest), Paquito le dijo a Quique:

—Tú sabes mucho acerca de las matemáticas.

El pobre Quique, que apenas sabía sumar dos y dos sin usar los dedos, movió la cabeza afirmativamente. Un hombre que estaba sentado al lado de los dos amigos oyó esta conversación, y pronto dio la noticia a sus amigos. Dentro de una semana todo el pueblo hablaba del gran talento de Quique. Todos los que le encontraban en la calle le saludaban con mucho respeto. Su país le mandó a un Congreso Internacional para dar un discurso. Su discurso tuvo mucho éxito porque nadie entendía lo que decía. Habló en español, lengua que nadie hablaba en el Congreso. Todo el mundo le hacía preguntas acerca de su vida privada, sus intereses, sus platos favoritos, qué programas de televisión prefería, etc. Pero nadie se atrevía a hacerle preguntas sobre las matemáticas, porque creían que sus respuestas serían muy complejas y difíciles de comprender. Se decía que Quique tenía en su casa una computadora misteriosa, pero a nadie le era permitido verla. Quique llegó a ser una de las personas más famosas de su época.

Por desgracia, después de un fuerte ataque de corazón, Quique murió. Toda la nación lloró su muerte. Una comisión de matemáticos decidió inspeccionar el cuarto donde guardaba su computadora. Al entrar, descubrieron un cuarto tan vacío como la cabeza de su dueño. No había nada: ni computadora, ni papeles, ni cuadernos. Algunas personas creían que Quique había sido un embustero (faker). Otros creían que toda su sabiduría (wisdom), que estaba en su cabeza, murió con él.

1. ¿Qué hacían los dos amigos?
   a. Estaban conversando en una taberna.
   b. Estaban andando por el centro del pueblo.
   c. Hablaban de sus familias.
   d. Estaban cenando.

2. ¿Cómo llegaron todos a saber del talento de Quique?
   a. Quique se lo anunció a todo el mundo por radio.
   b. Se anunció en la televisión.
   c. Se leyó en un periódico.
   d. Alguien escuchaba la conversación de los dos.

3. ¿Por qué aceptaron el discurso de Quique?
   a. Quique habló muy bien.
   b. Nadie lo comprendió.
   c. Todos sabían las matemáticas.
   d. Sus amigos le aplaudieron mucho.

4. ¿Por qué continuaba Quique con su reputación?
   a. Nadie podía disputar su talento.
   b. Él sabía mucho sobre las matemáticas.
   c. Nadie le preguntaba sobre las matemáticas.
   d. Los matemáticos decían que él era un gran hombre.

5. ¿Qué encontraron en la habitación de Quique?
   a. nada
   b. muchas obras de matemáticas
   c. libros complicados
   d. papeles importantes

PART TEN

LISTENING COMPREHENSION

To the teacher: The passages pertaining to this exercise will be found in the Answer-Key booklet.

To the student: Your teacher will read aloud some short passages in Spanish. Each passage will be read twice. After the second reading, the teacher will pause briefly, then read aloud the question (below) that refers to the passage. Circle the letter of the correct answer.

1. ¿Con quién habla la persona al teléfono?
   a. con Paco
   b. con su hermano
   c. con el padre de Paco
   d. con María

2. ¿De qué se habla?
   a. de una fiesta
   b. de una familia
   c. del tiempo
   d. de una cita

3. ¿Qué consejos se dan aquí?
   a. Es necesario viajar en seguida.
   b. No hay que esperar la luna nueva.
   c. La luna nueva no trae nada importante.
   d. No se debe viajar hasta cierto tiempo.

4. ¿Para quiénes es la clínica?
   a. para los que tienen problemas con la vista
   b. para los mentalmente enfermos
   c. para los que sufren de enfermedades de los dientes
   d. sólo para los pacientes ricos

5. ¿Quién va a realizar el proyecto?
   a. un animal grande
   b. un artista famoso
   c. un matemático célebre
   d. una persona desconocida

6. ¿En qué estación estamos?
   a. en la primavera
   b. en el otoño
   c. en el verano
   d. en el invierno

7. ¿Dónde tiene lugar esta escena?
   a. en una casa
   b. en una escuela
   c. en un cine
   d. en un restaurante

8. ¿Cuándo ocurre esta escena?
   a. a la medianoche
   b. temprano por la mañana
   c. por la tarde
   d. el sábado por la noche

9. ¿Por qué tiene que levantarse Juana?
   a. Ella tiene que ir a la escuela.
   b. Su familia va a hacer un viaje en coche.
   c. Ella va a reunirse con unas amigas.
   d. El desayuno está listo.

10. ¿Para qué quiere Eduardo ir al centro?
    a. Quiere ver una película nueva.
    b. Tiene cita con una amiga.
    c. Desea comprar ropa.
    d. Va a reunirse con su mamá allí.

11. ¿Qué ocurre?
    a. Alguien aprende a conducir un coche.
    b. Dos personas hablan de un film que acaban de ver.
    c. Ha ocurrido un accidente entre dos automóviles.
    d. Unas amigas andan por el parque.

12. ¿Dónde tiene lugar esta escena?
    a. en un hotel
    b. en un teatro
    c. en un café
    d. en una escuela

13. ¿De qué trata la discusión?
    a. de un programa musical en la radio
    b. de una comida especial
    c. de un día en el campo
    d. de la selección de un programa de televisión

14. ¿Cómo se puede asistir al concierto?
    a. obteniendo los billetes el mismo día
    b. comprando los billetes al llegar
    c. entrando sin tener que pagar
    d. llamando por teléfono

15. ¿Quién habla?
    a. un padre de familia
    b. un guía turístico
    c. un profesor de música
    d. un anunciador de radio

16. ¿Con quién fue Manuelito al zoo?
    a. con su padre
    b. con su amigo
    c. con su madre
    d. con un primo

17. ¿Dónde están las Pirámides?
    a. en la ciudad de México
    b. no muy lejos de la ciudad de México
    c. fuera del país
    d. en la costa del norte

18. ¿Quién habla?
    a. un profesor a su clase
    b. un vendedor de libros a unos clientes
    c. un alumno a su profesor
    d. un alumno a otro alumno

19. ¿Qué nos indica esta observación?
    a. Alguien tiene que ir al hospital.
    b. Hace mucho calor.
    c. Una persona no se siente bien.
    d. Alguien ha tenido un accidente grave.

20. ¿Dónde están estas personas?
    a. en un teatro
    b. en una estación de gasolina
    c. en un hospital
    d. en una fiesta

21. ¿Cuál es el problema?
    a. Alguien está enfermo.
    b. Un coche no funciona bien.
    c. No hay agua en casa.
    d. Nadie quiere reparar un defecto.

22. ¿Dónde tiene lugar esta escena?
    a. en un parque
    b. en un cine
    c. en una escuela de conducir
    d. en un banco

23. ¿Por qué no puede ir Pablo a la playa temprano?
    a. Tiene algo que hacer por la mañana.
    b. No le gusta la playa por la mañana.
    c. No se siente bien.
    d. Su madre no le permite ir.

24. ¿Dónde pasa esto?
    a. en un tren
    b. en un avión
    c. en un barco
    d. en un autobús

25. ¿Por qué escribe esta carta la joven?
    a. Quiere tomar un curso de estenografía.
    b. Necesita informaciones de viaje.
    c. Busca empleo de verano.
    d. Quiere aprender el español durante el verano.

26. ¿Por qué se detuvo la persona?
    a. Quería escuchar la música.
    b. Conocía a uno de los músicos.
    c. No quería volver a su casa.
    d. No tenía ganas de comer.

27. ¿Qué espera la familia?
    a. la llegada de unos parientes
    b. una visita de unos amigos
    c. un paquete de la Florida
    d. una carta de la tía Sara

28. ¿Qué desea la señora?
    a. billetes de teatro
    b. direcciones para ir a un lugar
    c. la calle de la Victoria
    d. molestar a la otra persona

29. ¿Cómo pudo el chico obtener todos los juguetes?
    a. Su padre le había dado el dinero para comprarlos.
    b. Había robado el dinero para conseguirlos.
    c. Un empleado le dio los juguetes.
    d. Los recibió como regalo.

30. ¿Por qué se agrupaba mucha gente?
    a. Miraban a unos hombres en bicicleta.
    b. Escuchaban la música de unos jóvenes.
    c. Querían ver un accidente de coches.
    d. Miraban a unos animales interesantes.

31. ¿De dónde viene este anuncio?
    a. de un restaurante famoso
    b. de un banco de ahorros
    c. de una agencia de viajes
    d. de la compañía telefónica

32. ¿Por qué fue famosa Ana López?
    a. Murió a una edad muy joven.
    b. Había sido una célebre actriz.
    c. Había dado dinero a los pobres.
    d. Había sido una favorita de Hollywood.

33. ¿Por qué necesita quedarse en casa el padre de Francisco?
    a. Tiene mucho trabajo que terminar.
    b. Prefiere no ir al hospital.
    c. No le gusta salir de la casa.
    d. Tiene que recuperarse de una enfermedad.

34. ¿Por qué no tenían un problema los bomberos?
    a. Era una falsa alarma.
    b. El público ayudó a apagar el fuego.
    c. Llegaron en menos de treinta minutos.
    d. Nadie estaba en el teatro cuando vinieron.

35. ¿Por qué no corría el chico?
    a. Había roto una ventana de su casa.
    b. No podía correr tan rápidamente como sus amigos.
    c. El hombre no le dejó correr.
    d. Otro muchacho había roto la ventana.

Appendix

0 TO 99

0	cero	21	veinte y uno (veintiuno)
1	uno, un, una	22	veinte y dos (veintidós)
2	dos	23	veinte y tres (veintitrés)
3	tres	24	veinte y cuatro (veinticuatro)
4	cuatro	25	veinte y cinco (veinticinco)
5	cinco	26	veinte y seis (veintiséis)
6	seis	27	veinte y siete (veintisiete)
7	siete	28	veinte y ocho (veintiocho)
8	ocho	29	veinte y nueve (veintinueve)
9	nueve	30	treinta
10	diez	31	treinta y uno
11	once	40	cuarenta
12	doce	42	cuarenta y dos
13	trece	50	cincuenta
14	catorce	53	cincuenta y tres
15	quince	60	sesenta
16	diez y seis (dieciséis)	67	sesenta y siete
17	diez y siete (diecisiete)	70	setenta
18	diez y ocho (dieciocho)	80	ochenta
19	diez y nueve (diecinueve)	90	noventa
20	veinte	99	noventa y nueve

100 TO 1000

100	ciento, cien	400	cuatrocientos(-as)
104	ciento cuatro	500	quinientos(-as)
185	ciento ochenta y cinco	600	seiscientos(-as)
200	doscientos(-as)	700	setecientos(-as)
217	doscientos(-as) diecisiete	800	ochocientos(-as)
300	trescientos(-as)	900	novecientos(-as)
308	trescientos(-as) ocho	1000	mil

1,001 TO 100,000,000

1001	**mil uno**	*31.578	**treinta y un mil quinientos setenta y ocho**
1006	**mil seis**	501.010	**quinientos un mil diez**
1022	**mil veinte y dos**	713.102	**setecientos trece mil ciento dos**
1174	**mil ciento setenta y cuatro**	1.000.000	**un millón**
1508	**mil quinientos ocho**	2.000.000	**dos millones**
1776	**mil setecientos setenta y seis**	35.046.007	**treinta y cinco millones cuarenta y seis mil siete**
1945	**mil novecientos cuarenta y cinco**	100.000.000	**cien millones**
2000	**dos mil**		
7001	**siete mil uno**		
8012	**ocho mil doce**		

UN, UNO, UNA

¿Tienes **un** libro?	Do you have a book?
Sí, tengo **uno.**	Yes, I have one.
¿Cuántas pesetas tienes?	How many pesetas do you have?
Tengo **una** peseta. (Tengo **una.**)	I have *one* peseta. (I have *one.*)
¿Cuántos hombres hay aquí?	How many men are there here?
Hay **veintiún** hombres.	There are twenty-one men.
Hay **veintiuno.**	There are twenty-one.
¿Cuántos billetes tienes?	How many tickets do you have?
Tengo cincuenta y **un** billetes.	I have fifty-one tickets.
Tengo cincuenta y **uno.**	I have fifty-one.

1. **Uno** becomes **un** before a masculine noun. The form **uno** is used if the masculine noun is not expressed.

CIEN, CIENTO

Tenemos **ciento un** dólares.	We have 101 dollars.
Tenemos **ciento** ochenta y **un** dólares.	We have 181 dollars.
But:	
Tenemos **cien** dólares.	We have a hundred dollars.
Tenemos **cien.**	We have a hundred.

2. **Ciento** becomes **cien** before a noun or when used alone.

DOSCIENTOS(-AS), TRESCIENTOS(-AS), ETC.

doscient**os** chicos	quinient**os** trece **hombres**
doscient**as** chicas	quinient**as** trece **mujeres**

ochocient**os** cuarenta y un **edificios**
ochocient**as** cuarenta y una **casas**

---

*Spanish notation uses a period instead of a comma to indicate thousands. The comma is used to set off decimal fractions; for example, 5.16 ("five point sixteen") = 5,16 ("cinco coma dieciséis").

3. In **doscientos, trescientos,** etc., the ending **-os** becomes **-as** before a feminine noun—even when it is separated from the feminine noun by another number-word.

NUMBERS EXPRESSED WITH *Y*

4. The conjunction **y** is used only between the digits of two-digit numbers (where the second digit is not zero), that is, in the numbers from 16 to 19, from 21 to 29, from 31 to 39, etc:

cuarenta **y** tres   forty-three

NUMBERS 16 TO 19 AND 21 TO 29

5. These numbers may be written either as one word or as three words; for example, 24 = **veinticuatro** or **veinte y cuatro.** All other two-digit numbers must be written as three words; for example, 63 = **sesenta y tres.**

MILLÓN, MILLONES

6. These words are used with **de** when followed by the noun they modify:

a million dollars = un millón **de** dólares
five million inhabitants = cinco millones **de** habitantes

II. Ordinal Numbers

primero (primer), primera, first (see page 170)   **sexto, sexta,** sixth
segundo, segunda, second   **séptimo, séptima,** seventh
tercero (tercer), tercera, third (see page 170)   **octavo, octava,** eighth
cuarto, cuarta, fourth   **noveno, novena,** ninth
quinto, quinta, fifth   **décimo, décima,** tenth

1. The ordinal numbers are adjectives and agree in gender and number with the noun they modify. They may either precede or follow the noun:

la **segunda** lección *or* la lección **segunda**
los **primeros** capítulos *or* los capítulos **primeros**

2. The ordinal numbers are not ordinarily used beyond the tenth:

la lección **once**   the eleventh lesson
el siglo **veinte**   the twentieth century

III. Days of the Week

el **lunes,** Monday   el **viernes,** Friday
el **martes,** Tuesday   el **sábado,** Saturday
el **miércoles,** Wednesday   el **domingo,** Sunday
el **jueves,** Thursday

1. The Spanish names for the days of the week generally begin with small (lower-case) letters.

2. The article **el** means *on:*

Te veré **el** lunes. I'll see you on Monday.

3. *On* is translated as **los** when the days of the week are used in the plural:

No vamos a la escuela **los** domingos. We don't go to school on Sunday*s.*

Los viernes vamos al cine. On Fridays we go to the movies.

Caution: In English, the singular form of the day is often used with plural meaning. Before translating into Spanish, decide whether the singular or the plural is meant:

We are going downtown on Tuesday. Vamos al centro **el** martes.

>   *But:*

We go downtown on Tuesday Vamos al centro **los** martes.
  (= on Tuesday*s*, every Tuesday).

IV. Months of the Year

enero, January **julio,** July
febrero, February **agosto,** August
marzo, March **septiembre,** September
abril, April **octubre,** October
mayo, May **noviembre,** November
junio, June **diciembre,** December

The Spanish names for the months are not capitalized.

V. Expressing Dates

¿Cuál es la fecha de hoy? What is today's date?
Hoy es **el primero de mayo.** Today is May 1.
Es **el dos de abril.** It is April 2.
Es **el catorce de octubre.** It is October 14.
Vamos **el ocho de junio.** We are going on June 8.
Ayer fue domingo, **el veinte de julio de mil** Yesterday was Sunday, July 20, 1983.
  novecientos ochenta y tres.

1. Except for **el primero,** the cardinal numbers (**dos, tres, cuatro,** etc.) are used in dates.

2. The preposition **de** is used to separate the month from the number; for example, November 21 = el veintiuno **de** noviembre.

3. *On* is expressed in Spanish by **el;** for example, *on* January 1 = **el** primero de enero.

4. In Spanish, the year is expressed in thousands and hundreds; for example, 1921 = **mil novecientos veintiuno** (literally "one thousand nine hundred twenty-one").

VI. Telling Time

¿Qué hora es?	What time is it?
Es la una.	It is one o'clock.
Son las dos.	It is two o'clock.
Son las tres y cuarto (y quince).	It is 3:15.
Son las siete y media (y treinta).	It is 7:30.
Son las ocho y diez.	It is 8:10.
Son las diez menos cuarto.	It is 9:45 (a quarter to ten).
Son las tres menos veinte.	It is 2:40 (twenty minutes to three).
Es mediodía.	It is noon.
Es medianoche.	It is midnight.
Son las nueve y media de la mañana.	It is 9:30 A.M.
Es la una y cuarto de la tarde.	It is 1:15 P.M.
Son las diez menos cinco de la noche.	It is 9:55 P.M.
¿A qué hora empieza la clase?	At what time does the class begin?
La clase empieza **a las once menos diez de la mañana.**	The class begins at ten minutes to eleven in the morning (at 10:50 A.M.)
Salimos de la escuela **a las tres de la tarde.**	We leave school at three o'clock in the afternoon (at 3:00 P.M.)

1. To tell time in Spanish, start with **son las** and add the number of the hour. The exception is one o'clock: **Es la una.**

2. To express a quarter past the hour, add **y cuarto** to the hour. To express half past the hour, add **y media** to the hour.

3. To express time past the hour (but not beyond the half hour), add **y** and the number of minutes.

4. To express time after the half hour, start with the *next* hour and subtract the number of minutes from that hour. "It is 4:50" is the same as "It is ten minutes to five": **Son las cinco menos diez.***

5. To indicate A.M., we add **de la mañana.**

6. To express P.M., we add **de la tarde** between 12:01 P.M. (one minute after 12 noon) and nightfall. From nightfall to midnight, we add **de la noche.**

7. In Spanish-speaking countries, it is actual darkness that determines whether the afternoon has ended. Thus, if it is still light, we express 7:45 P.M. as "las ocho menos cuarto **de la tarde.**"

8. Do not confuse **son las tres** with **a las tres.** The expression **son las tres** means "*it is* 3 o'clock," whereas **a las tres** means "*at* 3 o'clock."

---

*It is also correct to express clock-time in the same way as we often do in English: *it is 4:50* = **son las cuatro y cincuenta.**

OTHER TIME EXPRESSIONS

Es la una **en punto**.	It is one o'clock *sharp*.
Venga Ud. **a tiempo**.	Come *on time*.
Llegaron **a eso de** las ocho.	They arrived *at about* 8 o'clock.
Es tarde.	It is late.
Se hace tarde.	It is getting late.
No es temprano.	It is not early.
Jugamos **por la tarde (por la noche, por la mañana)**.	We play *in the afternoon* (*in the evening, in the morning*).

9. The expressions **por la mañana, por la tarde,** and **por la noche** refer to parts of the day and are not used after expressions of clock time (see §5 and §6 on page 407).

VII. Special Uses of *Tener*, *Hacer*, and *Haber*

A. *TENER*

The verb **tener** means *to have*, but it is translated as *to be* in several idiomatic expressions:

¿Cuántos años **tiene** ella?	How old is she?
Ella **tiene** quince años.	She is 15 years old.
Tengo (mucho) calor.	I am (very) warm.
¿**Tiene** Ud. sueño?	Are you sleepy?

SOME COMMON IDIOMS WITH **tener**

tener . . . años	to be . . . years old
tener (mucho) calor	to be (very) warm
tener (mucho) cuidado	to be (very) careful
tener (mucho) éxito	to be (very) successful
tener (mucho) frío	to be (very) cold
tener (mucho) gusto en + *inf.*	to be (very) glad to
tener (mucha) hambre	to be (very) hungry
tener (mucho) miedo a	to be (very) afraid of (someone)
tener (mucho) miedo de + *inf.*	to be (very) afraid to
tener (mucha) prisa	to be in a (great) hurry
tener razón	to be right
no tener razón	to be wrong
tener (mucha) sed	to be (very) thirsty

B. *HACER*

Hacer in weather expressions is used only in the third person singular:

Hoy **hace** frío.	Today it is cold.
Ayer **hizo** calor.	Yesterday it was warm.
Mañana **hará** mucho sol.	Tomorrow it will be very sunny.

OTHER WEATHER EXPRESSIONS

¿Qué tiempo hace?	How is the weather?
Hace buen tiempo.	The weather is good.
Hace mal tiempo.	The weather is bad.
Hace (mucho) calor.	It is (very) warm.
Hace (mucho) fresco.	It is (very) cool.
Hace (mucho) frío.	It is (very) cold.
Hace (mucho) sol.	It is (very) sunny.
Hace (mucho) viento.	It is (very) windy.

C. *HABER*

Haber has the special form **hay,** *there is, there are.* When used in other tenses, this idiom is expressed by the forms of **haber** in the third person singular—even when the subject is in the plural:

Hay mucho trabajo hoy.	*There is* a lot of work today.
¿Hay cuadros en el cuarto?	*Are there* pictures in the room?
No **había** nada que hacer.	*There was* nothing to do.
Había veinte personas allí.	*There were* 20 people there.
¿Hubo refrescos en el baile?	*Were there* refreshments at the dance?
No **hubo** dinero.	*There was* no money.
Habrá una reunión mañana.	*There will be* a meeting tomorrow.
¿Habrá muchas cosas que hacer?	*Will there be* many things to do?
Ella contestó que **habría** treinta personas en la fiesta.	She answered that *there would be* 30 people at the party.
Ha habido una tormenta.	*There has been* a storm.
Ha habido cuatro tormentas.	*There have been* four storms.

VIII. Verbs With Spelling Changes

In most of these verbs, the spelling changes affect the consonant immediately before the **-ar, -er,** or **-ir** infinitive ending.

GROUP A: VERBS WITH INFINITIVES THAT END IN **-car, -gar, -zar**

-car changes **c** to **qu** before **e** ⎫ in the preterite first
-gar changes **g** to **gu** before **e** ⎬ person singular and in
-zar changes **z** to **c** before **e** ⎭ formal commands

Common **-car** verbs: **acercarse, atacar, buscar, explicar, sacar, tocar.**

Spelling changes in **tocar**:   *Preterite*   *Formal Commands*

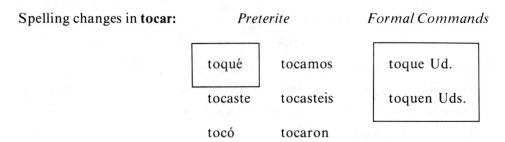

toqué	tocamos
tocaste	tocasteis
tocó	tocaron

toque Ud.
toquen Uds.

Common **-gar** verbs: **castigar, entregar, jugar (ue), juzgar, llegar, pagar.**

Spelling changes in **llegar**:   *Preterite*   *Formal Commands*

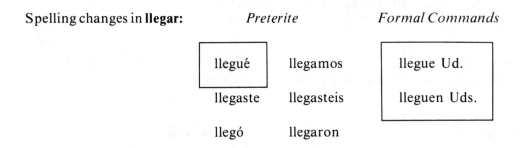

llegué	llegamos
llegaste	llegasteis
llegó	llegaron

llegue Ud.
lleguen Uds.

Common **-zar** verbs: **abrazar, almorzar (ue), comenzar (ie), cruzar, empezar (ie), gozar.**

Spelling changes in **gozar**:   *Preterite*   *Formal Commands*

gocé	gozamos
gozaste	gozasteis
gozó	gozaron

goce Ud.
gocen Uds.

   Note the formal commands of verbs that are stem-changing as well as orthographic-changing:

jugar:	**juegue** Ud.
	jueguen Uds.
almorzar:	**almuerce** Ud.
	almuercen Uds.
comenzar:	**comience** Ud.
	comiencen Uds.

GROUP B: Verbs With Infinitives That End in -ger, -gir, -guir

-ger changes **g** to **j** before **o** and **a** ⎫ in the first person singular
-gir changes **g** to **j** before **o** and **a** ⎬ of the present tense
-guir changes **gu** to **g** before **o** and **a** ⎭ and in formal commands

Common **-ger** verbs: **coger, escoger, proteger, recoger.**

Spelling changes in **escoger:**

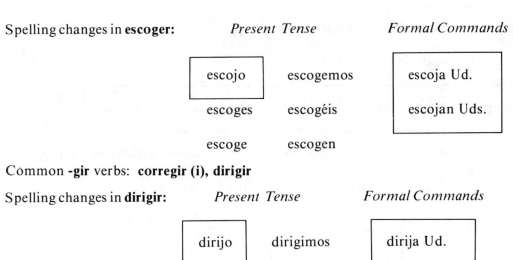

Present Tense		Formal Commands
escojo	escogemos	escoja Ud.
escoges	escogéis	escojan Uds.
escoge	escogen	

Common **-gir** verbs: **corregir (i), dirigir**

Spelling changes in **dirigir:**

Present Tense		Formal Commands
dirijo	dirigimos	dirija Ud.
diriges	dirigís	dirijan Uds.
dirige	dirigen	

Note the irregular forms of **corregir**, which is also stem-changing: yo **corrijo, corrija** Ud., **corrijan** Uds.

Common **-guir** verbs: **conseguir (i), seguir (i)**

Spelling changes in **conseguir:**

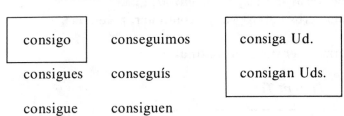

Present Tense		Formal Commands
consigo	conseguimos	consiga Ud.
consigues	conseguís	consigan Uds.
consigue	consiguen	

GROUP C: Verbs With Infinitives That End in **-ecer, -ocer, -ucir**

In these endings, **c** changes to **zc** in the first person singular of the present tense and in the formal commands.

Common verbs in this group:
agradecer, aparecer, conocer, desaparecer, merecer, nacer, obedecer, ofrecer, parecer, permanecer, reconocer; conducir, producir, reducir, traducir

Spelling changes in **merecer** and **traducir:**

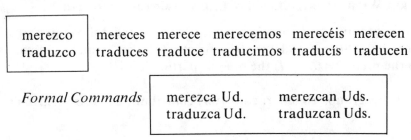

Present Tense

merezco	mereces	merece	merecemos	merecéis	merecen
traduzco	traduces	traduce	traducimos	traducís	traducen

Formal Commands

merezca Ud.	merezcan Uds.
traduzca Ud.	traduzcan Uds.

The preterite forms of verbs ending in **-ducir** change **c** to **j**:

Preterite of traducir

traduje	tradujiste	tradujo	tradujimos	tradujisteis	tradujeron

Note: The verb **vencer** has a consonant before the **-cer** ending, and is therefore conjugated as follows:

Present Tense

venzo	vencemos
vences	vencéis
vence	vencen

Formal Commands

venza Ud.

venzan Uds.

GROUP D: Some Verbs With Infinitives That End in -iar and -uar

In verbs of this group, the **i** in **-iar** and the **u** in **-uar** take an accent mark in the present tense, except for the **nosotros** and **vosotros** forms. These accent marks also occur in the formal commands.

Common **-iar** verbs in this group: **enviar, guiar.**
Common **-uar** verbs in this group: **continuar, graduarse.**

Accented forms in **enviar** and **continuar:**

Present Tense

envío	envías	envía	enviamos	enviáis	envían
continúo	continúas	continúa	continuamos	continuáis	continúan

Formal Commands	envíe Ud.	envíen Uds.
	continúe Ud.	continúen Uds.

Several verbs ending in **-iar** do not follow the pattern of **enviar;** for example, **anunciar, cambiar, copiar, estudiar, pronunciar.** Note the forms yo **cambio, copie** Ud., etc.

GROUP E: Verbs With Infinitives That End in -uir (but not -guir)

In verbs of this group, the **i** in **-uir** changes to **y** in the following cases: (*a*) the present tense, except for the **nosotros** and **vosotros** forms; (*b*) the formal commands; (*c*) the third-person forms of the preterite; and (*d*) the present participle.

Common verbs in this group: **concluir, construir, contribuir, destruir, distribuir.**

Spelling changes in **concluir:**

	Present Tense		*Formal Commands*
concluyo	concluimos		concluya Ud.
concluyes	concluís		concluyan Uds.
concluye	concluyen		

	Preterite	*Present Participle*
concluí	concluimos	concluyendo
concluiste	concluisteis	
concluyó	concluyeron	

IX. The *Nosotros* Commands ("Let's")

Bailemos.	Let's dance.
Comamos.	Let's eat.
Pidamos café.	Let's order coffee.
Durmamos hasta la una.	Let's sleep until one o'clock.
Vengamos temprano.	Let's come early.

1. The **nosotros** form of command is obtained from the **nosotros** form of the present subjunctive (see pages 124–125).

2. A **nosotros** command can also be expressed in the form **vamos a** + *infinitive*. This expression cannot be used in negative commands:

Vamos a poner la radio.	Let's turn on the radio.
But:	
No pongamos la radio.	Let's *not* turn on the radio.
Vamos a salir.	Let's leave.
But:	
No salgamos.	Let's *not* leave.

3. In spoken Spanish, *let's go* is expressed as **vamos** or **vámonos** rather than **vayamos,** which is used in negative constructions:

Vamos (Vámonos) ahora.	Let's go now.
But:	
No vayamos ahora.	Let's *not* go now.

NOSOTROS COMMANDS USED WITH OBJECT PRONOUNS

Visitemos a las muchachas.	Let's visit the girls.
Visitémos**las.** ⎫ Vamos a visitar**las.** ⎭	Let's visit them.
No **las** visitemos.	Let's *not* visit them.

4. *a.* Object pronouns are attached to the verb in the affirmative command but placed between **no** and the verb in a negative command. When an object pronoun is attached to the verb, an accent mark is placed on the vowel preceding the **-mos** ending.

b. If the expression **vamos a** + *infinitive* is used, the object pronouns are attached to the infinitive.

5. The rules governing the position of object pronouns also apply to the reflexive pronoun **nos.** When **nos** is attached to the command form, the **s** in the ending **-mos** is dropped:

Nos sentamos.	We sit (are sitting) down.
Sentémonos. ⎫ **Vamos a sentarnos.** ⎭	Let's sit down.
No nos sentemos.	Let's not sit down.
Vámonos.	Let's go (leave).
No nos vayamos.	Let's not go (leave).

X. The *Vosotros* Commands

Vosotros(-as) is the plural form of **tú,** which is used in familiar address. **Vosotros(-as)** and its verb forms are used only in Spain. In the rest of the Hispanic world, the plural of **tú** is **ustedes.**

The **vosotros** forms of command are obtained as follows:

Affirmative: Change the **-r** ending of the infinitive to **-d.** This rule applies to *all* verbs without exception:

-AR VERBS	*-ER* VERBS	*-IR* VERBS
empeza**r**	volve**r**	sali**r**
empeza**d,** begin	volve**d,** return	sali**d,** leave

Negative: Use the **vosotros** form of the present subjunctive (see pages 124–125):

no empecéis,	**no volváis,**	**no salgáis,**
don't begin	don't return	don't leave

Reminder: If an *-IR* verb has a stem-change in the preterite (see page 58), the same stem-change will occur in the **vosotros** form of the subjunctive. Examples: pedir—no pidáis; dormir—no durmáis.

FORMING *VOSOTROS* COMMANDS WITH REFLEXIVE VERBS

Affirmative: Drop the **-d** of the affirmative command form before attaching the reflexive pronoun **os.** For -*IR* verbs, add an accent mark to the **i** preceding the dropped **-d:**

-*AR* Verbs	-*ER* Verbs	-*IR* Verbs
senta**d**	pone**d**	conduci**d**
senta**os,**	pone**os** los guantes,	conducí**os** bien,
sit down	put on your gloves	behave yourselves

Exception: **idos,** leave, go away.

Negative: Insert the reflexive pronoun between **no** and the subjunctive verb form:

no os sentéis,	**no os pongáis** los	**no os conduzcáis** mal,
don't sit down	guantes, don't put	don't behave badly
	on your gloves	

Note the stem-changes in the negative command forms of **divertirse** and **dormirse:** no os divirtáis, no os durmáis.

USING OBJECT PRONOUNS WITH *VOSOTROS* COMMANDS

Habladle.	Speak to him.	No le habléis.	Don't speak to him.
Bebedlo.	Drink it.	No lo bebáis.	Don't drink it.
Escribidme.	Write to me.	No me escribáis.	Don't write to me.

Object pronouns used with **vosotros** commands take the same positions as the pronoun objects of the other command forms: the pronoun is attached to the verb in **affirmative** commands but precedes the verb in negative commands.

Verbs With Irregular Forms

Note: (1) Except for the forms needed to complete a conjugation, only irregular forms are displayed in this section.

(2) Only three verbs are irregular in the imperfect indicative:

ir: *iba, ibas, iba, íbamos, ibais, iban*
ser: *era, eras, era, éramos, erais, eran*
ver: *veía, veías, veía, veíamos, veíais, veían*

(3) The future indicative and the conditional have the same stem. For that reason, no conditional forms are shown in this section.

(4) The formal commands and the negative **tú** commands are the same as the corresponding forms of the present subjunctive.

Key: *a.* present indicative   *d.* present subjunctive
      b. preterite   *e.* imperfect subjunctive
      c. future   *f.* affirmative familiar singular (**tú**) command

1. **andar**   *b.* **anduve, anduviste, anduvo, anduvimos, anduvisteis, anduvieron**
   e. **anduviera(-se), anduvieras(-ses), anduviera(-se), anduviéramos(-semos), anduvierais(-seis), anduvieran(-sen)**

2. **caber**   *a.* **quepo,** cabes, cabe, cabemos, cabéis, caben
   b. **cupe, cupiste, cupo, cupimos, cupisteis, cupieron**
   c. **cabré, cabrás, cabrá, cabremos, cabréis, cabrán**
   d. **quepa, quepas, quepa, quepamos, quepáis, quepan**
   e. **cupiera(-se), cupieras(-ses), cupiera(-se), cupiéramos(-semos), cupierais(-seis), cupieran(-sen)**

3. **caer**   *pres. part.* **cayendo;** *past part.* **caído**
   a. **caigo,** caes, cae, caemos, caéis, caen
   b. **caí, caíste, cayó, caímos, caísteis, cayeron**
   d. **caiga, caigas, caiga, caigamos, caigáis, caigan**
   e. **cayera(-se), cayeras(-ses), cayera(-se), cayéramos(-semos), cayerais(-seis), cayeran(-sen)**

4. **creer**   *pres. part.* **creyendo**; *past part.* **creído**
    b. creí, **creíste, creyó, creímos, creísteis, creyeron**
    e. **creyera(-se), creyeras(-ses), creyera(-se), creyéramos(-semos), creyerais(-seis), creyeran(-sen)**

5. **dar**   *a.* **doy,** das, da, damos, **dais,** dan
    b. **di, diste, dio, dimos, disteis, dieron**
    d. **dé,** des, **dé,** demos, **deis,** den
    e. **diera(-se), dieras(-ses), diera(-se), diéramos(-semos), dierais(-seis), dieran(-sen)**

6. **decir**   *pres. part.* **diciendo**; *past part.* **dicho**
    a. **digo, dices, dice,** decimos, decís, **dicen**
    b. **dije, dijiste, dijo, dijimos, dijisteis, dijeron**
    c. **diré, dirás, dirá, diremos, diréis, dirán**
    d. **diga, digas, diga, digamos, digáis, digan**
    e. **dijera(-se), dijeras(-ses), dijera(-se), dijéramos(-semos), dijerais(-seis), dijeran(-sen)**
    f. **di**

7. **dormir**   *pres. part.* **durmiendo**
    a. **duermo, duermes, duerme,** dormimos, dormís, **duermen**
    b. dormí, dormiste, **durmió,** dormimos, dormisteis, **durmieron**
    d. **duerma, duermas, duerma, durmamos, durmáis, duerman**
    e. **durmiera(-se), durmieras(-ses), durmiera(-se), durmiéramos(-semos), durmierais(-seis), durmieran(-sen)**
    f. **duerme**

8. **estar**   *a.* **estoy, estás, está,** estamos, estáis, **están**
    b. **estuve, estuviste, estuvo, estuvimos, estuvisteis, estuvieron**
    d. **esté, estés, esté,** estemos, estéis, **estén**
    e. **estuviera(-se), estuvieras(-ses), estuviera(-se), estuviéramos(-semos), estuvierais(-seis), estuvieran(-sen)**
    f. **está**

9. **haber**   *a.* **he, has, ha, hemos,** habéis, **han**
    b. **hube, hubiste, hubo, hubimos, hubisteis, hubieron**
    c. **habré, habrás, habrá, habremos, habréis, habrán**
    d. **haya, hayas, haya, hayamos, hayáis, hayan**
    e. **hubiera(-se), hubieras(-ses), hubiera(-se), hubiéramos(-semos), hubierais(-seis), hubieran(-sen)**

10. **hacer**   *past part.* **hecho**
    a. **hago,** haces, hace, hacemos, hacéis, hacen
    b. **hice, hiciste, hizo, hicimos, hicisteis, hicieron**
    c. **haré, harás, hará, haremos, haréis, harán**
    d. **haga, hagas, haga, hagamos, hagáis, hagan**
    e. **hiciera(-se), hicieras(-ses), hiciera(-se), hiciéramos(-semos), hicierais(-seis), hicieran(-sen)**
    f. **haz**

11. **ir**   *pres. part.* **yendo**
         a. **voy, vas, va, vamos, vais, van**
         b. **fui, fuiste, fue, fuimos, fuisteis, fueron**
         d. **vaya, vayas, vaya, vayamos, vayáis, vayan**
         e. **fuera(-se), fueras(-ses), fuera(-se), fuéramos(-semos), fuerais(-seis), fueran(-sen)**
         f. **ve**

12. **oír**   *pres. part.* **oyendo;** *past part.* **oído**
         a. **oigo, oyes, oye, oímos,** oís, **oyen**
         b. oí, **oíste, oyó, oímos, oísteis, oyeron**
         c. **oiré, oirás, oirá, oiremos, oiréis, oirán**
         d. **oiga, oigas, oiga, oigamos, oigáis, oigan**
         e. **oyera(-se), oyeras(-ses), oyera(-se), oyéramos(-semos), oyerais(-seis), oyeran(-sen)**
         f. **oye**

13. **oler**   *a.* **huelo, hueles, huele,** olemos, oléis, **huelen**
         d. **huela, huelas, huela,** olamos, oláis, **huelan**
         f. **huele**

14. **pedir**   *pres. part.* **pidiendo**
         a. **pido, pides, pide,** pedimos, pedís, **piden**
         b. pedí, pediste, **pidió,** pedimos, pedisteis, **pidieron**
         d. **pida, pidas, pida, pidamos, pidáis, pidan**
         e. **pidiera(-se), pidieras(-ses), pidiera(-se), pidiéramos(-semos), pidierais(-seis), pidieran(-sen)**
         f. **pide**

15. **poder**   *pres. part.* **pudiendo**
         a. **puedo, puedes, puede,** podemos, podéis, **pueden**
         b. **pude, pudiste, pudo, pudimos, pudisteis, pudieron**
         c. **podré, podrás, podrá, podremos, podréis, podrán**
         d. **pueda, puedas, pueda,** podamos, podáis, **puedan**
         e. **pudiera(-se), pudieras(-ses), pudiera(-se), pudiéramos(-semos), pudierais(-seis), pudieran(-sen)**

16. **poner**   *past part.* **puesto**
         a. **pongo,** pones, pone, ponemos, ponéis, ponen
         b. **puse, pusiste, puso, pusimos, pusisteis, pusieron**
         c. **pondré, pondrás, pondrá, pondremos, pondréis, pondrán**
         d. **ponga, pongas, ponga, pongamos, pongáis, pongan**
         e. **pusiera(-se), pusieras(-ses), pusiera(-se), pusiéramos(-semos), pusierais(-seis), pusieran**
         f. **pon**

17. **querer**   *a.* **quiero, quieres, quiere,** queremos, queréis, **quieren**
         b. **quise, quisiste, quiso, quisimos, quisisteis, quisieron**
         c. **querré, querrás, querrá, querremos, querréis, querrán**
         d. **quiera, quieras, quiera,** queramos, queráis, **quieran**
         e. **quisiera(-se), quisieras(-ses), quisiera(-se), quisiéramos(-semos), quisierais(-seis), quisieran(-sen)**
         f. **quiere**

18. **reír**   *pres. part.* **riendo**; *past part.* **reído**
    a. **río, ríes, ríe, reímos,** reís, **ríen**
    b. reí, **reíste, rió, reímos, reísteis, rieron**
    c. **reiré, reirás, reirá, reiremos, reiréis, reirán,**
    d. **ría, rías, ría, riamos, riais, rían**
    e. **riera(-se), rieras(-ses), riera(-se), riéramos(-semos), rierais(-seis), rieran(-sen)**
    f. **ríe**

19. **saber**
    a. **sé,** sabes, sabe, sabemos, sabéis, saben
    b. **supe, supiste, supo, supimos, supisteis, supieron**
    c. **sabré, sabrás, sabrá, sabremos, sabréis, sabrán**
    d. **sepa, sepas, sepa, sepamos, sepáis, sepan**
    e. **supiera(-se), supieras(-ses), supiera(-se), supiéramos(-semos), supierais(-seis), supieran(-sen)**

20. **salir**
    a. **salgo,** sales, sale, salimos, salís, salen
    c. **saldré, saldrás, saldrá, saldremos, saldréis, saldrán**
    d. **salga, salgas, salga, salgamos, salgáis, salgan**
    f. **sal**

21. **seguir**   *pres. part.* **siguiendo**
    a. **sigo, sigues, sigue,** seguimos, seguís, **siguen**
    b. seguí, seguiste, **siguió,** seguimos, seguisteis, **siguieron**
    d. **siga, sigas, siga, sigamos, sigáis, sigan**
    e. **siguiera(-se), siguieras(-ses), siguiera(-se), siguiéramos(-semos), siguierais(-seis), siguieran(-sen)**
    f. **sigue**

22. **sentir**   *pres. part.* **sintiendo**
    a. **siento, sientes, siente,** sentimos, sentís, **sienten**
    b. sentí, sentiste, **sintió,** sentimos, sentisteis, **sintieron**
    d. **sienta, sientas, sienta, sintamos, sintáis, sientan**
    e. **sintiera(-se), sintieras(-ses), sintiera(-se), sintiéramos(-semos), sintierais(-seis), sintieran(-sen)**
    f. **siente**

23. **ser**
    a. **soy, eres, es, somos, sois, son**
    b. **fui, fuiste, fue, fuimos, fuisteis, fueron**
    d. **sea, seas, sea, seamos, seáis, sean**
    e. **fuera(-se), fueras(-ses), fuera(-se), fuéramos(-semos), fuerais(-seis), fueran(-sen)**
    f. **sé**

24. **tener**
    a. **tengo, tienes, tiene,** tenemos, tenéis, **tienen**
    b. **tuve, tuviste, tuvo, tuvimos, tuvisteis, tuvieron**
    c. **tendré, tendrás, tendrá, tendremos, tendréis, tendrán**
    d. **tenga, tengas, tenga, tengamos, tengáis, tengan**
    e. **tuviera(-se), tuvieras(-ses), tuviera(-se), tuviéramos(-semos), tuvierais(-seis), tuvieran(-sen)**
    f. **ten**

25. **traducir** *a.* **traduzco,** traduces, traduce, traducimos, traducís, traducen
    b. **traduje, tradujiste, tradujo, tradujimos, tradujisteis, tradujeron**
    d. **traduzca, traduzcas, traduzca, traduzcamos, traduzcáis, traduzcan**
    e. **tradujera(-se), tradujeras(-ses), tradujera(-se), tradujéramos(-semos), tradujerais(-seis), tradujeran(-sen)**

26. **traer** *pres. part.* **trayendo;** *past part.* **traído**
    a. **traigo,** traes, trae, traemos, traéis, traen
    b. **traje, trajiste, trajo, trajimos, trajisteis, trajeron**
    d. **traiga, traigas, traiga, traigamos, traigáis, traigan**
    e. **trajera(-se), trajeras(-ses), trajera(-se), trajéramos(-semos), trajerais(-seis), trajeran(-sen)**

27. **venir** *pres. part.* **viniendo**
    a. **vengo, vienes, viene,** venimos, venís, **vienen**
    b. **vine, viniste, vino, vinimos, vinisteis, vinieron**
    c. **vendré, vendrás, vendrá, vendremos, vendréis, vendrán**
    d. **venga, vengas, venga, vengamos, vengáis, vengan**
    e. **viniera(-se), vinieras(-ses), viniera(-se), viniéramos(-semos), vinierais(-seis), vinieran(-sen)**
    f. **ven**

28. **ver** *past part.* **visto**
    a. **veo,** ves, ve, vemos, veis, ven
    b. **vea, veas, vea, veamos, veáis, vean**

Spanish–English Vocabulary

Note: (1) Verbs marked with an asterisk (*) have irregular forms that appear in the list on pages 417–421. The number in parentheses indicates the verb's position in the list. For example, ***decir** (6) shows that **decir** is verb #6 (see page 418). A number following an unstarred verb indicates that the verb is conjugated like the starred verb with that number; for example, **proponer** (16).

(2) Verbs with spelling changes are followed by a letter in parentheses referring to a unit in Appendix VIII. For example, **dirigir** (B) indicates that **dirigir** undergoes the spelling changes shown in Group B on page 411.

(3) Also indicated in parentheses are stem-vowel changes. For example, **divertir (ie, i)** shows that **e** changes to **ie** in four forms of the present tense and to **i** in two forms of the preterite (see chapter 3). *Such changes are not indicated if the stem-changing verb is included in the list on pages 417–421.* When in doubt, consult the list of Verbs With Irregular Forms.

(4) Nouns that have both a masculine and a feminine form are displayed in the same style as adjectives. For example, **director, -ra** represents the forms **director,** *m,* and **directora,** *f.* Similarly, **médico, -a** indicates that a woman doctor is **una médica.**

a, to, at
abajo, below
abierto, -a, open
abogado, -a, lawyer
abrazar (A), to embrace
abrigo, *m,* coat
abril, *m,* April
abrir (*pp* **abierto**), to open
abrochar, to button, fasten; **abrochar el cinturón de seguridad,** to fasten the safety (seat) belt
absorto, -a, absorbed
abuelo, -a, *m* grandfather, *f* grandmother; **los abuelos,** grandparents
aburrido, -a, bored, boring
aburrimiento, *m,* boredom
aburrir, to bore
acabar de + *inf.,* to have just
aceptar, to accept
acera, *f,* sidewalk
acerca de, about, concerning
acercarse (A) **a,** to approach
acompañar, to accompany

acondicionador de aire, air conditioner
aconsejar, to advise
acordarse (ue) de, to remember
acostado, -a, lying down
acostarse (ue), to lie down, go to bed
actual, present (time); **actualmente,** at present
acuerdo, *m,* agreement; **estar de acuerdo,** to agree; **ponerse a un acuerdo,** to come to an agreement
adecuado, -a, adequate
además (de), besides, in addition (to)
adentro, inside
adivinar, to guess
¿adónde? (to) where?
adquirir (ie, i), to acquire
aéreo, -a, air, overhead
afortunadamente, fortunately
afuera, outside
agradable, pleasant
agradecer (C), to thank

agrícola, agricultural
agruparse, to group, cluster
agua (el), *f,* water
aguantar, to stand, endure, tolerate
águila (el), *f,* eagle
ahora, now; **ahora mismo,** right now
ahorrar, to save (money)
ahorros, *m pl,* savings
aire, *m,* air; **al aire libre,** outdoors; **aire acondicionado,** air conditioning
ají, *m,* chili
ala (el), *f,* wing; brim (of a hat)
alcalde, *m,* mayor
aldea, *f,* village
alegrarse de + *inf.,* to be glad to
alegre, happy, merry
alemán, alemana, German
Alemania, Germany
algo, something, anything; somewhat
algodón, *m,* cotton
alguien, someone, anyone

alguno, -a (algún), some; *pl* a
   few; **algunas veces,** sometimes
alimento, *m*, food
aliviar, to relieve, alleviate
almacén, *m*, department store
almendra, *f*, almond
almirante, *m*, admiral
almorzar (ue) (A), to eat lunch
almuerzo, *m*, lunch
alrededor de, around
altavoz (*pl* **altavoces**), *m*,
   loudspeaker
alto, -a, tall, high; **lo alto,** the top
altura, *f*, height, altitude
alumno, -a, pupil, student
allá, allí, there
amable, kind, nice (= obliging)
amar, to love
amarillo, -a, yellow
ambiente, *m*, atmosphere,
   ambience, surroundings
amenazar (A), to threaten
amigo, -a, friend
amistad, *f*, friendship
amor, *m*, love
ancho, -a, wide
*andar (1), to walk, go
anillo, *m*, ring
anoche, last night
anterior, previous; **anteriormente,**
   formerly
antes (de), before
antiguo, -a, old, ancient, former
anunciador, -ra, announcer
anunciar, to announce
anuncio, *m*, announcement,
   advertisement
añadir, to add
año, *m*, year
apagar (A), to put out,
   extinguish, turn off
aparato, *m*, apparatus, (radio or
   TV) set
aparecer (C), to appear
apellido, *m*, family name,
   surname; **apellido de soltera,**
   maiden name
apenas, hardly, scarcely
aperitivo, *m*, apéritif, *a wine or
   liquor taken customarily before
   a meal*
aplicado, -a, studious
aprender, to learn

aprobar (ue) un examen, to pass
   a test
aprovecharse de, to take
   advantage of
aquel, aquella, aquello, that;
   aquél, aquélla, that one; the
   former; **aquellos, -as,** those
aquí, here
árbol, *m*, tree
arena, *f*, sand
**arrancar (A): hacer arrancar el
   motor,** to start the engine
arreglar, to arrange; to fix, repair
arroz, *m*, rice
artículo, *m*, article
asaltante, *m*, attacker
ascensor, *m*, elevator
así, so, thus, (in) this way; **así
   que,** as soon as
asignar, to assign
asignatura, *f*, (school) subject
asistir, a, to attend
asociado, -a, associated
asombrado, -a, astonished
aspecto, *m*, aspect, appearance
asustarse, to become frightened
atacar (A), to attack
atención, *f*: **prestar atención,** to
   pay attention
atento, -a, attentive
atleta, *m & f*, athlete
atraer (26), to attract
atreverse a + *inf.*, to dare to
atún, *m*, tuna fish
aunque, although
ausencia, *f*, absence
ausente, absent
autobús, *m*, bus
automóvil, *m*, automobile
autor, -ra, author
avanzado, -a, advanced
avenida, *f*, avenue
avión, *m*, airplane
ayer, yesterday
ayudar, to help
azúcar, *m*, sugar
azul, blue

bachillerato, *m*, *diploma received
   upon graduation from a
   secondary school*

bahía, *f*, bay
bailar, to dance
baile, *m*, dance
bajar, to go down(stairs); to get
   off, out of (a train or vehicle)
bajo, under, below; **bajo, -a,** low,
   short
balneario, *m*, beach resort
banco, *m*, bank; bench
bañarse, to bathe, take a bath
baño, *m*, bath; **cuarto de baño,**
   bathroom
barato, -a, cheap
barco, *m*, boat, ship
barrio, *m*, neighborhood
basílica, *f*, large church
¡basta! that's enough!
bastante, enough, quite
bate, *m*, (baseball) bat
beber, to drink
bebida, *f*, drink, beverage
Belita, *nickname for Isabel*
belleza, *f*, beauty
bello, -a, beautiful
besar, to kiss
biblioteca, *f*, library
bicicleta, *f*, bicycle
bien, well
biftec, *m*, steak
bilingüe, bilingual
billete, *m*, ticket
bizcocho, *m*, cake, biscuit
blanco, -a, white
blusa, *f*, blouse
bolsillo, *m*, pocket
bollo, *m*, bun
bombero, *m*, fireman
bondad, *f*, kindness
bonito, -a, pretty
borracho, -a, drunk; drunkard
bosque, *m*, woods
botella, *f*, bottle
bracero, *m*, farm worker, day
   laborer
brazo, *m*, arm
breve, brief, short
brillar, to shine
broncearse, to get a suntan
bueno, -a (buen), good
busca: en busca de, in search of
buscar (A), to seek, look for

*caber (2), to fit
cabeza, *f*, head
cabina telefónica, telephone booth
cada, each, every
cadáver, *m*, corpse
*caer(se) (3), to fall
café, *m*, coffee; cafe
caja, *f*, box
cajero, -a, cashier
caída, *f*, fall
caliente, warm, hot
calor, *m*, heat; **hace calor,** it is warm; **tener calor,** to be (= feel) warm
caluroso, -a, warm, cordial
callarse, to become silent, stop talking
calle, *f*, street
cama, *f*, bed
camarero, -a, *m* waiter, *f* waitress
cambiar (de), to change
cambio, *m*, change; **en cambio,** on the other hand
caminar, to walk, go
camino, *m*, road, way; **ponerse en camino,** to start out
camisa, *f*, shirt
campeonato, *m*, championship
campesino, *m*, farmer, peasant
campo, *m*, country; field
canal, *m*, (television) channel
canción, *f*, song
cansado, -a, tired
cantante, *m* & *f*, singer
cantar, to sing
cantidad, *f*, quantity, amount
canto, *m*, singing, song
capítulo, *m*, chapter
cara, *f*, face
cariño, *m*, love, affection
cariñoso, -a, affectionate
Carlos, Charles
carne, *f*, meat; **carne de vaca,** beef
caro, -a, expensive
carrera, *f*, career; race (= running)
carretera, *f*, highway, road
carta, *f*, letter
cartaginés, -esa, Carthaginian
cartera, *f*, wallet
casa, *f*, house; **en casa,** at home;

ir (volver) a casa, to go (return) home
casarse (con), to get married (to)
casi, almost, nearly
casino, *m*, clubhouse, casino
caso, *m*, case; **no hacer caso a,** to ignore, pay no attention to (someone)
castellano, -a, Castilian
castigar (A), to punish
castillo, *m*, castle
catalán, -ana, Catalonian
Cataluña, *f*, Catalonia
catorce, fourteen
causa, *f*, cause; **a causa de,** because of
celebrar, to celebrate
célebre, famous
cena, *f*, supper
cenar, to have supper
centro, *m*, center; downtown; **en el centro,** downtown; **ir al centro,** to go downtown; **centro comercial,** business district; shopping mall
Centroamérica, *f*, Central America
cerca (de), near
cercano, -a, nearby
cerebro, *m*, brain
cereza, *f*, cherry
cero, *m*, zero
cerrado, -a, closed
cerrar (ie), to close
cerveza, *f*, beer
cesar (de), to stop (doing something)
cesta, *f*, basket
cielo, *m*, sky
cien, ciento, one hundred
ciencia, *f*, science
científico, -a, scientific; (*noun*) scientist
cierto, -a, certain; true
cigarrillo, *m*, cigarette
cinco, five
cincuenta, fifty
cine, *m*, movies, movie theater; **ir al cine,** to go to the movies
cinta, *f*, tape
cinturón, *m*, belt; **cinturón de seguridad,** safety belt, seat belt
cita, *f*, date, appointment

ciudad, *f*, city
ciudadano, -a, citizen
claro, -a, clear, light; **¡claro!** of course!
clase, *f*, class; kind, type
clásico, -a, classical
cliente, *m* & *f*, customer, client
clima, *m*, climate
cocina, *f*, kitchen
cocinar, to cook
cocinero, -a, cook
coche, *m*, car, automobile
coger (B), to take, catch, grab
colegio, *m*, secondary school
colina, *f*, hill
colocar (A), to place, put, set
colonizador, -ra, colonist
comedor, *m*, dining room
comenzar (ie) (A), to begin
comer, to eat
comerciante, *m*, merchant
comestibles, *m pl*, groceries
cometer, to commit
comida, *f*, food; meal; dinner; *midday meal in some countries*
comisionado, *m*, commissioner
como, as, like; **¿cómo?** how?
cómodo, -a, comfortable
compañero, -a, companion; **compañero(-a) de clase,** classmate
compañía, *f*, company
comparar, to compare
compartir, to share
complejo, -a, complex
completo: por completo, completely
componerse (16) **de,** to be composed of
compositor, *m*, composer
compra, *f*, purchase; **hacer (ir de) compras,** to go shopping
comprar, to buy
comprender, to understand
computadora, *f*, computer
común, common; **por lo común,** generally
comunidad, *f*, community
con, with
concierto, *m*, concert
concluir (E), to conclude
concurso, *m*, contest
conducir (C, 25), to drive;

licencia de conducir, driver's license

confesar (ie), to confess

confundir, to confuse

conmigo, with me

conocer (C), to know (persons or places)

conocido, -a, well known

conocimiento, *m,* knowledge

conquista, *f,* conquest

conquistador, *m,* conqueror

conquistar, to conquer

conseguir (21), to get, obtain

consejo, *m,* advice

consistir en, to consist of

construido, -a, constructed, built

construir (E), to build, construct

consultorio, *m,* (doctor's or lawyer's) office

contar (ue), to count; to tell, relate, narrate

contener (24), to contain

contento, -a, happy, glad

contestar, to answer

contigo, with you

continuar (D), to continue

contra, against

contrario: al contrario, on the contrary

conversar, to converse

copa, *f,* goblet, wine glass

corazón, *m,* heart

corbata, *f,* necktie

cordillera, *f,* mountain range

corregir (i) (B), to correct

correo, *m,* mail; **correo aéreo,** air mail

correr, to run

correspondencia: amigo(-a) por correspondencia, "pen pal," a friend acquired by correspondence

corrida de toros, bullfight

cortar, to cut

cortejar, to court

cortés, courteous, polite

cortina, *f,* curtain

corto, -a, short

cosa, *f,* thing; **cosa de,** about (with numbers)

costa, *f,* coast

costar (ue), to cost

costumbre, *f,* custom

*creer (4), to believe

criado, -a, servant, maid

crimen (*pl* **crímenes**), *m,* crime

cristianismo, *m,* Christianity

crucigrama, *m,* crossword puzzle

cruzar (A), to cross

cuaderno, *m,* notebook

cual: el (la) cual, los (las) cuales, which, who

cualquier, any

cuando, when; **¿cuándo?** when?

¿cuánto, -a? how much?; **¿cuántos, -as?** how many?; **cuanto antes,** as soon as possible; **unos cuantos (unas cuantas),** some, a few

cuarenta, forty

cuarto, *m,* room; quarter; **cuarto de baño,** bathroom; **a las dos y cuarto,** at a quarter past two (o'clock)

cuatro, four

cubano, -a, Cuban

cubrir (*pp* **cubierto**), to cover

cuchillo, *m,* knife

cuenta, *f,* bill, check; **darse cuenta de,** to realize; **tener en cuenta,** to bear in mind

cuento, *m,* story; **cuento policíaco,** detective story

cuero, *m,* leather

cuerpo, *m,* body

cueva, *f,* cave

cuidado, *m,* care; **con cuidado,** carefully; **tener cuidado,** to be careful

cuidar, to take care of

cumbre, *f,* top, summit

cumpleaños, *m,* birthday

cumplir con, to fulfill

cuyo, -a, whose

chaqueta, *f,* jacket

charlar, to chat

cheque, *m,* check

chico, -a, child, *m* boy, *f* girl

chiste, *m,* joke

dama, *f,* lady

*dar (5), to give; **dar un paseo,** to take a walk (ride)

de, of, from, in; **de joven,** as a young man (woman); **de repente,** suddenly

debajo (de), under, underneath, below

deber + *inf.,* should, to have to, be supposed to; **debes venir a las dos,** you should (are supposed to) come at two o'clock; **deber de +** *inf.,* must (= probably): **ella debe de estar en casa,** she must be (is probably) at home

débil, weak

*decir (6), to say, tell; **es decir,** that is (to say)

dedo, *m,* finger

defender (ie), to defend

dejar, to leave; to let, allow; **dejar de +** *inf.,* to stop (doing something)

delante de, in front of

delgado, -a, thin, slender

demás: los (las) demás, the others, the rest (of them)

demasiado, -a, too much; *pl* too many; *adv.* too

dentro de, inside (of)

dependiente, -a, sales clerk, shop assistant

deporte, *m,* sport

derecho, -a, right; **a la derecha,** at (to) the right; **todo derecho,** straight ahead

desarrollar(se), to develop

desarrollo, *m,* development

desayunarse, to have breakfast

desayuno, *m,* breakfast

descansar, to rest

descanso, *m,* rest

desconocido, -a, unknown

describir (*pp* **descrito**), to describe

descubrimiento, *m,* discovery

descubrir (*pp* **descubierto**), to discover

desde, from, since

desear, to wish, want

desgracia: por desgracia, unfortunately

deshacer (10), to undo; **deshacer la maleta,** to unpack

desierto, *m,* desert

desocupado, -a, unoccupied

despacio, slowly

despedirse (14) **de,** to say good-bye to

despegar (A), (*aircraft*) to take off
despertarse (ie), to wake up
después, afterward; **después (de) que**, after
destino, *m*, destination
destreza, *f*, skill
destruir (E), to destroy
detalle, *m*, detail
detenerse (24), to stop
detrás (de), behind, in back (of)
devolver (ue), to return, give back
día, *m*, day; **al día**, a day, per day; **día de fiesta**, holiday; **todos los días**, every day
diamante, *m*, diamond
diario, -a, daily
dibujo, *m*, drawing; **dibujo animado**, movie cartoon
dictadura, *f*, dictatorship
Diego, James
diente, *m*, tooth
diez, ten
diferirse (ie, i) de, to differ (be different) from
difícil, hard, difficult
dificultad, *f*, difficulty
dime, tell me
dinero, *m*, money
dios, *m*, god; idol
dirección, *f*, address
director, -ra, (school) principal; manager
dirigir (B), to direct
disco, *m*, phonograph record
discoteca, *f*, discothèque, *a small nightclub for dancing to live or recorded music*
discurso, *m*, speech
discutir, to discuss
disminuir (E), to diminish, decrease
disputa, *f*, argument
distinto, -a, distinct, different
diversos, -as, various
divertido, -a, amusing, enjoyable, fun
divertir (ie, i), to amuse, entertain; **divertirse**, to enjoy oneself, have a good time
dividir, to divide
doblar, to turn (a corner); **doble Ud. a la izquierda**, turn to the left

doce, twelve
dólar, *m*, dollar
dolor, *m*, pain; grief; **dolor de cabeza**, headache
domingo, *m*, Sunday
donde, where; **¿dónde?** where?; **¿adónde?** (to) where?
dormido, -a, asleep
***dormir** (7), to sleep; **dormirse**, to fall asleep
Dorotea, Dorothy
dudar, to doubt
dudoso, -a, doubtful
dueño, -a, owner
dulce, sweet; *m* piece of candy; *pl* candy
durante, during
durar, to last
duro, -a, hard

echar, to throw
edad, *f*, age
edificio, *m*, building
ejemplo, *m*, example; **por ejemplo**, for example
ejercicio, *m*, exercise
ejército, *m*, army
elegir (i) (B), to elect
Elena, Helen
embargo: sin embargo, nevertheless, however
emocionante, exciting
empanada, *f*, (meat) pie, patty
empezar (ie) (A), to begin
empleado, -a, employee, clerk
empresa, *f*, enterprise
en, in on, at; **en seguida**, at once, immediately
enamorarse (de), to fall in love (with)
encantador, -ra, charming
encantar, to enchant, charm; **me encanta manejar**, I love to drive
encender (ie), to light, turn on
encerrar (ie), to enclose, lock up, shut in
encima (de), above, on top of
encontrar (ue), to find; to meet; **encontrarse con**, to meet
enero, *m*, January
enfadarse, to get angry
enfermedad, *f*, sickness, illness

enfermo, -a, sick, ill
enfrente de, in front of; **de enfrente**, opposite
enojado, -a, angry, annoyed
Enrique, Henry
ensalada, *f*, salad
enseñanza, *f*, teaching, education
enseñar, to teach
entender (ie), to understand
entero, -a, entire, whole
enterrado, -a, buried
entonces, then
entrada, *f*, entry, entrance
entrar (en), to enter
entre, between, among
entregar (A), to deliver, hand over
enviar (D), to send
envolver (ue), to wrap
época, *f*, epoch, (historical) period
equipo, *m*, team; equipment
equivocarse (A), to be mistaken
erigir (B), to erect
escalera, *f*, staircase, stairs
escaparate, *m*, store window
escaparse, to escape
escena, *f*, scene; stage
escoger (B), to choose
escolar, (*adj.*) school; **libro escolar**, schoolbook
escribir (*pp* **escrito**), to write
escritorio, *m*, desk
escuchar, to listen (to)
escuela, *f*, school; **escuela primaria**, elementary school; **escuela intermedia**, intermediate school; **escuela secundaria**, secondary school
escultor, -ra, sculptor
escultura, *f*, sculpture
ese, -a, that; **esos, -as**, those; **eso**, that; **a eso de**, at about (with clock-time); **por eso**, for that reason, therefore
espacio, *m*, space
espectador, -ra, spectator
espejo, *m*, mirror; **espejo retrovisor**, rear-view mirror
esperar, to wait (for); to hope; to expect
esposa, *f*, wife
esquiar (D), to ski
esquina, *f*, street corner

establecerse (C), to settle (in a city or country)

estación, *f*, season; station

estadio, *m*, stadium

estado, *m*, state

Estados Unidos, *m pl*, United States

estante, *m*, bookshelf

*****estar** (8), to be; **está bien,** (it's) all right

estatua, *f*, statue

este, *m*, east

este, -a, this; **estos, -as,** these; **éste, -a, éstos, -as,** the latter

estereofónico, -a, stereophonic

estrecho, -a, narrow; **Estrecho de Magallanes,** Strait of Magellan

estrella, *f*, star; **estrella del cine,** movie star

estudiante, *m & f*, student

estudiar, to study

estudio, *m*, study

estúpido, -a, stupid

europeo, -a, European

evitar, to avoid

examen (*pl* **exámenes**), *m*, examination, test

excursión, *f*, outing, (pleasure) trip

éxito, *m*, success; **tener éxito,** to be successful

explicar (A), to explain

explorador, *m*, explorer

extranjero, -a, foreign

extraño, -a, strange

extremo, *m*, end

fábrica, *f*, factory

fácil, easy

falda, *f*, skirt

falta, *f*, mistake, error

faltar, to be lacking; **me falta dinero,** I lack (need) money

fama, *f*, fame; reputation; **tiene fama de ser,** (he, she, it) is reputed (said) to be

favor, *m*, favor; **haga Ud. el favor de** + *inf.*, please; **por favor,** please

febrero, *m*, February

fecha, *f*, date

Felipe, Philip

feliz (*pl* **felices**), happy

fenicio, -a, Phoenician

feo, -a, ugly

feroz (*pl* **feroces**), fierce

ferrocarril, *m*, railroad

fiebre, *f*, fever

fieltro, *m*, felt

fiesta, *f*, party; holiday; **fiesta patronal,** feast of the patron saint

fijarse en, to notice

fin, *m*, end; **a fines de,** at (toward) the end of; **fin de semana,** weekend; **poner fin a,** to put an end to; **por fin,** finally

final: al final de, at the end of

flaco, -a, skinny

flirtear, to flirt

flor, *f*, flower

flotar, to float

fluir (E), to flow

fomentar, to foster, encourage, promote

foro, *m*, forum

fortaleza, *f*, fortress

foto, *f*, photo; **sacar fotos,** to take pictures (snapshots)

francés, francesa, French

Francisca, Frances (girl's name)

Francisco, Francis (boy's name)

frase, *f*, phrase, sentence

frecuencia: con frecuencia, frequently

freno, *m*, brake

frente a, opposite

fresco, -a, cool; fresh; **hace fresco,** it is cool (weather)

frío, -a, cold; **hace frío,** it is cold (weather); **tener frío,** to be (= feel) cold

frito, -a, fried

frontera, *f*, frontier, border

frontón, *m*, jai-alai court

fuego, *m*, fire

fuera (de), outside

fuerte, strong

fuerza, *f*, force, strength

fui, fuiste, fue, etc., *forms of the preterite tense of* **ser** *and* **ir**

fumar, to smoke

fundar, to found, establish

fútbol, *m*, soccer

gana, *f*, desire; **tener ganas de** + *inf.*, to feel like; **tener muchas ganas de** + *inf.*, to be eager to

ganar, to win; to earn

garaje, *m*, garage

gaseosa, *f*, carbonated soda

gastar, to spend (money)

gato, -a, cat

general: por lo general, generally

gente, *f*, people

gobernador, *m*, governor

gobierno, *m*, government

godo, -a, Gothic; (*noun*) Goth

golpe, *m*, blow, stroke, hit; **dar un golpe,** to hit

golpear, to hit, strike

gorro, *m*, cap

gozar (A) **de,** to enjoy

grabadora, *f*, tape recorder

grabar (**en cinta**), to record (on tape)

gracias, thanks, thank you

grado, *m*, degree, grade

graduarse (D), to be graduated

gramática, *f*, grammar

gran, great

grande, big, large; (*preceding a noun in the plural*) great: **los grandes jefes,** the great leaders

grave, serious

griego, -a, Greek

gritar, to shout

grupo, *m*, group

guante, *m*, glove

guapo, -a, handsome, beautiful

guardar, to keep; **guardar cama,** to stay in bed

guerra, *f*, war; **guerra mundial,** world war

guiar (D), to guide; to drive

Guillermo, William

gustar, to please; **me gusta(n),** I like it (them)

*****haber** (9), to have (*aux. verb*): **haber hablado (tomado,** etc.), to have spoken (taken, etc.)

había, there was, there were

habitación, *f*, room

habitante, *m & f*, inhabitant

habitar, to inhabit

habla (el), *f*, speech; **de habla española,** Spanish-speaking

hablar, to speak, talk

habrá, there will be

*****hacer** (10), to do, make; **hace poco,** a short while ago; **hace un año,** a year ago; **hace bueno (hace buen tiempo),** the weather is nice; **hace calor,** it is warm (see VII-B); **hacer un papel,** to play a role; **hacerse,** to become

hacia, towards

hallarse, to be (situated), to find oneself

hambre, *f*, hunger; **tener hambre,** to be hungry

hasta, until; up to; even; **hasta que** + *verb*, until

hay, there is, there are; **hay que** + *inf.*, one must, it is necessary to; **no hay de qué,** you're welcome, don't mention it

helado, *m*, ice cream

henequén, *m*, hemp

herencia, *f*, inheritance, heritage

herir (ie, i), to injure, hurt, wound

hermano, *m*, brother; **hermana,** *f*, sister; **hermanos,** *m pl*, brother(s) and sister(s)

hermoso, -a, beautiful, handsome

hervido, -a, boiled

hielo, *m*, ice

hijo, *m*, son; **hija,** *f*, daughter; **hijos,** *m pl*, children (= sons and daughters)

hispánico, -a, Hispanic (= Spanish-speaking)

hispano, -a, Hispanic; (*noun*) person whose native language is Spanish

historia, *f*, story; history

hoja, *f*, leaf; sheet of paper

hombre, *m*, man

hombro, *m*, shoulder

honra, *f*, honor

honrar, to honor

hora, *f*, hour, time; **¿a qué hora?** at what time?

hoy, today; **hoy día,** nowadays; **hoy mismo,** this very day

hueso, *m*, bone

huevo, *m*, egg

ibérico, -a, ⎫ Iberian
ibero, -a ⎭

idioma, *m*, language

iglesia, *f*, church

imagen (*pl* **imágenes**), *f*, image, picture

imperio, *m*, empire

importar, to be important; to matter; **no me importa,** I don't care (it doesn't matter to me)

impresionante, impressive

incendio, *m*, fire

incesantemente, incessantly, continuously

incluir (E), to include

incluso, including

influjo, *m*, influx

informe, *m*, report; piece of information

ingeniería, *f*, engineering

Inglaterra, *f*, England

inglés, inglesa, English

iniciar, to initiate, begin

inmediatamente, immediately

inolvidable, unforgettable

insistir (en), to insist (on)

interés, *m*, interest

interesante, interesting

interesarse en, to be interested in

interminable, endless

invierno, *m*, winter(time)

invitado, -a, guest

invitar, to invite

*****ir** (11), to go; **ir a** + *inf.*, to be going to: **voy a hablar,** I'm going to speak; **irse,** to go away, leave

isla, *f*, island

izquierdo, -a, left; **a la izquierda,** at (to) the left

jabón, *m*, soap

jamás, ever, never

jamón, *m*, ham

jardín, *m*, garden

jefe, *m* ⎫ leader, boss, head
jefa, *f* ⎭

Jorge, George

José, Joseph

joven (*pl* **jóvenes**), young; **de joven,** as a young man (woman)

joya, *f*, jewel

Juan, John; **Juana,** Joan

juego, *m*, game

jueves, *m*, Thursday

juez, *m*, judge

jugador, -ra, player

jugar (ue) (A), to play; **jugar al béisbol,** to play baseball; **jugar a las cartas,** to play cards

jugo, *m*, juice

juguete, *m*, toy

julio, *m*, July

junto a, next to

juntos, -as, together

juntar, to join

jurar, to swear

juzgar (A), to swear

kilo, *m*, kilogram (about 2.2 lb.)

kilómetro, *m*, kilometer (about 5/8 mile)

lado, *m*, side; **al lado de,** next to

ladrón, -ona, thief

lago, *m*, lake

lana, *f*, wool

lápiz (*pl* **lápices**), *m*, pencil

largo, -a, long; **a lo largo de,** along

lástima, *f*, pity; **es lástima,** it's a pity

lavar(se), to wash (oneself)

lección, *f*, lesson

lectura, *f*, reading, reading selection

leche, *f*, milk

leer (4), to read

lejano, -a, distant, far-away

lejos (de), far (from)

lengua, *f*, language, tongue

león (*pl* **leones**), *m*, lion

levantarse, to rise, get up

leyenda, *f*, legend

libertad, *f*, liberty, freedom

libre, free

librería, *f*, bookstore

libro, *m*, book
licencia de conducir, driver's license
ligero, -a, light (in weight)
limpiar, to clean
limpio, -a, clean
lindo, -a, pretty
línea, *f*, line
listo, -a, ready
litoral, *m*, coast, shore
lobo, *m*, wolf
loco, -a, crazy; **volver loco(-a) a,** to drive (someone) crazy
lograr + *inf.*, to succeed in
Lola, *nickname for Dolores*
lo que, what, that which
lucha, *f*, struggle, fight
luchar, to struggle, fight
luego, then; **hasta luego,** so long, see you later
lugar, *m*, place; **tener lugar,** to take place
lujo, *m*, luxury
luna, *f*, moon
lunes, *m*, Monday
Luisa, Louise
luz (*pl* **luces**), *f*, light

llamado, -a, called, named
llamar, to call; **llamarse,** to be called, named; **llamar por teléfono,** to call up
llanura, *f*, plain
llave, *f*, key
llegada, *f*, arrival
llegar (A), to arrive; **llegar a ser,** to become
llenar, to fill
lleno, -a, full
llevar, to wear; to carry; to take (someone somewhere); **llevarse bien con,** to get along (well) with (someone)
llorar, to weep, grieve
llover (ue), to rain
lluvia, *f*, rain

madera, *f*, wood; **de madera,** wooden
madre, *f*, mother; **madre patria,** mother country

maestro, -a, teacher (*elementary school*)
magnífico, -a, magnificent; **¡Magnífico!** Great! "Super!"
maíz, *m*, corn
mal, badly
maleta, *f*, suitcase
malo, -a (mal), bad
mamá, *f*, mother, mama
mandar, to send; to order
mando, *m*, command, control
manejar, to drive
manera, *f*, way, manner
mano, *f*, hand
mantequilla, *f*, butter
manzana, *f*, apple
mañana, tomorrow; *f* morning; **de la mañana,** in the morning, A.M.; **por la mañana,** in (= during) the morning
mapa, *m*, map
máquina, *f*, machine; **escribir a máquina,** to typewrite
maquinaria, *f*, machinery
mar, *m*, sea
Mar Cantábrico, Bay of Biscay
marcharse, to leave, go away
María, Mary
marido, *m*, husband
mariscos, *m pl*, shellfish, seafood
marzo, *m*, March
más, more, most
máscara, *f*, mask
matar, to kill
matemático, *m*, mathematician
matrimonio, *m*, marriage, married couple
maya, Mayan (Indian)
mayor, older, oldest; greater, greatest; **la mayor parte (de),** most (of)
mayoría, *f*, majority
mecánico, *m*, mechanic
medianoche, *f*, midnight
médico, -a, physician, doctor
medio, -a, half; **a las dos y media,** at half past two (o'clock); **media hora,** half an hour; **por medio de,** by means of
mediodía, *m*, noon
medir (i), to measure
mejor, better, best
mejorar, to improve
melocotón, *m*, peach

menor, younger, youngest
menos, less, fewer; except; **por lo menos,** at least
mensaje, *m*, message
mentir (ie), to lie
mentira, *f*, lie
menudo: a menudo, often
mercado, *m*, market
merecer (C), to deserve
meridional, southern
merienda, *f*, afternoon snack
mes, *m*, month
mesa, *f*, table; **a la mesa,** at the table
meseta, *f*, plateau
mestizo, -a, of mixed Indian and Spanish origin
meter, to put in(to), insert
metro, *m*, subway; meter (= 3.3 feet)
mezcla, *f*, mixture
miedo, *m*, fear; **tener miedo,** to be afraid
miembro, *m*, member
mientras, while; **mientras tanto,** meanwhile
miércoles, *m*, Wednesday
milla, *f*, mile
millares, *m pl*, thousands
millón (*pl* **millones**), million
mío, -a, -os, -as, mine, of mine
mirar, to look at; **mirar la televisión,** to watch TV
misa, *f*, mass (*in church*)
misionero, *m*, missionary
mismo, -a, same; **lo mismo,** the same (thing)
mitad, *f*, half
moda, *f*, style, fashion
modo, *m*, way, means
mojarse, to get wet
molestar, to bother, disturb
moneda, *f*, coin
montaña, *f*, mountain
montañoso, -a, mountainous
montar (un caballo), to ride (a horse)
monte, *m*, mount, mountain
morder (ue), to bite
morir (ue) (*pp* **muerto**) (7), to die
moro, -a, Moorish; (*noun*) Moor
mostrar (ue), to show
motocicleta, *f*, motorcycle

moverse (ue), to move
muchedumbre, *f*, crowd
muchísimo, -a, very much, *pl* very many
mucho, -a, much, a great deal of; **muchos, -as,** many
muerte, *f*, death
muerto, -a, dead
mujer, *f*, woman
mundo, *m*, world; **todo el mundo,** everyone, everybody
muralla, *f*, wall
museo, *m*, museum
música, *f*, music
músico, *m*, musician
muy, very; too

nacer (C), to be born
nacimiento, *m*, birth
nación, *f*, nation
nada, nothing, (not) anything; **de nada,** you're welcome
nadador, -ra, swimmer
nadar, to swim
nadie, no one, nobody, (not) anybody
naranja, *f*, orange
narrador, -ra, narrator
Navidad, *f*, Christmas
navigar (A), to sail
necesario, -a, necessary
necesitar, to need
negar (ie) (A), to deny; **negarse a + inf.,** to refuse to
negocio, *m*, business; **hombre de negocios,** businessman
negro, -a, black
nevar (ie), to snow
nevera, *f*, refrigerator
ni . . . ni, neither . . . nor; **ni siquiera,** not even
nieto, -a, *m* grandson, *f* granddaughter; grandchild
nieve, *f*, snow
nilón, *m*, nylon
ninguno, -a (ningún), none, no, (not) any
niño, -a, *m* boy, *f* girl; child; *pl* children
nivel, *m*, level; **nivel del mar,** sea level; **nivel de vida,** standard of living
noche, *f*, night, evening; **buenas**

noches, good evening, good night; **esta noche,** tonight; **por la noche,** in the evening, at night; **de la noche,** in the evening, P.M.
nombrar, to name, appoint
nombre, *m*, name
nordeste, *m*, northeast
noroeste, *m*, northwest
norte, *m*, north
norteamericano, -a, American
nos, us, ourselves
nota, *f*, note; grade, mark (in school); **sacar buenas (malas) notas,** to get good (bad) marks
noticia, *f*, news item; *pl* news
noticiario, *m*, news broadcast
novela, *f*, novel
noveno, -a, ninth
novio, -a, sweetheart, fiancé(e)
nube, *f*, cloud
nuestro, -a, our
nueve, nine
nuevo, -a, new
número, *m*, number
nunca, never, (not) ever

o, or; **o sea,** or rather
obedecer (C), to obey
obra, *f*, work; **obra maestra,** masterpiece
obrero, -a, worker
obtener (24), to obtain
occidental, western
ocupado, -a, busy, occupied
ocupar, to occupy
ocuparse de, to be concerned with, deal with, take care of (a matter)
ocurrir, to occur
ocho, eight
odiar, to hate
oeste, *m*, west
oficina, *f*, office
ofrecer (C), to offer
oído, *m*, hearing; (inner) ear
***oír** (12), to hear
ojo, *m*, eye
***oler** (13), to smell
olor, *m*, smell, odor
olvidar ⎫ to forget
olvidarse de ⎭
once, eleven

orilla, *f*, bank (of a river); **a orillas de,** on the banks of
oro, *m*, gold; **de oro,** golden
orquesta, *f*, orchestra
oscuro, -a, dark
oso, *m*, bear
otoño, *m*, autumn, fall
otro, -a, other, another

Pablo, Paul
Paca, *nickname for Francisca (Frances)*
Paco = Pancho
padre, *m*, father; *pl* parents
paella, *f*, *stew of chicken, seafood, and rice with vegetables*
pagar (A), to pay (for)
país, *m*, country, nation
paisaje, *m*, landscape, countryside
pájaro, *m*, bird
palabra, *f*, word
palacio, *m*, palace
palo, *m*, stick
pan, *m*, bread
Pancho, Frank (*nickname for Francisco*)
panecillo, *m*, roll
pantalones, *m pl*, pants
papa, *f*, potato (Spanish America)
papel, *m*, paper; **hacer un papel,** to play a role
paquete, *m*, package
Paquita, *diminutive of Paca*
par, *m*, pair
para, for; in order to
paraguas, *m*, umbrella
parar, to stop
parecer (C), to seem; **parecerse a,** to resemble, look like
parecido, -a, similar, alike
pared, *f*, wall
pariente, *m & f*, relative
parque, *m*, park; **parque zoológico,** zoo
parte, *f*, part; **por todas partes,** everywhere
partido, *m*, game, match
partir, to leave, depart
pasado, -a, past, last; **el año pasado,** last year**

pasar, to pass, go; to spend (time); to happen; **pasar un buen rato,** to have a good time; **¿qué te pasa?** what's the matter with you?

pasear(se), to take a walk (ride)

paseo, *m,* walk, stroll, ride; **dar un paseo,** to take a walk (ride)

paso, *m,* footstep

pastel, *m,* pie, pastry

patata, *f,* potato (Spain)

patín, *m,* skate

patinaje, *m,* skating

patinar, to skate

patria, *f,* (native) country, fatherland; **madre patria,** mother country

pavo, *m,* turkey

paz, *f,* peace

pedazo, *m,* piece; **hacer pedazos,** to tear or smash to pieces

*pedir (14), to ask (for)

Pedro, Peter

pegar (A), to hit, strike

peinar, to comb

película, *f,* film, movie

peligroso, -a, dangerous

pelo, *m,* hair

pelota, *f,* ball

pena, *f,* effort, trouble; **valer la pena,** to be worthwhile

pensar (ie), to think; **pensar +** *inf.,* to intend to; **pensar en,** to think of

peor, worse, worst

Pepe, Joe (*nickname for José*)

pequeño, -a, small, little

perder (ie), to lose; to miss; **perderse,** to get lost

perfectamente, perfectly

periódico, *m,* newspaper

periodista, *m & f,* journalist

perla, *f,* pearl

permanecer (C), to stay, remain

permitir, to permit, allow

pero, but

perro, *m,* dog

persona, *f,* person; *pl* people

personaje, *m,* character (in a play, story, or novel)

pesado, -a, heavy

pesar: a pesar de, in spite of

pescado, *m,* fish (*ready to be cooked and eaten*)

pez, *m,* fish (*alive and still in the water*)

pico, *m,* (mountain) peak

pie, *m,* foot; **de pie,** standing; **ir a pie,** to walk (*instead of ride*); **ponerse en pie,** to stand up

piedra, *f,* stone

piel, *f,* fur, hide

pieza, *f,* room; (theater) play

pintor, -ra, painter

pintoresco, -a, picturesque

pintura, *f,* painting, picture

Pirineos, *m pl,* Pyrenees

piscina, *f,* pool

piso, *m,* floor; apartment

pista, *f,* skating rink; ski run

pizarra, *f,* chalkboard

planear, to plan

plata, *f,* silver

plato, *m,* dish, plate

playa, *f,* beach

plaza, *f,* square; **plaza mayor,** main square; **plaza de toros,** bullring

población, *f,* population

poblado, -a, populated

pobre, poor

pobreza, *f,* poverty

poco, *adv.,* little; **poco, -a,** little (*in quantity*); **pocos, -as,** few; **hace poco,** a short while ago; **poco a poco,** little by little

*poder (15), to be able, can, could

policía, *m,* policeman; *f* police; **mujer policía,** policewoman

pollo, *m,* chicken

*poner (16), to put; to turn on (the radio, TV, etc.); **poner la mesa,** to set the table; **ponerse,** to put on (a garment); to become; **ponerse en camino,** to start out; **ponerse en marcha,** to get moving

por, through, by, for, in, along; **por eso,** for that reason, therefore; **por favor,** please; **por fin,** finally; **por supuesto,** of course

¿por qué? why?

porque, because

porvenir, *m,* future

postre, *m,* dessert

practicar (A), to practice

precio, *m,* price

preferir (ie, i), to prefer

pregunta, *f,* question; **hacer una pregunta,** to ask a question

preguntar, to ask

premio, *m,* prize, reward

preocuparse (por), to worry (about)

preparar, to prepare

preparativos, *m pl,* preparations

prestar, to lend; **prestar atención,** to pay attention

pretolteca, before the Toltec period (see **tolteca**)

primario, -a, primary; **escuela primaria,** elementary school

primavera, *f,* spring(time)

primero, -a (primer), first

primo, -a, cousin

principio, *m,* beginning; **al principio,** at first

prisa: de prisa, fast; **darse prisa,** to hurry; **tener prisa,** to be in a hurry

privado, -a, private

probar (ue), to try, test, taste

problema, *m,* problem

profesor, -ra, teacher

programa, *m,* program; **ver un programa,** to watch a program

prohibir, to prohibit, forbid

prometer, to promise

pronto, soon; **de pronto,** suddenly; **lo más pronto posible,** as soon as possible

pronunciar, to pronounce

propio, -a, own

proponer (16), to propose

propósito, *m,* purpose; **a propósito,** by the way, incidentally

proteger (B), to protect

Provincias Vascongadas, Basque Provinces

próximo, -a, next; **la semana próxima,** next week

proyecto, *m,* project

prueba, *f,* test

pueblo, *m,* town; people

puente, *m,* bridge

puerta, *f,* door

puerto, *m,* port

puertorriqueño, -a, Puerto Rican

pues, well, then, well then

puesto, *m*, booth, stand; position (= job)

pulsera, *f*, bracelet

punto, *m*, point; **en punto** (with clock time), sharp, exactly

que, who, that, which; than; **¿qué?** what?

quedarse, to stay, remain

quejarse, to complain

***querer** (17), to want, wish; to love; **querer decir,** to mean: **¿qué quiere decir esa palabra?** what does that word mean?

querido, -a, dear

queso, *m*, cheese

¿quién, -es? who?; **¿a quién, -es?** (to) whom?; **¿de quién, -es?** whose?

químico, -a, chemical

quince, fifteen

quinientos, -as, five hundred

quinto, -a, fifth

quitarse, to remove, take off (clothes)

Ramón, Raymond

rápido, -a, fast, rapid

raqueta, *f*, (tennis) racquet

raro, -a, rare

rato, *m*, while; **pasar un buen rato,** to have a good time

razón, *f*, reason; **tener razón,** to be right; **no tener razón,** to be wrong

recibir, to receive

recientemente, recently

recoger (B), to pick up

reconocer (C), to recognize

recordar (ue), to remember; to remind

recorrer, to tour, go through (*a city, country, region*)

referirse (ie, i) a, to refer to

reflejar, to reflect

refresco, *m*, soft drink; *pl* refreshments

refrigerador, *m*, refrigerator

refugiado, -a, refugee

regalar, to give as a gift

regalo, *m*, gift, present

regla, *f*, rule; ruler (= straight-edge)

regresar, to return, come (go) back

reina, *f*, queen

***reír** (18), to laugh; **reírse de,** to laugh at, make fun of

reloj, *m*, watch, clock

rendirse (i), to surrender, give up

repente: de repente, suddenly

repetir (i), to repeat

representación, *f*, show, performance

reserva, *f*, reservation

resolver (ue), to resolve, solve; to settle (an issue)

responder, to answer, reply

respuesta, *f*, answer, response

resultar, to result (in), turn out (to be)

retreta, *f*, outdoor band concert

retrovisor: espejo retrovisor, rear-view mirror

reunión, *f*, meeting

reunirse, to meet, get together

revista, *f*, magazine

rey, *m*, king; *pl* king and queen, rulers

rico, -a, rich

rincón, *m*, corner

riqueza, *f*, wealth; *pl* riches

río, *m*, river

robar, to steal, rob

robo, *m*, theft, robbery

rojo, -a, red

romper (*pp* **roto**), to break; to tear (up)

ropa, *f*, clothing, clothes

rosbif, *m*, roast beef

roto, -a, broken; torn

rubio, -a, blond

ruido, *m*, noise

ruta, *f*, route

sábado, *m*, Saturday

***saber** (19), to know; **saber +** *inf.*, to know how: **¿sabe Ud. nadar?** do you know how to swim?; *preterite:* found out, learned

sacar (A), to take out, extract; **sacar fotos,** to take pictures

(with a camera); **sacar buenas (malas) notas,** to get good (bad) marks (grades)

sal, *f*, salt

sala, *f*, living room; **sala de clase,** classroom

***salir** (20) **de,** to leave, come (go) out; **salir bien (mal) en un examen,** to pass (fail) a test

salón, *m*, meeting room; **salón de actos,** auditorium

salto, *m*, jump

salud, *f*, health

saludar, to greet

sangre, *f*, blood

santo, -a (san), saint; **San Juan Bautista,** St. John the Baptist

santo patrón (santa patrona), patron saint

santuario, *m*, sanctuary

satisfacer (10), to satisfy

sé (*first person singular, present indic., of saber*), I know

seco, -a, dry

secundario, -a, secondary

sed, *f*, thirst; **tener sed,** to be thirsty

seda, *f*, silk

seguida: en seguida, at once, immediately

***seguir** (21), to follow; to continue, keep on: **sigue hablando,** he continues (keeps on) talking; **seguir un curso,** to take a course

según, according to

segundo, -a, second

seguro, -a, sure

seis, six

sello, *m*, postage stamp

semana, *f*, week; **por semana,** a week: **dos veces por semana,** twice a week

semejante, similar

semestre, *m*, (school) term, semester

sentado, -a, seated, sitting

sentarse (ie), to sit down

***sentir** (22), to be sorry, regret; **sentirse,** to feel (sick, well, etc.)

señal, *f*, sign, signal

señor, gentleman, sir, Mr.

señora, lady, Mrs.; **señorita,** young lady, Miss

separar, to separate

*ser (23), to be; (*noun*) *m,* being

serio, -a, serious

servir (i), to serve; **servir de,** to serve as

sesenta, sixty

setenta, seventy

severo, -a, strict

si, if

sí, yes

sí: para sí, to himself (herself, etc.)

siempre, always; **para siempre,** forever

sierra, *f,* mountain range

siesta, *f, traditional afternoon rest period observed in some Hispanic countries;* **echar una siesta,** to take a nap

siete, seven

siglo, *m,* century

significar (A), to mean

siguiente, following

silla, *f,* chair

sillón, *m,* armchair

simpático, -a, nice, likeable

sin, without; **sin embargo,** however, nevertheless

sino, but (*after a negative phrase*); **no solamente . . . sino también,** not only . . . but also

siquiera: ni siquiera, not even

sitio, *m,* place

situado, -a, situated, located

sobre, on, on top of, over; about (= concerning); **sobre todo,** especially

sobrino, -a, *m* nephew, *f* niece

sol, *m,* sun; **tomar el sol,** to sunbathe, lie in the sun

solamente, only

soldado, *m,* soldier

solicitar, to apply (for)

sólo = solamente

solo, -a, alone

soltar (ue), to loosen, release; **soltar el freno,** to release the brake

soltera, *f,* unmarried woman; **soltero,** *m,* bachelor

sombrero, *m,* hat

sonar (ue), to ring, sound

sonido, *m,* sound

sonreír (18), to smile

soñar (ue), to dream; **soñar con,** to dream of

sopa, *f,* soup

sorprender, to surprise

sospechar, to suspect

sótano, *m,* basement, cellar

subir, to climb, rise, go up; to get into (a vehicle); **subir la escalera,** to go upstairs; **subir al coche,** to get into the car

suceso, *m,* event

sucio, -a, dirty

Sudamérica, *f,* South America

sudeste, *m,* southeast

sudoeste, *m,* southwest

suelo, *m,* ground; floor

sueño, *m,* sleep; dream; **tener sueño,** to be sleepy

suerte, *f,* luck; **tener suerte,** to be lucky

suéter, *m,* sweater

sufrir, to suffer

suizo, -a, Swiss

sumamente, very, exceedingly

sumar, to add

supermercado, *m,* supermarket

supuesto: por supuesto, of course

sur, *m,* south

suyo, -a, -os, -as, yours, his, hers, theirs

taberna, *f,* tavern

tal, such

también, also, too

tambor, *m,* drum

tampoco, neither, (not) either

tan, so, as

tanto, -a, so much, as much; **tantos, -as,** so many, as many

tardar en + *inf.,* to take (time): **tardé 5 horas en llegar allí,** it took me 5 hours to get there

tarde, late; **más tarde,** later; *f* afternoon; **de la tarde,** in the afternoon, P.M.; **por la tarde,** in (= during) the afternoon

tarea, *f,* task, homework; *pl* homework assignments

tarjeta, *f,* card

taza, *f,* cup

teatro, *m,* theater

techo, *m,* ceiling; roof

teléfono, *m,* telephone

televisión: mirar la televisión, to watch television

televisor, *m,* television set; **televisor en colores,** color TV set

tema, *m,* theme, topic, composition

temer, to fear

temporada, *f,* season

temprano, -a, early

*tener (24), to have; **tener que** + *inf.,* to have to; **tener . . . años,** to be . . . years old; **tener lugar,** to take place; **tener prisa,** to be in a hurry; *see also Appendix VII*

tenis, *m,* tennis

tercero, -a (tercer), third

terminación, *f,* ending

terminar, to end, finish

terremoto, *m,* earthquake

terreno, *m,* land, ground, plot, terrain

tertulia, *f,* party, social gathering

tesoro, *m,* treasure

tiempo, *m,* time; weather; **a tiempo,** on time; **mucho tiempo,** a long time; **¿cuánto tiempo?** how long?; **hace buen tiempo,** the weather is nice; *see also Appendix VII*

tienda, *f,* store

tierra, *f,* land, earth; **la Tierra,** the Earth

tigre, *m,* tiger

timbre, *m,* bell

tío, -a, *m* uncle, *f* aunt

típico, -a, typical

tipo, *m,* type

título, *m,* title; degree, diploma

tocadiscos, *m,* record player, phonograph

tocar (A), to play (an instrument); to touch; to ring (a bell)

todavía, still, yet

todo, -a, all, every; **toda la mañana,** all morning; **todas las semanas,** every week; **todos,** everybody

tolteca, *m & f,* Toltec Indian; (*adj.*) *pertaining to the civiliza-*

tion of the Toltec Indians, which flourished in Mexico from A.D. 900-1200

tomar, to take; to have (food or drink)

tonto, -a, silly, foolish, stupid

tormenta, *f,* storm

toro, *m,* bull

torre, *f,* tower

trabajador, -ra, industrious, hardworking; (*noun*) worker

trabajar, to work

trabajo, *m,* work; **trabajo escolar,** schoolwork

***traducir** (25), to translate

***traer** (26), to bring

traje, *m,* suit, dress; **traje de baño,** swimsuit

tranquilo, -a, calm, peaceful, quiet

tratar, to treat; **tratar de,** to deal with, be about: **el cuento trata de la vida militar,** the story deals with (is about) army life; **tratar de** + *inf.,* to try to

través: a través de, across, through

trece, thirteen

treinta, thirty

tren, *m,* train

tres, three

tribu, *f,* tribe

trigo, *m,* wheat

triste, sad

tristeza, *f,* sadness

tu, tus, your (*fam. sing.*)

tú, you (*fam. sing.*)

tumba, *f,* tomb

tuyo, -a, -os, -as, yours

último, -a, last

un, uno, una, a, an, one; **a la una,** at one o'clock; **unos, -as,** some, a few

único, -a, only

universidad, *f,* university, college

usar, to use

útil, useful

uva, *f,* grape

va, vas, vamos, vais, van, *forms of the present tense of **ir***

vacaciones, *f pl,* vacation; **de vacaciones,** on vacation

vacío, -a, empty

valer (*pres. subj.* **valga, valgas,** etc.), to cost, be worth; **más vale** + *inf.,* it is better to; **valer la pena,** to be worthwhile

valiente, brave

valor, *m,* value; bravery

valle, *m,* valley

vaquero, *m,* cowboy

varios, -as, several, various

vasco, -a, Basque

vascuence, *m,* the Basque language

vaso, *m,* (drinking) glass

véase, see (*referring to a page or chapter*): **véase la página 45,** see page 45

vecindario, *m,* neighborhood

vecino, -a, neighbor

vegetal, *adj. & m,* vegetable

veinte, twenty

vencer (C), to conquer

vendedor, -ra, seller, vendor

vender, to sell

Venecia, Venice

***venir** (27), to come

venta, *f,* sale

ventana, *f,* window; **ventanilla,** *f,* car or train window

***ver** (28), to see

verano, *m,* summer(time)

verdad, *f,* truth; **es verdad,** it is true, that's right; **¿verdad? (¿no es verdad?)** right? isn't it so? isn't she? don't they? aren't you? etc.

verdadero, -a, true, real

verde, green

verduras, *f pl,* vegetables

vestido, *m,* dress

vestir (i), to dress; **vestirse,** to dress oneself, get dressed

vez (*pl* **veces**), *f,* time; **a veces,** at times; **de vez en cuando,** from time to time; **otra vez,** again; **una vez,** once; **dos veces,** twice; **muchas veces,** often; **en vez de,** instead of

viajar, to travel

viaje, *m,* trip, voyage; **hacer un viaje,** to take a trip

vida, *f,* life

viejo, -a, old; (*noun*) *m* old man, *f* old woman

viento, *m,* wind; **hace viento,** it's windy

viernes, *m,* Friday

vino, *m,* wine

visitar, to visit

vista, *f,* view, sight; **hasta la vista,** see you again

vivir, to live

vivo, -a, alive; lively

volar (ue), to fly

volcán (*pl* **volcanes**), *m,* volcano

volver (ue) (*pp* **vuelto**), to return, come (go) back; **volver a** + *inf.,* to . . . again; **volver loco(-a) a,** to drive (someone) crazy

voy, I am going (see **ir**)

voz (*pl* **voces**), *f,* voice; **en voz baja,** in a low (soft) voice; **en voz alta,** aloud

y, and

ya, already; **ya no,** no longer, not . . . anymore

yate, *m,* yacht

zapato, *m,* shoe

Zona Templada del Norte, North Temperate Zone

Zona Tórrida, Torrid Zone

English–Spanish Vocabulary

Concerning the Spanish verbs marked with an asterisk (*) and the indications in parentheses: see the first three Notes on page 423.

able: to be able, *pøder (15)

about, (*concerning*) acerca de, sobre; (*approximately*) alrededor de, cosa de, unos, -as,

activity, la actividad

actress, la actriz

advantage: to take advantage of, aprovecharse de

affection, el cariño

affectionate, cariñoso, -a

afraid: to be afraid, *tener miedo

after, después (de); **afterward,** después, luego

afternoon, la tarde; **in the afternoon,** por la tarde; (*with clock time*) de la tarde; **yesterday afternoon,** ayer por la tarde

again, otra vez, volver a + *inf*.; **he is speaking again,** vuelve a hablar

ago: a year ago, hace un año

agree, *estar de acuerdo

airplane, el avión

all, todo, -a, todos, -as; **all day,** todo el día

along, por, lo largo de

already, ya

also, también

always, siempre

a.m., de la mañana

angry: to get angry, enfadarse, enojarse

Anne, Ana

another, otro, -a,

answer, la respuesta; contestar, responder

anybody (*see* **anyone**)

anyone, alguien, nadie; **did you see anyone?** ¿viste a alguien?; **I did not see anyone,** no vi a nadie (a nadie vi)

anything, algo, nada; **did you see anything?** ¿viste algo?; **I did not see anything,** no vi nada

apartment, el apartamento; **apartment house,** la casa de apartamentos

apple, la manzana

April, abril

Argentina, la Argentina

around, alrededor (de)

arrange, arreglar

arrival, la llegada

arrive, llegar (A)

Arthur, Arturo

article, el artículo

ask, preguntar; **to ask for** (= *request*), *pedir (14)

at, a, (*with place*) en

athlete, el (la) atleta

attend, asistir a

attention, la atención

attentive, atento, -a

aunt, la tía

author, el autor, la autora

automobile, el automóvil

ax, el hacha, *f*

bad, malo, -a (mal)

badly, mal

band, la banda

bank, el banco

baseball, el béisbol

basement, el sótano

be, *estar (8), *ser (23)

beach, la playa

beautiful, hermoso, -a, bello, -a

because, porque; **because of,** a causa de

bed, la cama; **to go to bed,** acostarse (ue)

beer, la cerveza

before, antes (de)

begin, comenzar (ie) (A), empezar (ie) (A)

believe, *creer (4)

best, el (la) mejor, los (las) mejores; **to like best,** gustarle más (a uno): **the sports I like best are . . . ,** los deportes que me gustan más son . . .

better, mejor, mejores

bicycle, la bicicleta

big, grande, grandes

bill, la cuenta

birthday, el cumpleaños

blind, ciego, -a

blouse, la blusa

blue, azul

book, el libro

bookstore, la librería

bored: to be bored, *estar aburrido, -a

bottle, la botella

box, la caja

boy, el muchacho, el chico; **boys and girls,** los muchachos, los chicos

bracelet, la pulsera

break, romper (*pp* roto)

breakfast, el desayuno; **to have breakfast,** tomar el desayuno, desayunarse

bridge, el puente

bring, *traer (26)

brother, el hermano

building, el edificio

bus, el autobús; (*in Cuba & Puerto Rico*) la guagua

businessman, el comerciante

buy, comprar

cafe, el café

cafeteria, la cafetería

call, llamar

can (= *be able*), *poder (15)

car, el coche, el carro

card, la tarjeta

care, el cuidado

careful, cuidadoso, -a; **to be careful,** *tener cuidado

center, el centro

chair, la silla

Charles, Carlos

chat, charlar

cheap, barato, -a

child, el niño, la niña

chocolate, el chocolate

Christmas, la Navidad; **Christmas vacation,** las vacaciones de Navidad

church, la iglesia

city, la ciudad

class, la clase

classroom, la sala de clase

climate, el clima

close, cerrar (ie)

closed, cerrado, -a

clothes, clothing, la ropa

club, el club

coat, el abrigo

coffee, el café

cold, frío, -a, (*noun*) el frío; **to be cold,** (*persons*) *tener frío, (*things*) *estar frío, -a, (*weather*) *hacer frío; **I am very cold,** tengo mucho frío; **the soup is very cold,** la sopa está muy fría; **it's very cold today,** hoy hace mucho frío

comb, el peine; peinarse

come, *venir (27); **to come in,** entrar (en)

comfortable, cómodo, -a

complain, quejarse

concert, el concierto

construct, construir (E)

continue, continuar (D), *seguir (21); **he continues to work (keeps on working),** continúa (sigue) trabajando

converse, conversar

cook, el cocinero, la cocinera; cocinar

corner, el rincón; (*street corner*) la esquina

could, (past tense of **can**) *use the preterite or the imperfect of* *poder (*see page 71*); (conditional form of **can**) *use the conditional form of* *poder; **I could not see them yesterday,** no *pude* verlos ayer; **in those days I could walk to school,** en aquellos tiempos yo *podía* ir a la escuela a pie; **I could leave now but I don't want to,** yo *podría* salir ahora pero no quiero

country, (*nation*) el país; (*opposite of the city*) el campo

course, el curso; **of course,** claro, por supuesto

courteous, cortés

courtesy, la cortesía

cousin, el primo, la prima

cover, cubrir (*pp* cubierto)

criticize, criticar

crossword puzzle, el crucigrama

cup, la taza

dance, el baile; bailar

dangerous, peligroso, -a

dark, oscuro, -a

day, el día; **all day,** todo el día; **every day,** todos los días

decide, decidir

delicious, sabroso, -a, delicioso, -a

dentist, el (la) dentista

department store, el almacén

describe, describir (*pp* descrito)

dessert, el postre

diamond, el diamante

die, morir (ue) (*pp* muerto) (7)

difficult, difícil

dinner, la comida, la cena

dish, el plato

divide, dividir

do, *hacer (10)

doctor, el médico, la médica; el doctor, la doctora

dollar, el dólar

door, la puerta

Dorothy, Dorotea

doubt, dudar

doubtful, dudoso, -a

downtown: to go downtown, ir al centro

drama, el drama

dream, soñar (ue); **to dream of,** soñar con

drink, la bebida; beber; tomar; **do you drink coffee or tea?** ¿toma Ud. café o té?

drive, conducir (25), manejar

driver, el conductor, la conductora

dry, seco, -a

during, durante

eager: to be eager to, *tener muchas ganas de + *inf.*

early, temprano, -a

earn, ganar

ease, la facilidad

east, el este

easy, fácil

eat, comer; **to eat lunch,** tomar el almuerzo

education, la educación

elevator, el ascensor

employee, el empleado, la empleada

engineer, el ingeniero

English, inglés, inglesa; (*language*) el inglés

enjoy, gustar, gozar (A) de; **I enjoyed the movie,** me gustó la película; **to enjoy life,** gozar de la vida; **to enjoy oneself,** divertirse (ie, i)

enjoyable, divertido, -a

enough, bastante, suficiente

enter, entrar (en)

error, el error

evening, la noche; **in the evening,** por la noche; (*with clock time*) de la noche; **good evening,**

buenas noches; **this evening,** esta noche

ever, jamás

every, cada, todos los, todas las

examination, el examen (*pl* exámenes)

exciting, emocionante

expensive, caro, -a

explain, explicar (A)

extremely, . . . -ísimo, . . . -ísima; **extremely high,** altísimo, -a

eye, el ojo

eyeglasses, las gafas

face, la cara

fail a test, salir mal en un examen, no aprobar (ue) un examen

fair, la feria

fall, *caer(se) (3); **fall asleep,** *dormirse (7)

family, la familia

famous, célebre, famoso, -a

far (from), lejos (de)

fast, (*adj.*) rápido, -a; (*adv.*) rápidamente, de prisa

father, el padre

favor, el favor

feel, *sentirse (22); **I don't feel well,** no me siento bien

few, pocos, -as; **fewer,** menos: **fewer than** 15, menos de 15

fifteen, quince

filled, lleno, -a; **to be filled with,** *estar lleno(-a) de

film, la película

finally, por fin, al fin

finish, terminar

first, primero, -a (primer); **the first time,** la primera vez

fish, (*in its natural habitat*) el pez; (*caught and ready to be eaten*), el pescado

fit, *caber (2)

five, cinco

Florida, la Florida

flower, la flor

follow, *seguir (21)

food, el alimento, la comida

for, para, por (*see ch. 34*)

forbid, prohibir

foreign, extranjero, -a

forget, olvidar, olvidarse de

Francis, Francisco

Frank, Francisco; Pancho

French, francés, francesa; (*language*) el francés

Frenchman, el francés

friend, el amigo, la amiga

from, de

front: in front of, delante de

gallery, la galería

garden, el jardín

general, general; **generally,** generalmente, por lo general

gentleman, el caballero, el señor

German, alemán, alemana; (*language*) el alemán

get, obtener (24), conseguir (21); **to get along with (someone),** llevarse bien con; **to get angry,** enfadarse, enojarse; **to get dressed,** vestirse (i); **to get off, out of (a vehicle),** bajar (de); **to get together,** reunirse; **to get to school,** llegar a la escuela; **to get up,** levantarse

gift, el regalo

girl, la muchacha, la chica

give, *dar (5)

glad: to be glad to, alegrarse de + *inf.*

glass (*for water*), el vaso

glove, el guante

go, *ir (11); **to go away,** *irse, marcharse; **to go out,** *salir (20) (de); **to go up,** subir

going: to be going to, ir a + *inf.*

gone (*pp* of **go**), ido

good, bueno, -a (buen)

good-by, adiós; **to say good-by to,** despedirse (14) de

grandmother, la abuela

grandparents, los abuelos

great, gran *or* grandes + *noun*; **a great actress,** una gran actriz; **the great artists,** los grandes artistas

greet, saludar

group, el grupo

guest, el invitado, la invitada

guitar, la guitarra

hair, el pelo

half, medio, -a; **half hour,** media hora; **at half past two,** a las dos y media

hamburger, la hamburguesa

hand, la mano

handkerchief, el pañuelo

handsome, hermoso, -a, guapo, -a

happy, contento, -a, feliz; **to be happy,** *estar contento, -a, *ser feliz

hat, el sombrero

have, *tener (24); (*a meal or beverage*) tomar; **to have a good time,** divertirse (ie, i), pasar un buen rato; **to have to,** (*obligation*) deber + *inf.*, (*necessity*) tener que + *inf.*

hear, *oír (12)

heat, el calor

Helen, Elena

help, la ayuda; ayudar

Henry, Enrique

her, (*direct object*) la, (*indirect object*) le, (*object of prep.*) ella; (*possessive adj.*) su, -s, de ella

here, aquí

hers, el suyo, la suya, los suyos, las suyas; **this book is hers,** este libro es suyo (. . . es de ella)

high school, la escuela superior, el colegio

him, (*direct object*) lo, (*in Spain*) le; (*indirect object*) le; (*object of prep.*) él

his, (*adj.*) su, -s, de él; (*pron.*) el suyo, la suya, los suyos, las suyas, de él; **this box is his,** esta caja es suya (. . . es de él)

home: at home, en casa; **to go (return) home,** *ir (regresar) a casa; **to leave home,** *salir de casa

hope, esperar

horizontal, horizontal

hot = very warm (*see* **warm**)

hotel, el hotel

hour, la hora

house, la casa; **apartment house,** la casa de apartamentos

how? ¿cómo?; **how many?** ¿cuántos, -as; **how much?** ¿cuánto, -a?

hundred: one hundred, cien, ciento

hungry: to be (very) hungry, *tener (mucha) hambre

hurry: to be in a hurry, *tener prisa

husband, el marido, el esposo

I, yo; **I like,** me gusta(n)

ice cream, el helado

idea, la idea

ignore (= *to snub or show no interest in someone*), no *hacer caso a

important, importante

impossible, imposible

inhabitant, el (la) habitante

innocence, la inocencia

innocent, inocente

insist, insistir (en)

instead of, en vez de

intelligence, la inteligencia

intelligent, inteligente

intend, pensar (ie) + *inf.*

interested: to be interested in, interesarse en

interesting, interesante

invite, invitar

iron, el hierro

island, la isla

it, *as subject, usually not expressed;* (*direct object*) lo, la; (*indirect object*) le; (*object of prep.*) él, ella; **I like it,** me gusta

job, el empleo, el puesto; (*task*) el trabajo

John, Juan

Joseph, José

just: to have just, acabar de + *inf.*: **I have just arrived,** acabo de llegar; **I had just arrived,** acababa de llegar

king, el rey; **king and queen,** los reyes

kitchen, la cocina

knife, el cuchillo

knock (at the door), llamar (a la puerta)

know, (*facts*) *saber (19); (*persons and places*) conocer (C)

lady, la dama, la señora; **young lady** (*unmarried*), la señorita

landscape, el paisaje

language, la lengua, el idioma

large, grande

last, último, -a; **last month,** el mes pasado; **last night,** anoche

late, tarde

later, más tarde; **see you later,** hasta luego

lawyer, el abogado, la abogada

lazy, perezoso, -a

learn, aprender

least, menos; **at least,** por lo menos

leather, el cuero

leave, *salir (20) (de), partir, *irse (11); **to leave for (a place),** salir para

lend, prestar

less, menos

lesson, la lección (*pl* lecciones); **the Spanish lesson,** la lección de español

let (= *allow*), dejar; **I let him drive,** le dejo conducir

letter, la carta

let us (let's), vamos a + *inf., or use present subjunctive, 1st pers. plural*: **let's eat,** vamos a comer, comamos; **let's leave,** vamos a salir, salgamos; **let's not . . . ,** *use present subjunctive, 1st pers. plural*: **let's not go there,** no vayamos allí

lie, la mentira

light, la luz (*pl* luces); claro, -a

like (be pleasing), gustar; **I like,** me gusta(n)

listen (to), escuchar

little, (*in size*) pequeño, -a; (*in quantity*) poco, -a

live, vivir

living room, la sala

long, largo, -a; **a long time,** mucho tiempo

look at, mirar; **look for,** buscar (A)

lose, perder (ie)

lot: a lot (of), mucho, -a

Louis, Luis

Louise, Luisa

luck, la suerte

lunch, el almuerzo; **to eat (have) lunch,** almorzar (ue) (A), tomar el almuerzo

madam, señora

magazine, la revista

magnificent, magnífico, -a

make, *hacer (10)

mall (= *shopping center*), el centro comercial

man, el hombre

many, muchos, -as

map, el mapa

March, marzo

marry, casarse (con)

Mary, María

match (game), el partido

matter: it doesn't matter, no importa

meal, la comida

meat, la carne

medicine, la medicina

meet, encontrar (ue), encontrarse con; (*to get together*) reunirse; (*to make the acquaintance of*) conocer (C)

meeting, la reunión

Mexico City, la ciudad de México

midnight, la medianoche

milk, la leche

mine, el mío, la mía, los míos, las mías; **she is a friend of mine,** es una amiga mía; **these books are mine,** estos libros son míos

minute, el minuto

miss, (la) señorita

mister, (el) señor

modern, moderno, -a

moment, el momento; **at this moment,** en este momento

money, el dinero

month, el mes

more, más

morning, la mañana; **in the morning,** por la mañana; (*with clock time*) de la mañana; **good**

morning, buenos días;
tomorrow morning, mañana
   por la mañana
most of, la mayoría de, la mayor
   parte de
motorcycle, la motocicleta
movie, la película
movies: to go to the movies, ir al
   cine
much, mucho, -a; **very much,**
   muchísimo
museum, el museo
music, la música
must, (*obligation*) deber + *inf.*,
   (*necessity*) *tener que + *inf.*,
   (*probability*) deber de + *inf.*
mustard, la mostaza
my, mi, -s

name, el nombre; **to be named,**
   llamarse
narrow, estrecho, -a
near, cerca (de); **nearest,** más
   cerca (a)
necessary, necesario, -a
necklace, el collar
necktie, la corbata
need, necesitar; (= *to lack*)
   faltarle a uno: **I need (lack)**
   pencils, me faltan lápices
neighbor, el vecino, la vecina
neighborhood, el vecindario, el
   barrio
nervous, nervioso, -a; **to be too**
   nervous to (do something),
   *estar muy nervioso(-a) para
never, nunca, jamás
new, nuevo, -a
news, las noticias; (*news item*)
   la noticia
newspaper, el periódico
next, próximo, -a
nice, (*likeable*) simpático, -a;
   (*kind, obliging*) amable;
   (*weather*) bueno
night, la noche; **at night,** por la
   noche
no = not any, ninguno, -a
   (ningún)
nobody, nadie
noise, el ruido
noon, el mediodía; **at noon,**
   a mediodía

north, el norte
notebook, el cuaderno
nothing, nada
novel, la novela
now, ahora; **right now,** ahora
   mismo
nylon, el nilón

o'clock: at seven o'clock, a las
   siete; **it is one o'clock,** es la una
old, viejo, -a; (= *ancient*) antiguo,
   -a; **how old is she?** ¿cuántos
   años tiene ella?; **I am 15 years**
   old, tengo 15 años; **the oldest,**
   el (la) mayor, los (las) mayores
on, en; **on Thursday,** el jueves;
   on Fridays, los viernes; **on**
   July 4, el cuatro de julio;
   on . . . -ing, al + *inf.:* **on**
   arriving, al llegar
once, una vez; **at once,** en seguida
open, abrir (*pp* abierto)
opposite, enfrente de
order, la orden; (*from a menu*)
   *pedir (14); **in order to,**
   para + *inf.*
other, otro, -a
our, nuestro, -a
ours, el nuestro, la nuestra, los
   nuestros, las nuestras; **these**
   chairs are ours, estas sillas son
   nuestras
outside, afuera, fuera de

package, el paquete
page, la página
painting, la pintura
paper, el papel; (*newspaper*) el
   periódico
parents, los padres
park, el parque
party, la fiesta
pass, pasar; **to pass a test,** *salir
   bien en un examen, aprobar
   (ue) un examen
past: half past six, las seis y
   media
patience, la paciencia
patient, paciente
patio, el patio
pay, pagar (A); **I paid for the**
   book, pagué el libro; **I paid ten**

dollars for the book, pagué
   diez dólares por el libro; **to pay**
   attention, prestar atención; **to**
   pay a visit, *hacer una visita
pearl, la perla
pen, la pluma
pencil, el lápiz (*pl* lápices)
people, (*as a group*) la gente; (*as*
   individuals) las personas;
   (= *nation or race*) el pueblo;
   the people are waiting for the
   train, la gente espera el tren;
   many people are learning
   Spanish, muchas personas
   aprenden el español; **the mexi-**
   can people, el pueblo mexicano
pepper, la pimienta
perfect, perfecto, -a
perfection, la perfección
person, la persona
Peter, Pedro
Philip, Felipe
phone, el teléfono; **on the phone,**
   al teléfono
photo, la foto; **photograph,** la
   fotografía
pie, el pastel
pity, la lástima; **it is a pity,** es
   lástima
place, el lugar, el sitio; **to take**
   place, *tener lugar
play, (*theater*) la pieza, la come-
   dia; jugar (ue) (A); (*a musical*
   instrument) tocar (A); **to play**
   a role, *hacer un papel
player, el jugador, la jugadora
please, por favor, haga el favor
   de + *inf.*; **please sit down,**
   siéntese, por favor, haga el
   favor de sentarse
p.m., de la tarde, de la noche; **at**
   4 P.M., a las cuatro de la tarde;
   it is 11 P.M., son las once de la
   noche
pool, la piscina
poor, pobre
popcorn, las palomitas de maíz
popular, popular
port, el puerto
possible, posible; **as soon as**
   possible, lo más pronto posible
postcard, la tarjeta postal
potato, (*Spain*) la patata,
   (*Spanish America*) la papa

practice, practicar (A)
prefer, preferir (ie, i)
prepare, preparar
president, el presidente
pretty, bonito, -a
problem, el problema
program, el programa
promise, prometer
put, *poner (16); **to put on** (*the radio, TV*), poner, (*clothes*) ponerse

quarter: a quarter past two, las dos y cuarto
queen, la reina
question, la pregunta; **to ask a question,** *hacer una pregunta

race (= *running competition*), la carrera; competir (i) en una carrera
racquet, la raqueta
radio, la radio; (*radio set*) el radio
rain, la lluvia; llover (ue)
raincoat, el impermeable
read, leer (4)
ready: to be ready, *estar listo, -a
receive, recibir
recently, recientemente
record, el disco; **record player,** el tocadiscos
red, rojo, -a
refreshments, los refrescos
refuse, negarse (ie) (A) a + *inf.;* **he refuses to leave,** se niega a salir
relative, el (la) pariente
religious, religioso, -a
remain, quedarse, permanecer (C)
repeat, repetir (i)
rest, descansar
restaurant, el restaurante
return, (*go back*), regresar, volver (ue) (*pp* vuelto); (*give back*) devolver (ue) (*pp* devuelto)
rich, rico, -a
ride: to go for a ride (in a car), dar un paseo (en coche)
right, el derecho; (*opposite of left*) derecho, -a; **on the right (side),** a la derecha; **to be right,** *tener razón; **right now,** ahora mismo
ring, el anillo; **diamond ring,** el anillo de diamantes; sonar (ue): **the bell (phone) rang,** sonó el timbre (teléfono)
road, el camino, la carretera
Robert, Roberto
rock music, música *rock*
role: to play a role, *hacer un papel
room, el cuarto, la habitación; **to be room** (= *space*) **for,** *caber (2): **there was no room for me in the car,** no cupe en el coche
route, la ruta
rug, la alfombra
run, correr

sad, triste
sadness, la tristeza
saint, el santo, la santa; **Saint Francis,** San Francisco; **Saint Joseph,** San José
salad, la ensalada
salt, la sal
same, mismo, -a
sand, la arena
Saturday, sábado; **on Saturday,** el sábado
say, *decir (6); **to say good-bye to,** despedirse (i) de
school, la escuela; **to school,** a la escuela; **in (at) school,** en la escuela
sea, el mar
seated, sentado, -a
see, *ver (28)
seem, parecer (C)
sell, vender
send, mandar, enviar (D)
serve, servir (i)
set: television set, el televisor; **to set the table,** *poner la mesa
several, varios, -as
shelf, el estante
shirt, la camisa
shoe, el zapato
shopping: to go shopping, *ir de compras

shopping center (mall), el centro comercial
should, deber + *inf.;* **I should study,** debo estudiar
show, el espectáculo, la función; mostrar (ue)
sick, enfermo, -a
sign, la señal
since (= *because*), puesto que
sing, cantar
singer, el (la) cantante
sir, señor
sister, la hermana
sit, (*to be seated*) *estar sentado, -a; (*to sit down*) sentarse (ie)
situated, situado, -a
six, seis
skate, el patín; patinar
ski, el esquí; esquiar (D); **ski run,** la pista de salto; **to go skiing,** *ir a esquiar
skirt, la falda
sky, el cielo
sleep, *dormir (7)
sleepy: to be (very) sleepy, *tener (mucho) sueño
slow, lento, -a; **slowly,** despacio, lentamente
small, pequeño, -a
smart, inteligente
smile, sonreír (18)
snow, la nieve; nevar (ie)
sock, (*footwear*) el calcetín (*pl* calcetines)
soda, la gaseosa
sofa, el sofá
soldier, el soldado
solution, la solución
some, alguno, -a (algún); (= *a few*) unos, -as, algunos, -as
somebody, someone, alguien
something, algo
so much, tanto, -a; **so many,** tantos, -as
soon, pronto; **as soon as,** así que; **as soon as possible,** lo más pronto posible
sorry: to be sorry, *sentir (22); **I'm sorry,** lo siento
south, el sur
Spain, España
Spanish, español, -la; (*language*) el español
speak, hablar

speech, el discurso

spend, (*time*) pasar, (*money*) gastar

sport, el deporte

stairs, la escalera

stamp, el sello

standing, de pie; **I am standing,** estoy de pie

start out, *ponerse en camino

stay, quedarse

steel, el acero

stereophonic, estereofónico, -a

Steven, Esteban

stop: to stop . . . -ing, cesar de + *inf.*: **he stopped running,** cesó de correr; (*to halt*) parar: **the bus stops at the corner,** el autobús para en la esquina

store, la tienda

story, el cuento, la historia

strawberry, la fresa

street, la calle; **along (through) the street,** por la calle

stripe, la raya

strong, fuerte

student, el (la) estudiante

studious, aplicado, -a

study, estudiar

summer, el verano

sunbathe, tomar un baño de sol

Sunday, domingo; **on Sunday,** el domingo

supermarket, el supermercado

sure: to be sure, *estar seguro, -a

Susan, Susana

sweater, el suéter

sweet, dulce

swim, nadar

swimming: to go swimming, *ir a nadar

table, la mesa

take, tomar; (*to take someone or something somewhere*) llevar; **to take a ride,** *dar un paseo (en coche, en bicicleta, etc.); **to take a sunbath,** tomar un baño de sol; **to take a trip,** *hacer un viaje; **to take a walk,** *dar un paseo; **to take off (clothes),** quitarse; **to take part in,** tomar parte en

talk, hablar

tall, alto, -a

tape, la cinta; **to tape** (= *record on tape*) grabar en cinta

tape recorder, la grabadora

taste, el sabor

tea, el té

teach, enseñar

teacher, (*elementary school*) el maestro, la maestra; (*high school and university*) el profesor, la profesora; **Spanish teacher** (= *teacher of Spanish*) el (la) profesor(-ra) de español

team, el equipo

telephone, el teléfono; (*verb*) telefonear, llamar al teléfono

television, la televisión; **television set,** el televisor

tell, *decir (6); (= *to narrate*) contar (ue)

ten, diez

tennis, el tenis; **tennis match,** el partido de tenis

test, el examen (*pl* exámenes), la prueba

than, que, de; **she is taller than I,** ella es más alta que yo; **there were more than 50 guests,** había más de 50 invitados

thank, *dar las gracias a

that, (*conj.*) que; (*dem. adj.*) ese, esa, aquel, aquella; **that one,** ése, -a, aquél, -la; **what is that?** ¿qué es eso (aquello)?

theater, el teatro

their, su(-s), de ellos(-as); **theirs,** el suyo, la suya, los suyos, las suyas; **this box is theirs,** esta caja es suya (. . . es de ellos, -as)

them, (*direct object*) los, las; (*indirect object*) les; (*object of prep.*) ellos, -as

then, (*afterward*) después, luego; (*at that time*) entonces

there, allí, allá

there is, there are, hay (*see VII-C*)

these, (*adj.*) estos, -as; (*pron.*) éstos, -as

they, ellos, ellas; **they like it,** les gusta

thing, la cosa

think, pensar (ie); **to think of,** pensar en

third, tercero, -a (tercer)

thirsty: to be (very) thirsty, *tener (mucha) sed

this, este, -a; **this one,** éste, -a; **what is this?** ¿qué es esto?

those, (*adj.*) esos, -as, aquellos, -as; (*pron.*) ésos, -as, aquéllos, -as

through, por

ticket, el billete, (*Mexico, South America*) el boleto

tie = necktie, la corbata

time, el tiempo, la hora, la vez; **a long time,** mucho tiempo; **at what time?** ¿a qué hora?; **on time,** a tiempo; **four times,** cuatro veces

tired: to be tired, *estar cansado, -a

to, a; (= *in order to*) para + *inf.*

today, hoy

together, juntos, -as

tomorrow, mañana; **tomorrow morning,** mañana por la mañana

tonight, esta noche

train, el tren

travel, viajar

trip, el viaje; **to take a trip,** *hacer un viaje

truck, el camión

truth, la verdad

try, tratar de + *inf.*; (*to taste*) probar (ue)

turn off (a light, etc.), apagar (A)

twenty, veinte

type, el tipo

umbrella, el paraguas (*pl* los paraguas)

uncle, el tío

understand, comprender, entender (ie)

university, la universidad

us, nos; (*object of prep.*) nosotros, -as

use, usar

used to, *use the imperfect tense*: **I used to swim well,** yo nadaba bien

value, el valor
verb, el verbo
very, muy; **very much,** muchísimo; *expressed by* mucho, -a *in idioms with* hacer *and* tener; *see Appendix VII*
visit, la visita; visitar; **to pay a visit,** *hacer una visita
voice, la voz (*pl* voces)

wait (for), esperar
waiter, el camarero, el mozo
wake up, despertar(se) (ie)
walk, *andar, caminar; (*instead of ride*) *ir a pie; **to take a walk,** pasearse, *dar un paseo
want, desear, *querer (17)
warm: to be warm, (*weather*) *hacer calor, (*persons*) *tener calor, (*things*) *estar caliente; **it is very warm today,** hoy hace mucho calor; **we are (= feel) very warm,** tenemos mucho calor; **the soup is very warm,** la sopa está muy caliente
wash: to wash oneself, "get washed," lavarse
watch, (*wristwatch*) el reloj; **to watch TV,** mirar la televisión; **to watch a program (film, etc.),** ver un programa (una película, etc.); **to watch a baseball game,** mirar un partido de béisbol
water, el agua (*f*)
we, nosotros, nosotras

weak, débil
wear, llevar
weather, el tiempo (*see VII-B*)
week, la semana
weekend, el fin de semana
welcome: you're welcome, de nada, no hay de qué
well, bien
what? ¿qué?
when? ¿cuándo?
where? ¿dónde?
while, mientras; el rato
white, blanco, -a
who? ¿quién, -es?
whole, todo, -a: **the whole day,** todo el día
whom? ¿a quién, -es?
why? ¿por qué?
wide, ancho, -a
wife, la esposa
William, Guillermo
win, ganar
window, la ventana; (*in car, train, etc.*) la ventanilla
wine, el vino
winter, el invierno
wish, desear, querer
with, con; **with me,** conmigo; **with you,** contigo, con Ud. (Uds.)
within, dentro (de)
without, sin
wood, la madera; **wooden,** de madera
wool, la lana; **woolen,** de lana
word, la palabra

work, el trabajo; trabajar
worry, preocuparse (de); **don't worry,** no tenga(n) cuidado, pierda(n) cuidado
worse, worst, peor
worth: to be worth, valer; **it is worthless (not worth anything),** no vale nada
would like: I would like to go, me gustaría ir
write, escribir (*pp* escrito)

year, el año
yesterday, ayer; **yesterday afternoon,** ayer por la tarde
yet, todavía
you, (*subject*) tú, Ud., Uds., vosotros, -as; (*direct object*) te, lo(-s), la(-s), os; (*indirect object*) te, le(-s), os; (*object of prep.*) ti, Ud., Uds., vosotros, -as
young, joven (*pl* jóvenes); **young man (woman),** el (la) joven; **younger,** menor; **the youngest,** el (la) menor, los (las) menores
your, tu(-s), su(-s), de Ud., de Uds., vuestro, -a
yours, el tuyo, la tuya, etc.; el suyo, la suya, etc.; el vuestro, la vuestra, etc.; **these things are yours,** estas cosas con tuyas (suyas, vuestras, . . . son de Ud., de Uds.)